Non-verbal Reasoning

Rapid Tests 5

Rebecca Brant

Schofield&Sims

Introduction

This book gives you practice in answering non-verbal reasoning questions quickly.

The questions are like the questions on the 11+ and other school selection tests. You must find the correct answers.

School selection tests are usually timed, so you need to get used to working quickly. Each test has a target time for you to work towards. You should time how long you spend on each test, or you can ask an adult to time you.

All the questions in this book are multiple choice. For each question you are given a choice of answers. Choose the answer you think is correct and draw a circle round the letter beneath it.

What you need

- A pencil
- An eraser
- A clock, watch or stopwatch
- A sheet of rough paper
- An adult to help you work out how long you take and to mark the test for you

What to do

- Turn to **Section 1 Test 1** on page 4. Look at the grey box at the top of the page labelled **Target time**. This tells you how long the test should take.

- When you are ready to start, write down the time or start the stopwatch. Or the adult helping you will tell you to begin.

- Find this black arrow ⬇ near the top of the first page. Start each test here.

- Find this square ▪. The instructions for the first set of questions are beside it. Read them carefully.

- Look below the instructions. Read the **Example**. Work out why the answer given is correct.

- Using similar methods, answer each question.

- Try to answer every question. If you do get stuck on a question, leave it and go on to the next one. Work quickly and try your best.

- When you have finished the first page, go straight on to the next page without waiting. Here you will find a different question type. Again, read the instructions and the example. Then answer the questions.

- When you reach the end, stop. Write down the time or stop the stopwatch. Or tell the adult that you have finished.

- With the adult, work out how long you took to do the test. Fill in the **Time taken** box at the end of the test.

- The adult will mark your test and fill in the **Score** and **Target met?** boxes.

- Turn to the **Progress chart** on page 40. Write your score in the box and colour in the graph to show how many questions you got right.

- Did you get some questions wrong? You should always have another go at them before you look at the answers. Then ask the adult to check your work and help you if you are still not sure.

- Later, you will do some more of these tests. You will soon learn to work through them more quickly. The adult who is helping you will tell you what to do next.

Published by **Schofield & Sims Ltd**,
7 Mariner Court, Wakefield, West Yorkshire WF4 3FL, UK
Telephone 01484 607080
www.schofieldandsims.co.uk
First published in 2014
This edition copyright © Schofield & Sims Ltd, 2018
Eighth impression 2022
Author: **Rebecca Brant**. Rebecca Brant has asserted her moral right under the Copyright, Designs and Patents Act, 1988, to be identified as the author of this work.
British Library Cataloguing in Publication Data. A catalogue record for this book is available from the British Library.

Commissioned by **Carolyn Richardson Publishing Services**
Design by **Oxford Designers & Illustrators**
Front cover design by **Ledgard Jepson Ltd**
Printed in the UK by **Page Bros (Norwich) Ltd**
ISBN 978 07217 1467 7

Contents

A **pull-out answers section** (pages A1 to A8) appears in the centre of this book, between pages 20 and 21. It also gives simple guidance on how best to use this book. Remove this section before the child begins working through the tests.

Section **1** Test **1**

Target time: **7 minutes**

Which picture on the right belongs to the group on the left? Circle the letter.

Example

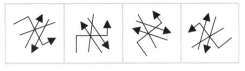

a　　　　b　　　　c　　　　ⓓ　　　　e

1.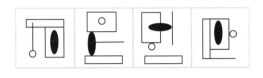

a　　　　b　　　　c　　　　d　　　　e

2.

a　　　　b　　　　c　　　　d　　　　e

3.

a　　　　b　　　　c　　　　d　　　　e

4.

a　　　　b　　　　c　　　　d　　　　e

5.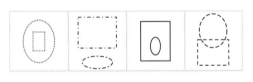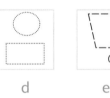

a　　　　b　　　　c　　　　d　　　　e

6.

a　　　　b　　　　c　　　　d　　　　e

Now go on to the next page ➜

Schofield & Sim

There is a pair of pictures on the left. Which one of the five pictures on the right goes with the single picture on the left to make a pair in the same way? Circle the letter.

Example

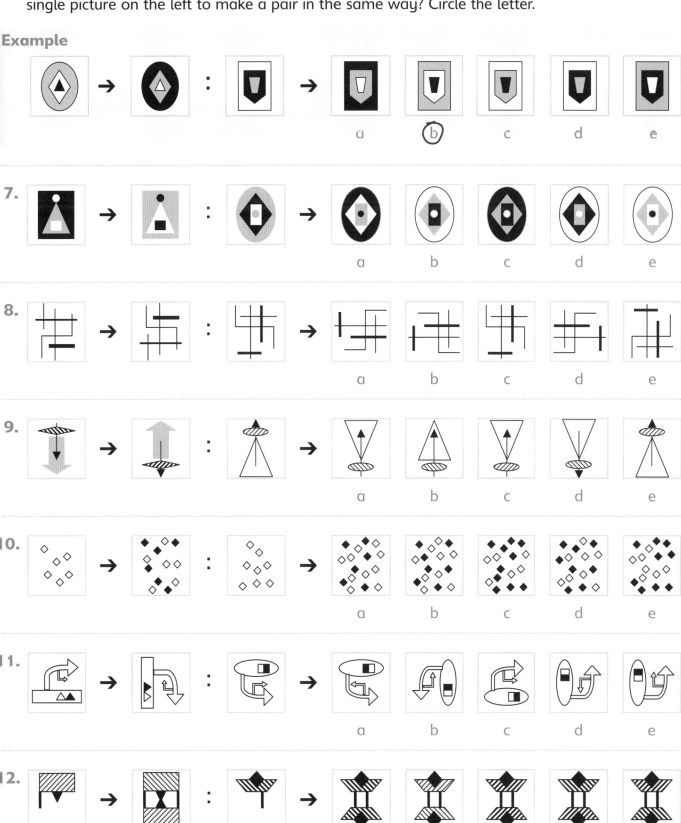

End of test

| Score: | | Time taken: | | Target met? | |

Target time: **7 minutes**

Which picture on the right belongs to the group on the left? Circle the letter.

Example

                                          a   b   c   ⓓ   e

1.

                                          a   b   c   d   e

2.

                                          a   b   c   d   e

3.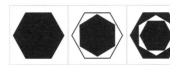

                                          a   b   c   d   e

4.

                                          a   b   c   d   e

5.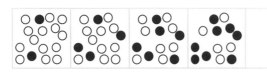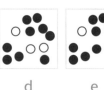

                                          a   b   c   d   e

6.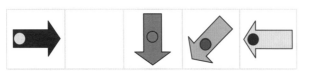

                                          a   b   c   d   e

Now go on to the next page ➡

Which picture on the right best fits into the space in the grid on the left? Circle the letter.

Example

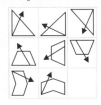

a   b   c   (d)   e

7.

a   b   c   d   e

8.

a   b   c   d   e

9.

a   b   c   d   e

10.

a   b   c   d   e

11.   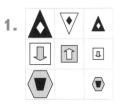

a   b   c   d   e

12.   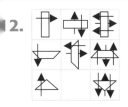

a   b   c   d   e

End of test

Score:	Time taken:	Target met?

In which picture on the right is the picture on the left hidden? Circle the letter.

Example

a   b   c   d   e

1.

a   b   c   d   e

2.

a   b   c   d   e

3.

a   b   c   d   e

4.

a   b   c   d   e

5.

a   b   c   d   e

6.

a   b   c   d   e

Now go on to the next page ➡

Which picture is the odd one out? Circle the letter.

Example

a   ⓑ   c   d   e

7.

a   b   c   d   e

8.

a   b   c   d   e

9.

a   b   c   d   e

0.

a   b   c   d   e

1.

a   b   c   d   e

2.

a   b   c   d   e

End of test

Score:		Time taken:		Target met?	

Which picture on the right is a reflection of the picture on the left? Circle the letter.

Example

a   b   c   d   e

1.

a   b   c   d   e

2.

a   b   c   d   e

3.

a   b   c   d   e

4.

a   b   c   d   e

5.

a   b   c   d   e

6.

a   b   c   d   e

Now go on to the next page ➡

What is the code of the final picture? Circle the letter.

Example

    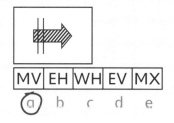

WV	EX	MH	WX	MV	EH	WH	EV	MX

ⓐ   b   c   d   e

7.

   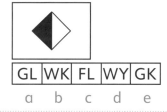

FY	WL	GY	FK	GL	WK	FL	WY	GK

a   b   c   d   e

8.

    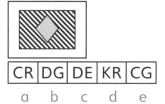

KE	DR	KG	CE	CR	DG	DE	KR	CG

a   b   c   d   e

9.

 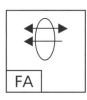 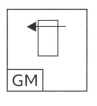 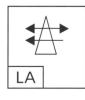 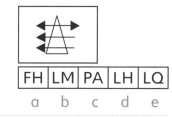

GQ	FA	PH	GM	LA	FH	LM	PA	LH	LQ

a   b   c   d   e

10.

    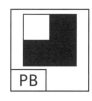 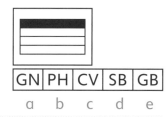

GH	PV	CH	SN	PB	GN	PH	CV	SB	GB

a   b   c   d   e

11.

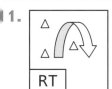  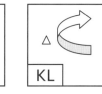 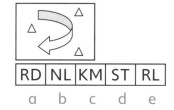

RT	SD	NM	ND	KL	RD	NL	KM	ST	RL

a   b   c   d   e

12.

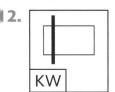 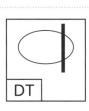 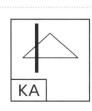 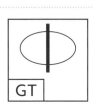 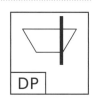 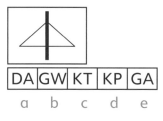

KW	DT	KA	GT	DP	DA	GW	KT	KP	GA

a   b   c   d   e

End of test

Score:	Time taken:	Target met?

Which picture on the right can be made by combining the two shapes on the left? Circle the letter

Example

 + =

a   b   c   d   (e)

1. + =

a   b   c   d   e

2. + =

a   b   c   d   e

3. + =

a   b   c   d   e

4. + =

a   b   c   d   e

5. + =

a   b   c   d   e

6. + =

a   b   c   d   e

Now go on to the next page ➡

Which cube can be made from the net? Circle the letter.

Example

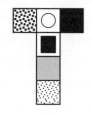

a   b   c   d   e

7.

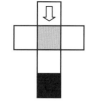

a   b   c   d   e

8.

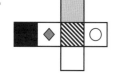

a   b   c   d   e

9.

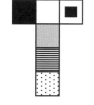

a   b   c   d   e

10.

a   b   c   d   e

11.

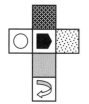

a   b   c   d   e

12.

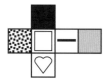

a   b   c   d   e

End of test

Score:	Time taken:	Target met?

Which picture on the right belongs to the group on the left? Circle the letter.

Example

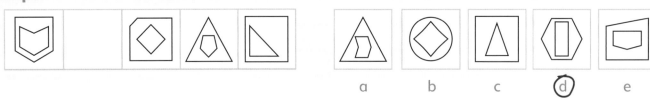

1.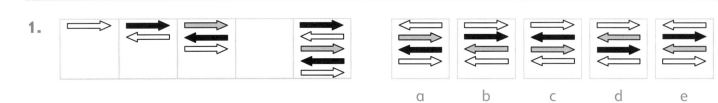

2.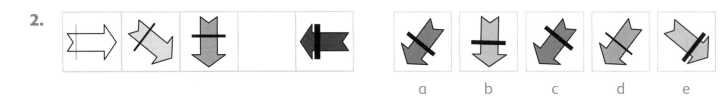

3.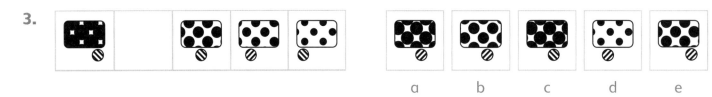

4.

5.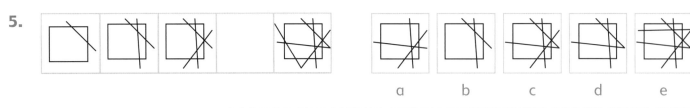

6.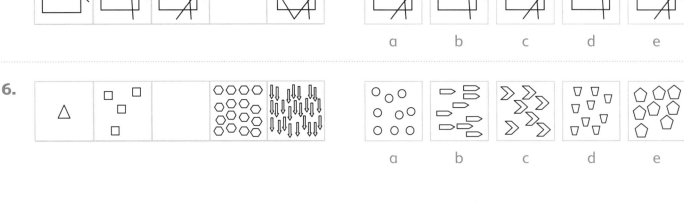

Now go on to the next page ➡

Which blocks on the right make up the 3D shape on the left? Circle the letter.

Example

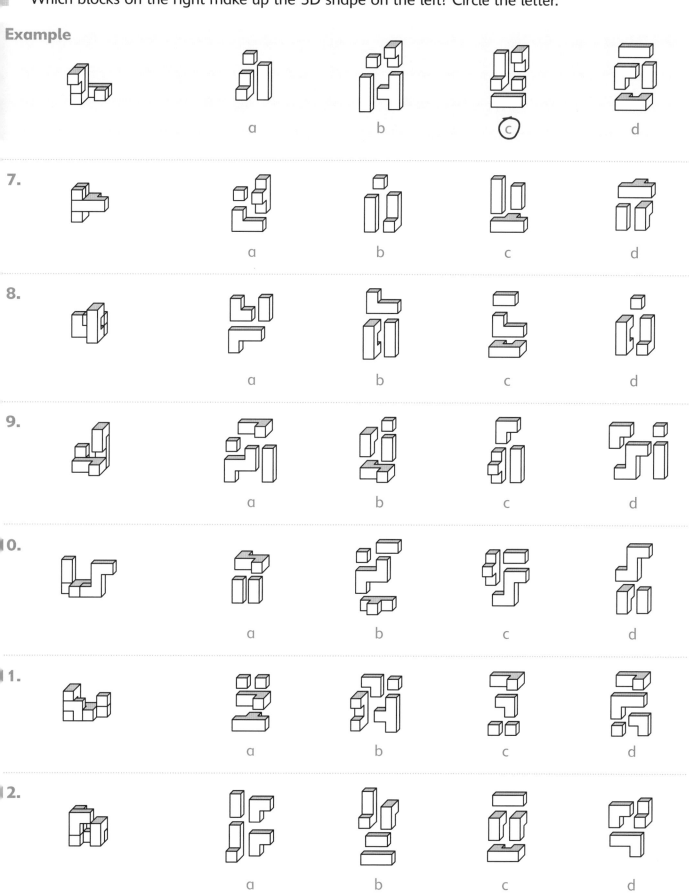

7.

8.

9.

10.

11.

12.

End of test

| Score: | Time taken: | Target met? |

Target time: **7 minutes**

Which 2D plan view on the right belongs to the 3D shape on the left? Circle the letter.

Example

  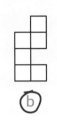

a   ⓑ   c   d

1.

  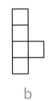 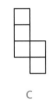 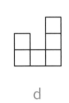

a   b   c   d

2.

a   b   c   d

3.

a   b   c   d

4.

  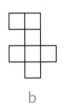 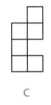 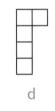

a   b   c   d

5.

   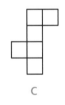 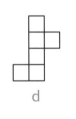

a   b   c   d

6.

 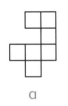 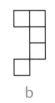 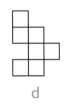

a   b   c   d

Now go on to the next page ➡

Which picture is the odd one out? Circle the letter.

Example

a   ⓑ   c   d   e

7.

a   b   c   d   e

8.

a   b   c   d   e

9.

a   b   c   d   e

10.

a   b   c   d   e

11.

a   b   c   d   e

12.

a   b   c   d   e

End of test

Score:		Time taken:		Target met?	

Which net can be made from the cube? Circle the letter.

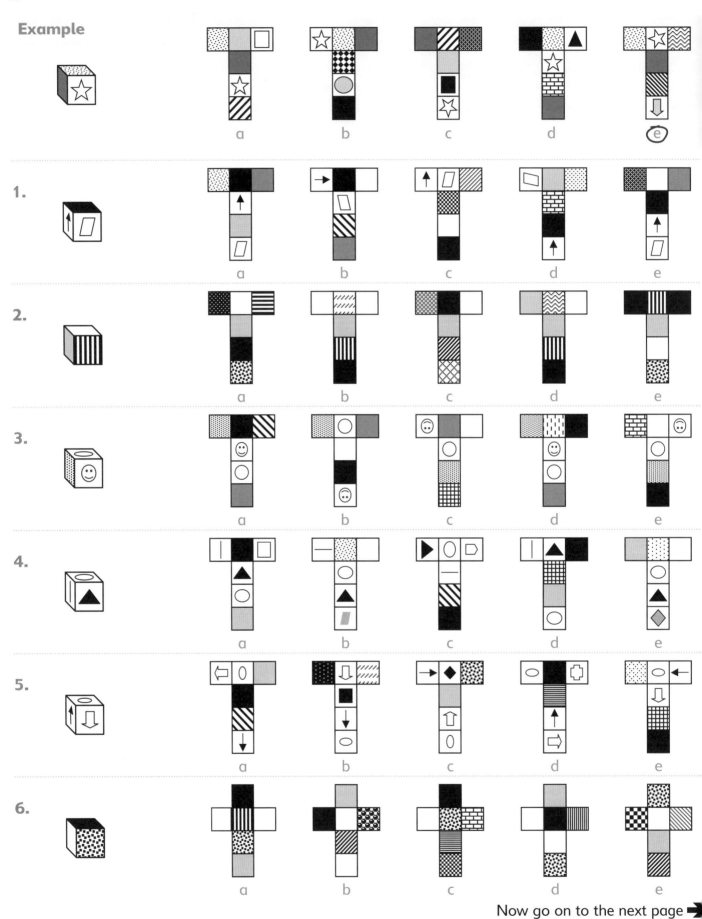

In which picture on the right is the picture on the left hidden? Circle the letter.

Example

7.

8.

9.

10.

11.

12.

End of test

Score:	Time taken:	Target met?

Which picture on the right best fits into the space in the grid on the left? Circle the letter.

Example

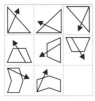

                    a   b   c   **(d)**   e

1.

                    a   b   c   d   e

2.

                    a   b   c   d   e

3.

                    a   b   c   d   e

4.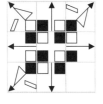

                    a   b   c   d   e

5.

                    a   b   c   d   e

6.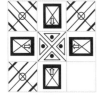

                    a   b   c   d   e

Now go on to the next page ➡

Non-verbal Reasoning Rapid Tests 5 Answers

Notes for parents, tutors, teachers and other adult helpers

- **Non-verbal Reasoning Rapid Tests 5** is designed for 10- and 11-year-olds, but may also be suitable for some children of other ages.

- Remove this pull-out section before giving the book to the child.

- Before the child begins work on the first test, together read the instructions headed **What to do** on page 2. As you do so, point out to the child the different elements in **Section 1 Test 1**.

- Make sure that the child understands how to answer multiple choice questions and has a pencil, an eraser and a sheet of rough paper. Also ensure that the child is able to see a clock or a watch.

- Explain to the child how they should go about timing the test. Alternatively, you may wish to time the test yourself. When the child has finished the test, together work out the **Time taken** and complete the box that appears at the end of the test.

- Mark the child's work using this pull-out section, giving one mark for each correct answer. There are a total of 12 marks available for each test. Then complete the **Score** box at the end of the test.

- This table shows you how to mark the **Target met?** box and the **Action** notes help you to plan the next step. However, these are suggestions only. Please use your own judgement as you decide how best to proceed.

Score	Time taken	Target met?	Action
1–6	Any	Not yet	Give the child the previous book in the series. Provide help and support as needed.
7–9	Any	Not yet	Encourage the child to keep practising using the tests in this book. The child may need to repeat some tests. If so, wait a few weeks or the child may simply remember the correct answers. Provide help and support as needed.
10–12	Over target – child took too long	Not yet	
10–12	On target – child took suggested time or less	Yes	Encourage the child to keep practising using further tests in this book, and to move on to the next book when you think this is appropriate.

- After finishing each test, the child should fill in the **Progress chart** on page 40.

- Whatever the test score, always encourage the child to have another go at the questions that they got wrong – without looking at the solutions. If the child's answers are still incorrect, work through these questions together. Demonstrate the correct method if necessary.

- If the child struggles with particular question types, help them to develop the strategies needed.

Answers

1. **c** Each picture contains two rectangles, a black oval, a line and a circle.
2. **e** Each picture contains an even number of rhombuses.
3. **b** Each picture contains two identical shapes where one has been rotated 90° clockwise.
4. **a** Each picture contains a line crossing into a quadrilateral, both with the same line width.
5. **d** Each picture contains a rectangle and an oval with the same line type.
6. **d** Each picture contains a large shape and a small rectangle in the same colour, attached to another shape.
7. **b** The colours change – grey becomes white, black becomes grey and white becomes black.
8. **e** The picture is reflected in the horizontal mirror line.
9. **a** The picture is reflected in the horizontal mirror line but the thin arrow stays in the same orientation.
10. **d** The number of rhombuses doubles and half become black.
11. **b** The picture is rotated 90° clockwise, the black and white shapes swap places, and the small right-angled arrow is then reflected.
12. **e** The shape is rotated 180° and added to the existing shape. The stripes in the original shape are reflected.

Section 1 Test 2
(pages 6–7)

1. **b** The circle moves gradually down and is on alternating sides, while the horizontal line gradually moves up.
2. **b** Repeating pattern
3. **a** A smaller hexagon is added to each picture and all the hexagons change colour each time.
4. **d** The picture is rotated 90° clockwise.

5. **e** Two black circles are added and three white circles are removed each time.
6. **c** The arrow is rotated 45° clockwise and gets paler, while the circle gets darker and moves towards the arrow head.
7. **b** The picture is rotated 90° clockwise.
8. **a** The picture is rotated 90° clockwise.
9. **d** The outer central squares are rotated 90°.
10. **e** The shape matches the row, while its size matches the column, and there is a dark, medium and light shaded shape in each row and column.
11. **a** The picture is reflected in the horizontal mirror line, gets smaller and alternates in colour across each row.
12. **c** The picture is rotated 90° clockwise, and an extra arrow is added which faces in the opposite direction and alternates being over or under the white shape.

Section 1 Test 3
(pages 8–9)

1. **c**
2. **d**
3. **e**
4. **b**
5. **b**
6. **c**

7. **d** The others are all triangles.
8. **b** The others have only one black rectangle.
9. **e** The others have seven arrow heads.
10. **e** The others all have the circle on a corner of the large shape.
11. **c** The others are all quadrilaterals.

12. a The others are rotations of the same picture.

Section 1 Test 4
(pages 10–11)

1. c

2. a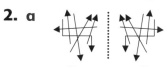

3. e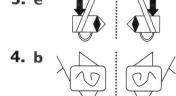

4. b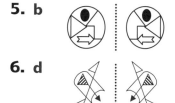

5. b

6. d

7. a First letter – shape
Second letter – position of black half

8. b First letter – stripe direction
Second letter – colour of internal shape

9. d First letter – shape
Second letter – number of arrow heads

10. c First letter – shape
Second letter – fraction coloured

11. d First letter – arrow direction
Second letter – number of triangles

12. e First letter – line position
Second letter – shape

Section 1 Test 5
(pages 12–13)

1. d

2. c

3. e

4. b

5. a

6. e

If in doubt about the nets of cubes, copy them onto a piece of paper and fold them up.

7. b	**10. d**
8. c	**11. b**
9. e	**12. c**

Section 1 Test 6
(pages 14–15)

1. d One arrow facing in the opposite direction is added to the bottom each time and the colours move down.

2. a The arrow rotates 45° clockwise and gets darker, while the line moves towards the arrow head and gets thicker.

3. a The black dots get smaller, the circle moves from right to left and its stripe direction alternates.

4. b The picture is rotated 45° anticlockwise.

5. c One extra line is added each time.

6. b The shapes increase in square numbers and the number of sides on the shapes goes up one each time.

7. a This is made up of a single block (dark orange), a T-shaped block (white) and what looks like a long L-shaped block (purple).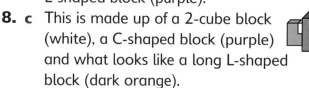

8. c This is made up of a 2-cube block (white), a C-shaped block (purple) and what looks like a long L-shaped block (dark orange).

9. d This is made up of what looks like a Z-shaped block (white), a short L-shaped block (purple), a 3-cube block (dark orange) and a single cube (pale orange).

Answers

10. **c** This is made up of a Z-shaped block (white), what looks like a T-shaped block (purple) and a 2-cube block (dark orange).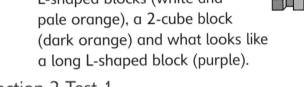

11. **b** This is made up of a single cube (pale orange), what looks like a T-shaped block (purple), a short L-shaped block (dark orange) and what looks like a C-shaped block (white).

12. **a** This is made up of two short L-shaped blocks (white and pale orange), a 2-cube block (dark orange) and what looks like a long L-shaped block (purple).

Section 2 Test 1
(pages 16–17)

1. **c**

2. **a**

3. **b**

4. **d**

5. **b**

6. **c**

7. **b** The others are rotations of the same picture.
8. **e** The others are rotations of the same picture.
9. **e** The others all have a rhombus too.
10. **b** The others all have an even number of sides.
11. **d** The others all have a line of symmetry.
12. **c** The others all have one solid line.

Section 2 Test 2
(pages 18–19)

If in doubt about the nets of cubes, copy them onto a piece of paper and fold them up.

1. **c**
2. **a**
3. **e**
4. **d**
5. **a**
6. **c**
7. **e**
8. **d**
9. **c**
10. **e**
11. **b**
12. **a**

Section 2 Test 3
(pages 20–21)

1. **c** The corners are reflective.
2. **d** The corners are reflective.
3. **d** The shapes move outward but the colours stay in the same order.
4. **b** The corners rotate 90° and the small squares alternate colour.
5. **a** The corners are reflective.
6. **d** The corners are reflective.
7. **c**
8. **a**
9. **e**
10. **c**
11. **b**
12. **d**

Section 2 Test 4
(pages 22–23)

1. c   (note position of rectangle and overlaps)

2. b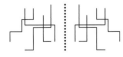

3. e

4. d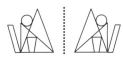

5. d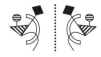

6. a

7. b The shape has been rotated 135° anticlockwise.

8. d The shape has been rotated 45° anticlockwise.

9. c The shape has been rotated 135° anticlockwise.

10. b The shape has been rotated 180°.

11. d The shape has been rotated 45° anticlockwise.

12. d The shape has been rotated 135° anticlockwise.

Section 2 Test 5
(pages 24–25)

1. a First letter – stripe direction
Second letter – internal shape colour

2. d First letter – outline thickness
Second letter – colour

3. a First letter – star shape
Second letter – internal shape shading

4. b First letter – line type
Second letter – rectangle position

5. e First letter – number of sides
Second letter – line direction

6. a First letter – arrow direction
Second letter – arrow thickness

7. c The parallelogram and stripes alternate direction, while the star moves down on alternate sides.

8. b The rectangle gets darker and the diagonal and horizontal lines increase by one, while the horizontal lines move lower.

9. d The stripes alternate while the circle moves clockwise around the rectangle and alternates its colour.

10. c The picture is rotated 45° anticlockwise and the design of the arrow alternates.

11. b The rectangle gets darker, the oval gets paler, and the star alternates colour.

12. d The picture is rotated 45° anticlockwise.

Section 2 Test 6
(pages 26–27)

1. c

2. b

3. c

4. b

5. a

6. c

7. e The outer shape is reflected in the horizontal mirror line and the arrow is rotated 90° clockwise.

8. c The outer shape is rotated 90° clockwise and the arrow rotates 90° anticlockwise.

9. c The picture is reflected in the horizontal mirror line.

10. b The picture is reflected in the vertical mirror line.

11. c Two smaller shapes are created with the same pattern and total number of sides as the larger shape which turns white.

12. a The colours change – black to white, grey to black and white to grey.

Section 3 Test 1
(pages 28–29)

1. b A quarter of the rectangles are shaded black in each picture.

2. a Each picture contains a dashed arrow.

3. b The style of lines and their direction are the same in each picture.

4. c Each picture contains 15 sides.

5. d Each picture contains an arrow facing anticlockwise within a circle, plus two shapes which are the same.

6. c Each picture contains a large white shape with the same shape inside but shaded.

If in doubt about the nets of cubes, copy them onto a piece of paper and fold them up.

7. b	**10. b**
8. a	**11. c**
9. c	**12. e**

Section 3 Test 2
(pages 30–31)

1. c Reflective corners

2. e Reflective outer central squares

3. d Reflective corners

4. b The picture is rotated 90° clockwise, and gets smaller and darker.

5. a Reflective corners (note triangle)

6. e The arrow rotates 90° anticlockwise and the main shape rotates 90° clockwise.

7. d

8. d

9. b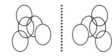

10. b (note overlaps)

11. d

12. a

Section 3 Test 3
(pages 32–33)

1. b

2. e

3. e

4. c (note overlaps)

5. e (note overlaps)

6. a

7. b The others all have one angled line and three straight lines.

8. d The others are all rotations of the same picture.

9. b The others have a reflection of the larger shape inside.

10. e The others all have five lines (and four line crosses).

11. b The others have half the number of black squares as white squares.

12. d The others all have one small shape inside the larger shape.

Section 3 Test 4
(pages 34–35)

If in doubt about the nets of cubes, copy them onto a piece of paper and fold them up.

1. c   4. a
2. d   5. c
3. d   6. e
7. b

8. a

9. b

10. a

11. c

12. a

Section 3 Test 5
(pages 36–37)

1. **b** The small internal shape becomes the largest, the other two shapes shrink and the top shape becomes black.
2. **a** The picture gets larger and then the top shape is reflected in the horizontal mirror line and becomes grey.
3. **a** The line moves up, the striped shape moves to the other end of the line and is reflected in the horizontal mirror line.
4. **e** The picture is rotated 90° clockwise. Then the small white shapes are reflected in the vertical mirror line and change to black, while the large shape changes to white.

5. **b** The picture is rotated 180°.
6. **c** The picture is rotated 180°.
7. **d** The picture is rotated 45° clockwise.
8. **a** Repeating pattern
9. **b** The picture is rotated 90° clockwise.
10. **a** The double-headed arrows decrease by one each time.
11. **e** The shading and the lines move out concentrically.
12. **b** The circle moves up, while the vertical line moves left and the horizontal line moves down.

Section 3 Test 6
(pages 38–39)

1. **c** First letter – triangle colour
Second letter – number of circles
2. **e** First letter – internal shape
Second letter – external shape
3. **a** First letter – number of circles
Second letter – arrow position
4. **e** First letter – arrow direction
Second letter – triangle colour
5. **d** First letter – number of white shapes
Second letter – number of sides
6. **e** First letter – outer shape
Second letter – number of black circles
7. **e** Each picture contains three circles and three lines which cross twice.
8. **b** Each picture contains a large white shape with a small black shape inside, an angled line and a white star.
9. **a** Each picture contains an arrow.
10. **d** Each picture contains a total of 17 sides (including the larger shape) and the internal shapes are white.
11. **c** Each picture contains a white rectangle.
12. **d** The number of small shapes in each picture is equal to the number of sides of the large shape. The small shapes are the same shape as the large shape and one is black.

This book of answers is a pull-out section from
Non-verbal Reasoning Rapid Tests 5

Published by **Schofield & Sims Ltd**,
7 Mariner Court, Wakefield, West Yorkshire WF4 3FL, UK
Telephone 01484 607080
www.schofieldandsims.co.uk

First published in 2014
This edition copyright © Schofield & Sims Ltd, 2018
Eighth impression 2022

Author: **Rebecca Brant**
Rebecca Brant has asserted her moral right under the Copyright, Designs and Patents Act, 1988, to be identified as the author of this work.

British Library Cataloguing in Publication Data
A catalogue record for this book is available from the British Library.

Commissioned by **Carolyn Richardson Publishing Services**

Design by **Oxford Designers & Illustrators**
Printed in the UK by **Page Bros (Norwich) Ltd**

ISBN 978 07217 1467 7

Which picture on the right can be made by combining the two shapes on the left? Circle the letter.

Example

 =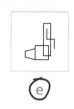

a   b   c   d   e

7.  =

a   b   c   d   e

8.  =

a   b   c   d   e

9. 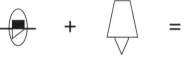 =

a   b   c   d   e

10.  =

a   b   c   d   e

11.  =

a   b   c   d   e

12. 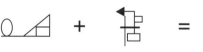 =

a   b   c   d   e

End of test

Score:	Time taken:	Target met?

Which picture on the right is a reflection of the picture on the left? Circle the letter.

Example

a   b   ⓒ   d   e

1.

a   b   c   d   e

2.

a   b   c   d   e

3.
          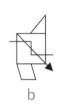         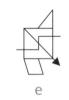

a   b   c   d   e

4.

a   b   c   d   e

5.

a   b   c   d   e

6.

a   b   c   d   e

Now go on to the next page ➡

Which 3D shape on the right is a rotation of the 3D shape on the left? Circle the letter.

Example

a   b   (c)   d

7.

  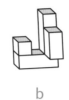

a   b   c   d

8.

a   b   c   d

9.

a   b   c   d

10.

a   b   c   d

11.

a   b   c   d

12.

a   b   c   d

End of test

Score:	Time taken:	Target met?

What is the code of the final picture? Circle the letter.

Example

  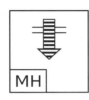  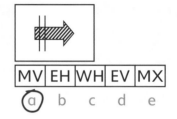

WV | EX | MH | WX | MV EH WH EV MX

ⓐ b c d e

1.

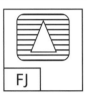   

FJ | DS | HQ | ZS | DJ | ZQ HS DQ ZJ FS

a b c d e

2.

    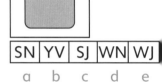

SC | YJ | WC | YN | SV | SN YV SJ WN WJ

a b c d e

3.

 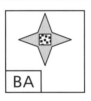    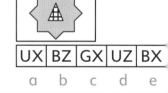

CX | BA | CZ | UR | GA | UX BZ GX UZ BX

a b c d e

4.

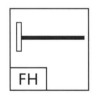 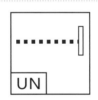 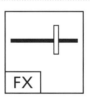 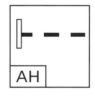 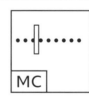 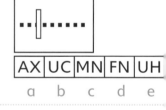

FH | UN | FX | AH | MC | AX UC MN FN UH

a b c d e

5.

    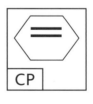 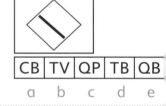

TP | CV | QV | MB | CP | CB TV QP TB QB

a b c d e

6.

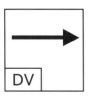 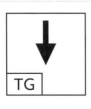  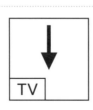 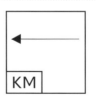 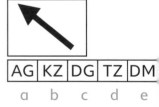

DV | TG | AZ | TV | KM | AG KZ DG TZ DM

a b c d e

Now go on to the next page ➡

Which picture on the right belongs to the group on the left? Circle the letter.

Example

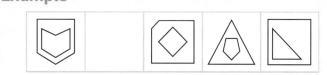

a   b   c   ⓓ   e

7.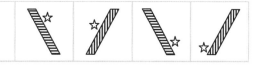

a   b   c   d   e

8.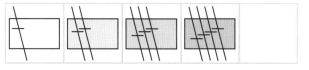

a   b   c   d   e

9.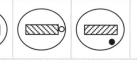

a   b   c   d   e

10.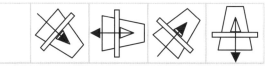

a   b   c   d   e

11.

a   b   c   d   e

12.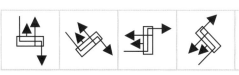

a   b   c   d   e

End of test

Score:		Time taken:		Target met?	

Target time: **7 minutes**

Which picture on the right shows the unfolded paper? Circle the letter.

Example

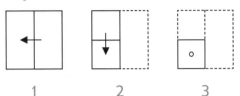

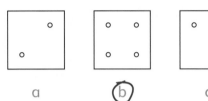

| 1 | 2 | 3 | a | b | c | d |

1.

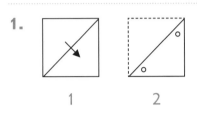

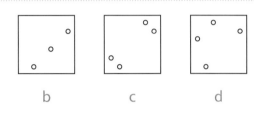

| 1 | 2 | a | b | c | d |

2.

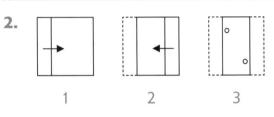

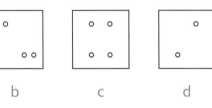

| 1 | 2 | 3 | a | b | c | d |

3.

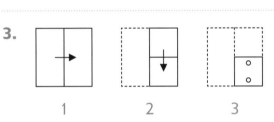

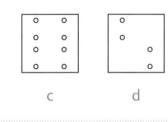

| 1 | 2 | 3 | a | b | c | d |

4.

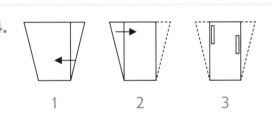

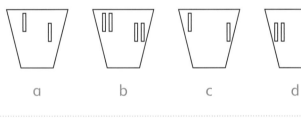

| 1 | 2 | 3 | a | b | c | d |

5.

| 1 | 2 | 3 | a | b | c | d |

6.

| 1 | 2 | 3 | a | b | c | d |

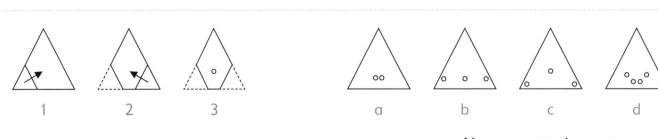

Now go on to the next page ➡

Schofield & Sims

There is a pair of pictures on the left. Which one of the five pictures on the right goes with the single picture on the left to make a pair in the same way? Circle the letter.

Example

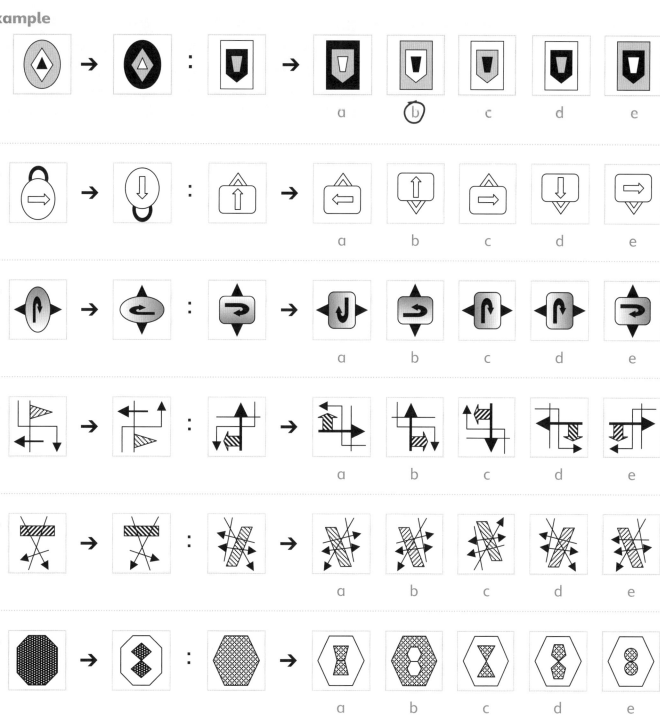

7.

8.

9.

10.

11.

12.

End of test

| Score: | | Time taken: | | Target met? | |

Target time: **7 minutes**

Which picture on the right belongs to the group on the left? Circle the letter.

Example

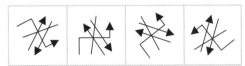

          a   b   c   ⓓ   e

1.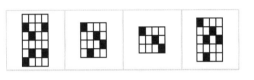

          a   b   c   d   e

2.

          a   b   c   d   e

3.

          a   b   c   d   e

4.

          a   b   c   d   e

5.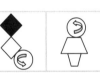

          a   b   c   d   e

6.

          a   b   c   d   e

Now go on to the next page ➡

Which cube can be made from the net? Circle the letter.

Example

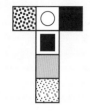

u   b   c   ⓓ   e

7.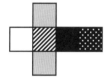

a   b   c   d   e

8.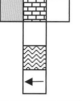

a   b   c   d   e

9.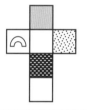

a   b   c   d   e

10.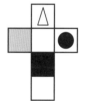

a   b   c   d   e

11.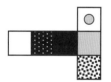

a   b   c   d   e

12.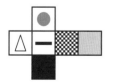

a   b   c   d   e

End of test

Score:	Time taken:	Target met?

Target time: **7 minutes**

 Which picture on the right best fits into the space in the grid on the left? Circle the letter.

Example

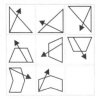

a

b

c

d

e

1.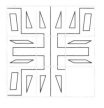

a

b

c

d

e

2.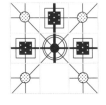

a

b

c

d

e

3.

a

b

c

d

e

4.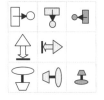

a

b

c

d

e

5.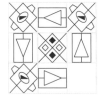

a

b

c

d

e

6.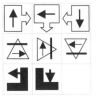

a

b

c

d

e

Now go on to the next page ➡

Which picture on the right is a reflection of the picture on the left? Circle the letter.

Example

a   b   ⓒ   d   e

7.

a   b   c   d   e

8.

a   b   c   d   e

9.

a   b   c   d   e

10.

a   b   c   d   e

11.

a   b   c   d   e

12.

a   b   c   d   e

End of test

Score:	Time taken:	Target met?

In which picture on the right is the picture on the left hidden? Circle the letter.

Example

a   b   c   d   e

1.

a   b   c   d   e

2.

a   b   c   d   e

3.

a   b   c   d   e

4.

a   b   c   d   e

5.

a   b   c   d   e

6.

a   b   c   d   e

Now go on to the next page ➡

Which picture is the odd one out? Circle the letter.

Example

a   ⓑ   c   d   e

7.

a   b   c   d   e

8.

a   b   c   d   e

9.

a   b   c   d   e

10.

a   b   c   d   e

11.

a   b   c   d   e

12.

a   b   c   d   e

End of test

Score:	Time taken:	Target met?

Which net can be made from the cube? Circle the letter.

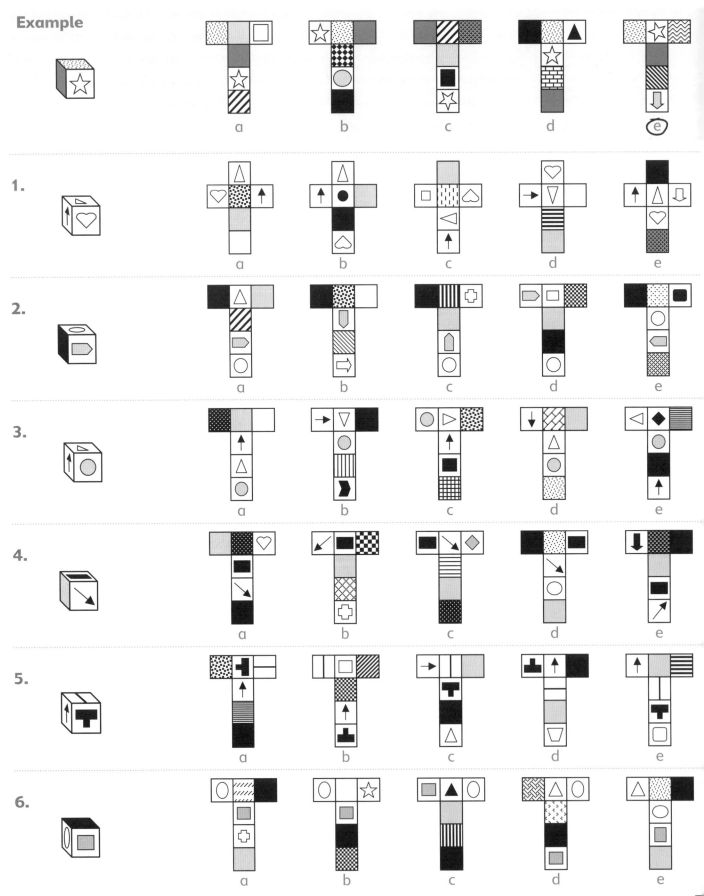

Now go on to the next page ➜

Which picture on the right can be made by combining the two shapes on the left? Circle the letter.

Example

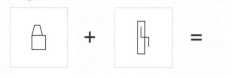 + =

                a   b   c   d   (e)

7. + 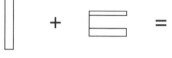 =

                a   b   c   d   e

8.  =

                a   b   c   d   e

9.  =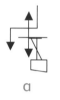

                a   b   c   d   e

10.

                a   b   c   d   e

11.

                a   b   c   d   e

12.

                a   b   c   d   e

End of test

Score:		Time taken:		Target met?	

There is a pair of pictures on the left. Which one of the five pictures on the right goes with the single picture on the left to make a pair in the same way? Circle the letter.

Example

a   (b)   c   d   e

1.

a   b   c   d   e

2.

a   b   c   d   e

3.

a   b   c   d   e

4.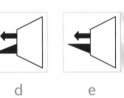

a   b   c   d   e

5.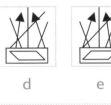

a   b   c   d   e

6.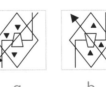

a   b   c   d   e

Now go on to the next page ➡

Which picture on the right belongs to the group on the left? Circle the letter.

Example

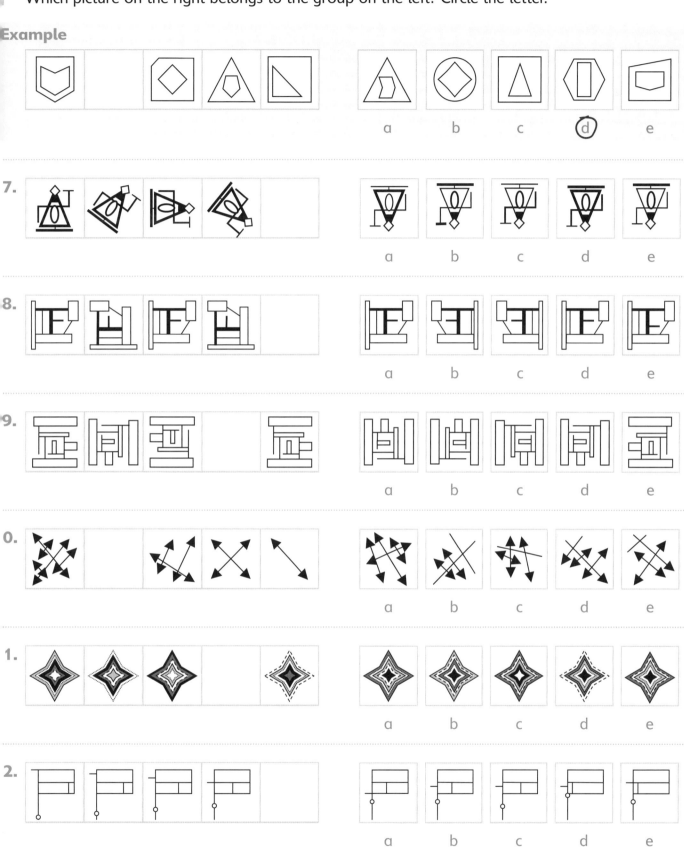

End of test

| Score: | | Time taken: | | Target met? | |

What is the code of the final picture? Circle the letter.

Example

 WV

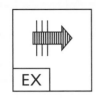 EX

 MH

 WX

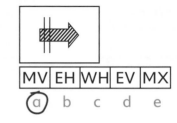

MV	EH	WH	EV	MX
ⓐ	b	c	d	e

1.

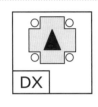 DX

 RG

 PZ

 DZ

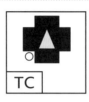 TC

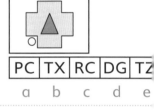

PC	TX	RC	DG	TZ
a	b	c	d	e

2.

 DF

 RT

 UJ

 DT

 US

UF	DJ	RJ	UT	RF
a	b	c	d	e

3.

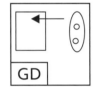 GD

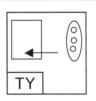 TY

 PD

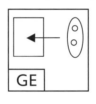 GE

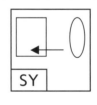 SY

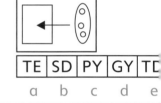

TE	SD	PY	GY	TD
a	b	c	d	e

4.

 ED

 RP

 CS

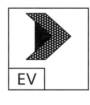 EV

 HD

HV	ES	CP	HS	RV
a	b	c	d	e

5.

 HS

 RN

 PZ

 DN

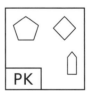 PK

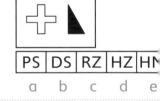

PS	DS	RZ	HZ	HN
a	b	c	d	e

6.

 CA

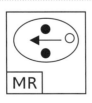 MR

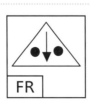 FR

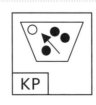 KP

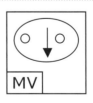 MV

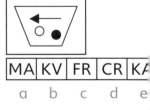

MA	KV	FR	CR	KA
a	b	c	d	e

Now go on to the next page ➡

Which picture on the right belongs to the group on the left? Circle the letter.

Example

a   b   c   (d)   e

7.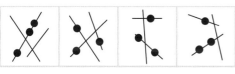

a   b   c   d   e

8.

a   b   c   d   e

9.

a   b   c   d   e

0.

a   b   c   d   e

1.

a   b   c   d   e

2.

a   b   c   d   e

End of test

Score:		Time taken:		Target met?	

Progress chart

Write the score (out of 12) for each test in the box provided on the right of the graph.
Then colour in the row next to the box to represent this score.

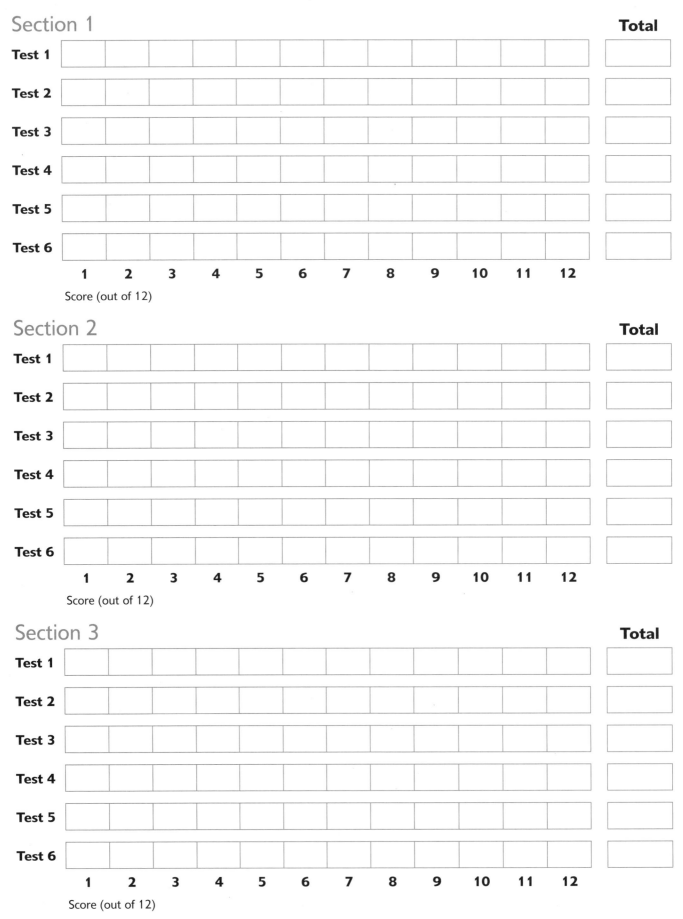

Section 1

Total

Test 1

Test 2

Test 3

Test 4

Test 5

Test 6

1   2   3   4   5   6   7   8   9   10   11   12

Score (out of 12)

Section 2

Total

Test 1

Test 2

Test 3

Test 4

Test 5

Test 6

1   2   3   4   5   6   7   8   9   10   11   12

Score (out of 12)

Section 3

Total

Test 1

Test 2

Test 3

Test 4

Test 5

Test 6

1   2   3   4   5   6   7   8   9   10   11   12

Score (out of 12)

Clem

B B C

Speak out

3RD EDITION

C1-C2

Student's Book and eBook

CONTENTS

LISTENING/VIDEO	SPEAKING	WRITING
	Talk about conventional wisdom	
Listen to an extract from a radio programme about future learning	Talk about future educational developments	Note-taking and summary writing **FUTURE SKILLS** Self-management
	Discuss ways of developing people's creativity at work or college **FUTURE SKILLS** Collaboration **MEDIATION SKILLS** share recommendations	
BBC **Street Interviews** about teaching and learning	Discuss education	Write a nomination for an award
	Talk about applying to be 'City of Arts'	
Understand a radio interview about interpreting	Talk about translation apps **FUTURE SKILLS** Communication	Write an informative summary for a careers brochure
	Talk about traditions and cultures **FUTURE SKILLS** Social responsibility **MEDIATION SKILLS** talk about a character and speculate on their motivation	
BBC **Programme** *Nadiya's American Adventure*	Propose a new restaurant	Write a blog post about a food hotspot
Listen to a question-and-answer session after a talk on job hunting	Record a video résumé **FUTURE SKILLS** Communication	Write a cover email/letter
	Talk about solutions to problems with remote working **FUTURE SKILLS** Communication	
	Discuss issues related to work **FUTURE SKILLS** Communication **MEDIATION SKILLS** share and listen to viewpoints	
BBC **Street Interviews** about jobs	Make suggestions for a better workplace	Write a report on work experience
	Have a debate about space exploration **FUTURE SKILLS** Critical thinking	
Understand a radio programme about a charity	Talk about designing an app to help people in need	Write an informal review of a product or service
	Present survey results **FUTURE SKILLS** Communication **MEDIATION SKILLS** explain a complex diagram	
BBC **Programme** *Extinction: The Facts*	Plan a documentary introduction	Write an opinion essay

CONTENTS

LISTENING/VIDEO	SPEAKING	WRITING
	Talk about positive and negative first impressions	
Understand a radio programme about a fake news story	Talk about fake news	Write a report
	Give a presentation **MEDIATION SKILLS** give opinions about a course of action	
BBC Street Interviews about people who influence us	Discussing types of influence	Write a contribution for a website
	Talk about books or films you think should become classics	Write a review of a book or film
Understand a radio discussion about poetry and song	Talk about and agree on a playlist for space	
	Tell an anecdote **MEDIATION SKILLS** process and report a range of opinions	
BBC Programme *Everyday Miracles*	Talk about selecting classic designs	Write an account of an exhibition
	Talk about decisions and their impacts **FUTURE SKILLS** Teamwork	
Understand a radio programme about reading	Talk about how to encourage people to read for pleasure	Write a blog post
	Oppose and defend statements **MEDIATION SKILLS** identify what is relevant in a talk	
BBC Street Interviews about choice	Prioritising essential items	Write a newspaper opinion piece
	Give a shout-out to somebody who deserves it	
Understand a radio programme about synaesthesia	Talk about sensory reactions	Write a description
	Discuss ways to create a healthier work environment **FUTURE SKILLS** Goal setting: time management **MEDIATION SKILLS** make a decision as a group	
BBC Programme *QI*	Describing psychological effects	Write a story about strange effects

MEDIATION BANK p144   **AUDIOSCRIPTS** p160   **VIDEOSCRIPTS** p171

PARTS OF SPEECH

1 A Work in pairs and discuss the questions.

1 How important is it to set goals for yourself when learning something new?

2 What different motivations might people have for studying a language to a high level?

B Read the article. What surprising facts did the recent survey throw up?

Goals and growth

'If you know your goals, you're more likely to reach them.' Quite clearly, this could be said about many things, including language learning. People who devote time and energy to learning a foreign language take on this challenge for several reasons. What is surprising, however, is that a significant proportion of advanced learners of English are unable to describe their motivation in anything but the vaguest of terms. In some cases, not only were the respondents to a survey about study goals unable to actually identify their goals, but they also admitted to being remarkably undisciplined when it came to their study habits, which were often part-time.

C Answer the questions and compare with a partner. Are you similar or different?

1 What is your motivation for learning English?

2 What opportunities do you have to use English in your daily life?

3 What are your study habits when it comes to learning English?

4 Which aspects of English do you hope to have improved by the end of this course?

D Find examples of the following in the article in Ex 1B.

1 a conjunction
2 a comment adverb
3 inversion
4 a relative pronoun
5 a compound adjective
6 a defining relative clause
7 a phrasal verb
8 a gerund
9 a passive form
10 a comparative structure

GRAMMAR

2 Work in pairs and discuss why the tenses and phrases in bold have been used and how they affect the meanings of the sentences.

1 **a** I **really enjoy** studying the intricacies of grammar.
   b I'm **really enjoying** studying the intricacies of grammar.

2 **a** We've **learnt** how to use a whole range of punctuation.
   b We've **been learning** how to use a whole range of punctuation.

3 **a** If I **were working** in England, I'**d be able** to practise my English every day.
   b If I **work** in England, I'**ll be able** to practise my English every day.

4 **a** **Despite the weather**, we completed the walk in just over an hour.
   b **Because of the weather**, we completed the walk in just over an hour.

5 **a** We'**ll have covered** the main grammatical structures by the end of the month.
   b We'**ll be covering** the main grammatical structures at the end of the month.

6 **a** The teacher said she **was** extremely pleased with the progress we'd made over the course.
   b The teacher said she'**d been** extremely pleased with the progress we'd made over the course.

7 **a** I've **tried to check out** some websites for advice.
   b I've **tried checking out** some websites for advice.

FUNCTIONS

3 A Work in pairs. What would you say in these situations (1–4)? How many different phrases could you use?

1 Your friend finds learning new vocabulary difficult and asks you for your advice.
   a ....
   b ....
   c ....

2 You'd like your friend to look over an essay you've written.
   a ....
   b ....
   c ....

3 Your friend asks for your opinion about the importance of trying to achieve perfect pronunciation in English.
   a ....
   b ....
   c ....

4 You borrowed a book from a friend and you've mislaid it.
   a ....
   b ....
   c ....

B Compare your ideas in Ex 3A with the class. Then work in pairs and discuss the questions about learning English.

1 What are the best ways of learning new vocabulary?

2 Is it important to have perfect pronunciation? Why/Why not?

3 Should a fear of making mistakes put students off speaking in English?

learning

1

VLOGS

Q: What's one thing you think everyone should learn to do?

1 ▶ Watch the video. What things do people mention that you think are essential for everyone to learn?

2 What other things would you recommend that everyone learns?

GSE LEARNING OBJECTIVES

1A READING | Read an article about attitudes to failure: describing attitudes; idioms

Pronunciation: *if* in natural speech

Talk about conventional wisdom: conditional forms

1B LISTENING | Understand a radio programme about future learning: collocations: education; compound nouns

Talk about future educational developments: nominal relative clauses

Pronunciation: emphatic syllable stress

Write a summary of an extract from a radio programme

1C HOW TO … | manage interaction during a discussion: creativity

Pronunciation: polite intonation

1D BBC STREET INTERVIEWS | Understand street interviews about teaching and learning

Talk about education: teaching and learning

Write a nomination for an award

1A Is that a fact?

GRAMMAR | conditional forms
VOCABULARY | describing attitudes; idioms
PRONUNCIATION | *if* in natural speech

READING

1 Look at the photos. Work in pairs and discuss the questions.

1 What is being learnt in each picture? What is the best way to learn these things?

2 When was the last time you learnt a new skill and how did you learn it?

3 In what ways is a learning process good for us?

4 In general, how do you cope when you do badly or fail at something? Give examples.

2 A Read the introduction to *Is failure good for you?*. What opinions might you find in the article? Scan the article to check.

B Which reporter holds a different view from the others? How is it different?

C Read the article again. Which reporter:

1 feels more strongly about the topic than the others? How do you know?

2 agrees with Kate that some often-repeated phrases are untrue?

3 is motivated to question their own attitudes by another's comments?

4 mentions an alternative career option?

5 compares two differing attitudes to failure from real experiences?

6 agrees with Molls that failing at something can in fact open up new opportunities?

VOCABULARY

describing attitudes

3 A Look at the phrases in bold in the article in Ex 2A. Which ones reflect the writer's opinion that a statement is:

1 true?   2 partially true?   3 completely wrong?

B Choose the correct options to complete the sentences.

1 Reading about how people sometimes just freeze in exams really **struck a chord / trotted out a trite phrase** with me. I've experienced the same thing, many times.

2 The advice about never giving up was, in my opinion, **spot on / way too oversimplistic**. It's misguided to say you should 'never' do something.

3 People might think it's **a sweeping statement / spot on**, but I'd say that to be successful at something you just need to practise.

4 It's **a complete fallacy / an element of truth** to claim you can become proficient in a foreign language within a few weeks, as the adverts suggest – we all know that can't be done. People **strike a chord / trot out these trite phrases** to get us to buy things.

5 I get irritated when I hear people coming out with **spot on / vacuous** comments on topics that are actually quite complex.

6 I think it's **an element of truth / patently not true** that our ability to learn a new language disappears as we become older.

7 It **rings true / is a complete fallacy** for me when people say that all things are good in moderation. Therefore, some level of failure is helpful to us, and beyond a certain point it becomes harmful.

C Work in pairs. Tell your partner about something you've read about or heard recently which:

a was patently not true.
b was a complete fallacy.
c was oversimplistic.
d was spot on.
e had an element of truth.
f struck a chord with you.

D Learn and practise. Go to the Vocabulary Bank.

▶▶ page 136 **VOCABULARY BANK** idioms

4 Work in pairs. Imagine you had been asked to write a comment for the article in Ex 2A. What would you have said?

Is failure good for you?

Have you messed up recently? Not achieved the right grades or had a cringe-worthy interview? Did friends pat you on the back and reassuringly murmur, 'Let it go, don't worry about it', 'Be resilient', 'Failure's not a bad thing – it's all part of the learning curve'? We are constantly being told failure can actually be a positive. But are you on board with this whole 'failure is good for you' thing? Recent research indicates that many of us are not and that comments like these are overly simplistic. In light of this, we asked four of our reporters from different departments how they feel about the topic. There might be a few surprises!

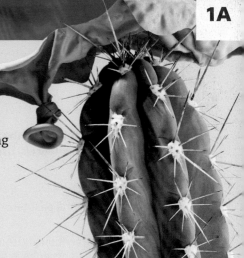

Molls Pickering | HEALTH

Well, no one likes to fail, do they? If you put your heart and soul into something, you don't want to be told it isn't good enough. But I think the whole attitude to failure has changed over the last fifty years, and in a good way. If we treat our failures as learning opportunities and not something to be ashamed of, we are going to make strides going forward in every aspect of our lives from learning at school, pursuing a career – even in relationships. My memories of the shame I felt when I failed school tests contrast dramatically with the way teachers used my son's failings to help him achieve success. Fear of failing can also entrap you and prevent you from taking risks. But for the intervention and encouragement of my son's drama teacher, he would never have risked going into acting. So, for me **the idea is spot on**. It definitely **rings true**. Failing can, and should, be a positive in that it makes you reassess and perhaps change tack, and I think this generation of young people are much better at dealing with it than mine was.

Kate Quinn | ARTS

I might be flying in the face of popular opinion and the results of numerous studies, but I simply cannot go along with the fashionable belief that failing is almost something to be pleased about because it allows you to learn and progress from what you've done wrong. OK, to me it **makes sense** that we shouldn't dwell on failure because that is – in itself – negative, and if we were to get hung up about all our mistakes, we would probably get nowhere in life. But, the old saying – try, try, try again – assumes that persistence will help you succeed. This is not necessarily true at all. It might be that however hard you try, however often you fail, you are not going to succeed because what you're trying to achieve lies outside your ability, or talent. It bugs me when I hear people saying that anyone can do anything, should they want it hard enough. Rubbish! **It is patently not true**. Give it a good go, but give up if you clearly don't have what it takes. Had I not accepted that I wasn't cut out to be a crime writer (seventy-one rejection letters!), I wouldn't be enjoying the rewards of being a reporter now! We need to get real about failure and think about what it is really telling us.

Ethan Knowles | SPORTS

Something **struck a chord with me** the other day. I was interviewing a local football manager, an intelligent guy, on the subject of criticism – and we all know football managers get their fair share of that! He admitted really resenting it and the sense of failure it brought, however constructive it was intended to be. In fact, he resented it so much that if it hadn't been for his love of the game, he would have thrown in the towel early on. He made the point that most humans probably feel the same, although we have been conditioned to accept criticism, and try to respond gratefully when we receive it. I could see where he was coming from, and I started to analyse my own reactions to being criticised (self-reflection being very on trend at the moment!). They are mixed. If I do my best and then get a critical reaction, the feeling of failure can be galling. After all, human beings are inherently self-centred creatures: we like to be liked, to be right, to succeed, to be praised. However, I also realised that as long as the person criticising me was someone I admired or respected, I was OK with it – at least to a certain extent … ☹

Jay Masters | BUSINESS

I, for one, simply cannot stand all these **vacuous comments** and **sweeping statements** we get on social media, like 'Failing is part of the journey.' I promise you, if I hear the word 'journey' once more in this context, I'm going to lose it. And as for 'failure is good for you', it's simply a saying that most definitely is not always true. I admit there is often **an element of truth** in there somewhere, but people overuse these phrases and treat them as if they're completely valid for all situations. They **trot out these trite phrases** regularly to explain or excuse whatever they've done or not done. For me, it's not just that **they are way too oversimplistic**, but were we to analyse them, we'd probably find some that are often actually wrong: **complete fallacies**. Failure is so often NOT good for you. It can have dire consequences: knock your confidence, lead to disasters, rob you of a job, lose you money. Honestly folks, whatever the trendy psychologists say, success is definitely better. And encouragement to prepare better, in order NOT to fail, is surely the best way forward.

GRAMMAR

conditional forms

5 A Complete the examples from the article with the correct words. Then decide which sentence(s) use:

a inversion.

b alternatives to *if*.

c an alternative to the past tense in the *if* clause.

d 'not be for'.

1 .... the intervention and encouragement of my son's drama teacher, he would never have risked going into acting.

2 If it hadn't .... his love of the game, he would have thrown in the towel early on.

3 It bugs me when I hear people saying that anyone can do anything, ... they want it hard enough.

4 If we .... to get hung up about all our mistakes, we would probably get nowhere in life.

5 .... we to analyse them, we'd probably find some that are often actually wrong.

B Rewrite the sentences in Ex 5A using a different conditional form. Use 'If' to start each sentence and retain the meaning.

C Complete the sentences with the correct forms of the verbs in brackets.

1 But for my teacher's advice on revising, I .... (not / pass) the exam with flying colours.

2 If it .... (not / be) for my brother's daily encouragement, I .... (not still be) on this course.

3 .... (have / you / not / check) your essay before handing it in yesterday, you .... (not / got) that A grade!

4 .... (be / you / take) constructive criticism on board and reapply for the job next month, you might stand a better chance of succeeding.

5 If it .... (not / be) for watching so many English films, I .... (never / become) so fluent in English.

D Read the situations and complete the sentence starters with your own ideas. Then compare with a partner.

1 about your college or workplace some time ago

• If it hadn't ....

• But for ....

2 about something that happened recently

• I wouldn't be .... if ....

• If it weren't ....

3 about something you're considering doing in the future

• If I were ....

• Should I ....

E Read the quote and say whether you agree with it. Tell your partner about a mistake that a) you learnt from, b) you didn't learn from.

'Mistakes are the portals of discovery.'

Absolutely. If it hadn't been for clicking on the wrong link, I'd never have discovered that amazing band, and I'm now a big fan.

F Learn and practise. Go to the Grammar Bank.

▶▶ page 112 GRAMMAR BANK

PRONUNCIATION

6 A 🔊 **1.01 | *if* in natural speech |** Listen to a sentence from the article being spoken at natural speed. What do you notice about the pronunciation of the word *if*?

… if it hadn't been for his love of the game, he would have thrown in the towel early on.

B Practise saying the sentences (1–3) as fast as you can.

1 If you believe that, you'll believe anything!

2 If people thought about these sayings more, they'd never repeat them.

3 If it's really true, then I'm definitely doing the wrong thing.

SPEAKING

7 Work in pairs and discuss points 1–3.

1 Choose two of these pieces of conventional wisdom and discuss how true you think they are. Give examples to support your opinion.

A little knowledge is a dangerous thing.

Practice makes perfect.

Tidy room, tidy mind.

Good things come to those who wait.

What doesn't kill you makes you stronger.

It doesn't matter as long as you do your best.

2 What other pieces of conventional wisdom have you come across that are either true or not true in your opinion?

3 Invent your own piece of conventional wisdom related to learning. Share it with the class and discuss how true you think others' contributions are.

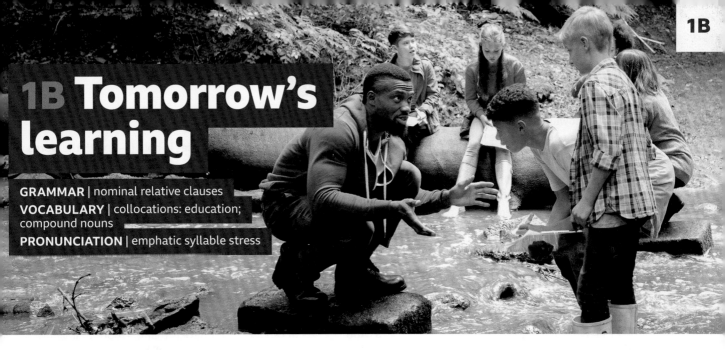

1B Tomorrow's learning

GRAMMAR | nominal relative clauses
VOCABULARY | collocations: education; compound nouns
PRONUNCIATION | emphatic syllable stress

VOCABULARY

collocations: education

1 A Work in pairs and discuss the questions.

1 Which educational experiences have you found enjoyable?
2 Which educational experiences have you found difficult?
3 What do you think is important in education?

B Work in pairs. Look at these different responses to Question 3 in Ex 1A. Match the collocations in bold in 1–10 with their meanings (a–j).

1 For me, **developing a nurturing environment** is essential.
2 In my opinion, **finding your own path** is key.
3 **Striving for excellence** has always got to be the aim.
4 **Fostering good relationships** is definitely one of the goals of a teacher.
5 I would say that **fulfilling your potential** is the main focus of education.
6 For a school or college, it's **delivering a quality curriculum** that is at the heart of education.
7 As a parent, I believe that **maintaining rigorous standards** is vital.
8 **Taking the initiative** is something we all need to learn for our future lives.
9 An educational environment is the ideal place to learn about **establishing mutual respect**.
10 A newer, but significant, element of teaching is **focusing on individuality**.

a never settling for second best
b doing things first, not waiting to be told to do them
c providing a context where someone is helped to grow
d becoming as good as you're able to be
e meeting challenging or difficult requirements
f not treating people as if they are all the same
g helping people to get along in a positive way
h encouraging the belief that the other person is as worthy as oneself
i providing educational content of a high standard
j discovering what interests you in life

C Complete the sentences with the correct form of the collocations in Ex 1B.

1 Nobody wanted to speak, so I .... and kicked off the discussion.
2 It took me a long time to .... and I tried several career options before settling on teaching.
3 If you do not strive for excellence in life, it's likely you won't .... and you'll feel undervalued.
4 A good manager should .... and realise what each person can bring to a team.
5 Arranging social events outside school or work will .... between classmates or colleagues.
6 In my school, we work hard to .... and we reassess it at the end of each academic year.

D Learn and practise. Go to the Vocabulary Bank.

▶▶ page 136 **VOCABULARY BANK** compound nouns

PRONUNCIATION

2 A | **emphatic syllable stress** | Look at the words in the collocations in Ex 1B. Which words have:

1 three syllables?
2 four syllables?

B 🔊 **1.02** | Underline the stressed syllables. Then listen and check.

1 a nurturing environment
2 striving for excellence
3 fostering good relationships
4 fulfilling your potential
5 a quality curriculum
6 rigorous standards
7 taking the initiative
8 mutual respect

C Work in pairs. Student A: Say the first part of one of the collocations in Ex 2B. Student B: Complete the collocation. Remember to stress the words correctly.

Student A: a quality …
Student B: … curriculum!

LISTENING

3 A What sort of knowledge do you think will be important for people to have in the future? Why?

B 🔊 **1.03 |** Listen to an extract from a radio programme about future learning. Which points (1–5) are covered?

1 past reforms in education
2 different types of knowledge
3 changes in teacher training
4 the changing nature of the world
5 the importance of exams

C 🔊 **1.03 |** Listen again and take notes about the key points you chose in Ex 3B.

D Work in pairs. Use your notes from Ex 3C to answer the questions.

1 What do we learn from the extract?
 a Changes in education over the last decades include ....
 b Despite many educational reforms, some countries ....
 c Considerations that will drive future changes in educational systems will be ....

2 Why are the following examples given during the extract?
 a a 19th-century classroom
 b Paris
 c using GPS
 d cooking a meal

E How far do you agree that 'knowing that' will no longer be important in the future?

4 A Work in pairs. Imagine a student and their learning environment in 100 years' time. Note down points about:

a learning routine.
b topics covered.
c educational tasks and interactions.
d the technology in use.
e the role of the classroom and teacher.
f types of assessment.

B Compare your ideas with the class. Which ideas are the most interesting, the most unusual and the most probable?

GRAMMAR

nominal relative clauses

5 A Complete the nominal relative clauses in bold (1–7) with the words in the box.

> however   what (x3)   whatever   whenever   whoever

1 .... **you look at it**, approaches to future education will need to change.
2 I think in your introduction you've laid out exactly .... **we need to be considering**.
3 … and that is .... **makes new learning easier**.
4 Of course, students in the future will adapt to .... **the educational system asks of them**.
5 And .... **I'm talking about here** is that it's more than knowing how to play an instrument or cook a meal …
6 .... **makes the big educational decisions** has set out that students should know maths, history or geography …
7 The students' role has been to store the knowledge and use it .... **they need it** …

B Find relative pronouns in the sentences in Ex 5A that mean:
 a the thing(s) that (object)
 b the thing(s) that (subject)
 c the person who
 d any way that
 e anything that
 f any time that

C Complete the sentences with your own ideas. Compare your answers in pairs.
 1 Whenever I find it challenging to learn something, ...
 2 What I think will be important in future education ....
 3 Whichever subjects are taught to children in the future, ...
 4 Exams are just ....

D Learn and practise. Go to the Grammar Bank.
▶▶ page 113 **GRAMMAR BANK**

SPEAKING

6 A Look at the questions. Think about your answers and make notes.
 1 What improvements could be made to the current educational experience?
 2 What changes will we definitely see in the future?

Consider areas such as:

- developing a nurturing environment and establishing mutual respect between learners and teachers.
- helping students to find their own path and deal with their individual needs.
- striving for excellence and fulfilling students' potential.
- delivering a curriculum relevant for modern learners.
- harnessing technology to improve the learning experience.

B Work in pairs. Discuss your answers to the questions, using your notes to help you.

WRITING

note-taking and summary writing

7 A Work in pairs and discuss the questions.

1 When do you usually need to take notes?
2 What kind of things do you note down and how?
3 What kind of problems do you have when note-taking?
4 How similar or different are the notes you took in Ex 3C?

B Read the tips for taking better notes. Which of the tips do you use the most or the least? Why?

Take better notes! •••

- Work out a system of note-taking that suits you.
- Don't write down everything – only main points.
- Don't let yourself be distracted – focus!
- Don't be so concerned with writing that you miss the next points.
- Use your own symbols to replace or abbreviate words.
- Look over your notes immediately – add other points or finish unfinished notes.
- Check over your notes later to improve recall.

8 A Read a summary of the extract you heard in Ex 3B and a list of what is important to remember when writing a summary (1–7). Discuss with a partner how the writer has used the advice.

1 condense the main points into one paragraph
2 link more than one idea in a sentence
3 avoid quoting directly
4 give an objective account
5 use reporting verbs to guide the reader through the summary
6 use the present tense for the summary
7 eliminate extra details or complex examples

In this extract about the future of learning the presenter, Sarah Butler, **begins** by outlining the way educational systems have changed and will continue to change in order to address the changing nature of the world. She **compares** classrooms and student and teacher roles from the past with the present but **accepts** that not all countries' systems and teaching methods are going in the same direction. Her guest, Rob Taylor, **gives** his views on the subject and **focuses on** different types of 'knowledge', knowing *that* and knowing *how*, explaining which he believes will be more important in the future and giving his reasons. He **goes on** to suggest that future generations will need to offload large quantities of fact-based knowledge technology in order to focus on learning skills required to collaborate in order to deal with global issues. He **cites** skills such as developing empathy, critical thinking, creative problem-solving and understanding each other, which in his opinion human beings are well suited to do. Both Sarah and Rob **point out** the vital role technology has already played and will continue to play in every aspect of education.

B Complete the sentences with the correct form of the verbs in bold in Ex 8A.

1 The lecturer .... a useful website as the source of his information.
2 Both guests .... out how classrooms need to physically change to accommodate new tech.
3 The speaker .... by asking us about our most interesting learning experiences.
4 The experts took it in turns to .... their views on how they saw learning developing in the future.
5 The expert .... the education systems in his country with those in the UK and .... on recent changes.
6 He .... on to suggest that more research should be carried out on the subject.
7 The psychologist .... that not all his colleagues agreed with his interpretation of the matter under discussion.

9 A ◀) **1.04** | Listen to another extract from the same programme. Take notes to include in a summary.

B Use your notes from Ex 9A to write a summary paragraph of the extract.

C Exchange your summary with a partner. Compare the ways you have summarised the information and the points you chose to include or not to include.

D Read the Future Skills box and answer the question.

FUTURE SKILLS
Self-management

Developing note-taking and summarising skills are important for breaking down complex information. This enables us to remember key points which we may need to recall at some point in the future.

Think about the note-taking skills you have learnt in this lesson. Will these skills be important for you in the future? Why/Why not?

1C Creativity

HOW TO ... | manage interaction during a discussion
VOCABULARY | creativity
PRONUNCIATION | polite intonation

VOCABULARY

creativity

1 A Work in pairs and discuss the questions.

   1 In what ways are you or people you know creative? Think about people at home, work, online, etc.

   2 What examples of creative things have you done in the last month?

B What do you know about the difference between people who are 'left-brained' and people who are 'right-brained'? Read the article and check your ideas.

C Do you agree with the conclusions of the article? Would you say that you have or don't have a particular left- or right-brain dominance? Why?

2 A Match the sentence beginnings (1–8) with the endings (a–h).

   1 An **intuitive** person is someone who

   2 If you have a **fertile** imagination, you

   3 Our **imagination** can be

   4 Many people believe that a **creative genius**

   5 People can be trained

   6 **Creative thinking** is all about coming

   7 Problems can sometimes be solved by

   8 Sometimes new ideas can

   a come completely **out of the blue**.

   b getting **flashes of inspiration** or **insight**.

   c relies on **instinct** rather than facts.

   d to think **outside the box**.

   e **sparked** by seeing or hearing something unusual.

   f are good at thinking of stories or good excuses.

   g up with **novel ideas** in business settings.

   h needs a degree of **innate** or **raw talent**.

B Work in pairs. Tell your partner, with examples, about someone you know who:

   1 has a fertile imagination.

   2 regularly comes up with novel ideas.

   3 is not good at thinking outside the box.

   4 has a raw talent for something.

   5 did something out of the blue.

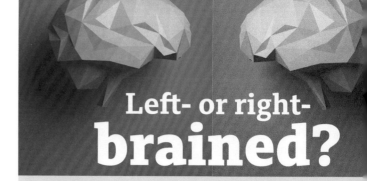

Left- or right-brained?

In the 1960s, research by the Nobel Prize winner Roger W. Sperry concluded that we are either right-brained or left-brained, meaning that one side of our brain is dominant. Left-brain dominance implies that a person is more analytical, logical and organised, better at dealing with facts, mathematics and linear thinking. The right brain is more concerned with intuitive and imaginative thinking, visualisation and daydreaming, and people with this dominance are more artistic, creative and able to think outside the box and come up with novel ideas, seemingly out of the blue.

However, a study of over a thousand people, published by a team of neuroscientists a decade ago, seems to have debunked this theory and showed that in fact both sides of the brain work in tandem. Whereas it is undoubtedly true that different areas of the brain have different functions and control, for example, movement, motivation, visual processing, aspects of language and so on, there is no real evidence to show that the two hemispheres play a significant part in determining our overall personalities in terms of whether we have a fertile imagination, more flashes of inspiration, better insight or whether we use logic and pay attention to detail. In fact, today it is believed that to become a good mathematician or artist, both sides of the brain need to collaborate.

So, there is no reason why an artistic person cannot also be strong at critical thinking and reasoning, nor for a scientist not to have ideas sparked by something unexpected, to appreciate colour or improvise on a musical instrument. To me, that makes a lot of sense.

How to ...
manage interaction during a discussion

3 A Do you think creativity can be learnt? Work in pairs and note down some ideas.

B 🔊 **1.05** | Listen to a radio programme about creativity and check if your ideas from Ex 3A were mentioned.

C 🔊 **1.05** | Listen again and answer the questions.

1 Would you say that all the participants share the discussion time equally?

2 Do they all take turns well? Give some examples.

3 Do you think the presenter manages the discussion well? Why/Why not?

4 A Complete the phrases (1–12) from the programme with the correct words.

1 To get the _____ rolling, let's start with …

2 If I can _____ in here, …

3 … and going back to _____ I was saying earlier …

4 Sorry, I didn't mean to _____ you off …

5 Sorry Kelly, you were _____ … ?

6 I'd like to hear Jake's _____ on this.

7 To go back to my _____ point, …

8 Let me _____ up on that …

9 … what I _____ to say was …

10 … as we _____ before, …

11 … if I can just _____ Jake back in …

12 Earlier you _____ an important point about …

B 🔊 **1.06** | Listen and check.

C Match the phrases from Ex 4A with the categories.

- interrupting
- returning to a previous point
- directing the interaction

D Learn and practise. Go to the Grammar Bank.

▶▶ page 114 **GRAMMAR BANK**

PRONUNCIATION

5 A 🔊 **1.07** | **polite intonation** | Listen to the comments said in two different ways. Which intonation, A or B, is more polite? Why? Listen again and repeat.

1 But surely we can't all be creative geniuses.   **A / B**

2 So you're saying that if I wanted, I could sit down and write a novel?   **A / B**

3 Did you just say 'green'? What's that got to do with being creative?   **A / B**

B 🔊 **1.08** | Practise saying these comments in two different ways, first politely and then impolitely. Listen and check.

1 But don't you think that's a bit of an exaggeration?

2 So you're saying that anyone can learn to paint a masterpiece?

3 Did you just say 'daydream'? What's daydreaming got to do with it?

SPEAKING

6 A Read the Future Skills box and do the task.

> ### FUTURE SKILLS
> ## Collaboration
>
>
> In a discussion, it is important to listen to others' opinions and to take turns, not to dominate. If you are leading a discussion or find yourself with others who are too outspoken, you can manage the discussion by politely bringing in other speakers, and if necessary, returning to a previous point to give them an opportunity to contribute.
>
> Talk to a partner about a time when you were in a discussion that needed management. What did you do?

B Work in groups of three or four. Do the task. You have been asked to come up with and discuss ways of developing people's creativity at college or work.

Here are some possible things your college or company could do:

- Organise creative skills sessions to encourage people to learn something new, e.g. a language, creative writing or art.
- Engage participants in team-building training days or activities.
- Introduce special courses on brainstorming and creative thinking.
- Invite guest speakers to give talks on a range of inspirational, creative projects.

Decide which two or three of the options (or your own ideas) might be most useful to develop people's creativity and discuss why. How would you set them up? Think about:

- looking at things from different perspectives.
- activating different areas of the brain.
- sparking ideas.
- putting people on the spot.
- raising people's awareness of their own abilities.
- getting people out of their comfort zones.

People might think they are not intuitive or don't have fertile imaginations, but raising people's awareness about their own abilities can …

C Think about the discussion you have just had and identify points where there were interruptions, returns to previous points and where the interaction was directed.

D Compare and discuss the choices your group made with the rest of the class.

> ### MEDIATION SKILLS
> ### describing genres
> share recommendations
>
>
> ▶▶ page 144 **MEDIATION BANK**

1D   BBC Street Interviews

Learning experiences

VOCABULARY | teaching and learning
SPEAKING | a discussion about education
WRITING | a nomination for an award

Serkan

Rahma

PREVIEW

1   Work in pairs. How many different answers can you predict people might give to questions 1 and 2 below?

BBC

Q1: What kind of things do you enjoy learning?

Q2: What makes a good teacher?

VIEW

2   ▷ Watch the interviews. How many of the speakers' answers did you predict?

3 A   Work in pairs. Look at the extracts from the interviews. Try to complete the phrases in bold.

  1 … someone who can connect with you and inspire you **on a personal** ....
  2 … you can sort of .... **your teaching to that**.
  3 … different pupils have different methods of learning and to .... **that into account**.
  4 … if they lead them to the answers rather than .... **them with the answers**.
  5 And not having too much of a **power** ....
  6 Someone … that **talks you** .... the different issues that you're having …

B   ▷ Watch the second part of the interviews again. Check your answers to Ex 3A.

VOCABULARY

teaching and learning

4 A   Complete the sentences with your own ideas.

  1 Feeding answers to students results in …
  2 In my view, the classroom dynamic should be …
  3 A teacher needs to adjust their teaching to …
  4 When deciding what to study, you have to take into account …
  5 At the beginning of the course, it's helpful if the teacher talks you through …
  6 … was a teacher who inspired me on a personal level because …

B   Work in pairs. Compare your answers to Ex 4A and give extra information to clarify what you mean.

I think you remember things more easily if you learn them for yourself, rather than being fed information.

Samuel

Farah

B B C

David

Ollie

Omri

SPEAKING

a discussion about education

5 A Imagine you've been invited to a discussion titled 'How would you redesign the secondary school experience?' Make notes about the following.

- What were the positives and negatives about your secondary school experience from a learning perspective?
- What subjects do you think should be removed from school curriculums or made optional?
- What subjects would you recommend be introduced as mandatory school subjects?
- How much freedom should students be allowed to have in directing their own learning?
- What do you think are the most essential characteristics in teachers?
- What role will technology have in shaping the school of the future?

B Look at the phrases in Ex 3A. Make a note of any that can help you explain your answers to Ex 5A.

C Work in groups. Use the questions in Ex 5A and your notes and discuss how to redesign the secondary school experience. Use the Key phrases to help you.

> ### KEY PHRASES
>
> What we need from our teachers is the ability to …
> One thing we didn't get enough guidance on was …
> While a lot of people found … completely useless, it was definitely useful for me because …
> We need far less … and far more …
> … is a pretty complicated subject but one that would …

D Summarise the key points from your discussion for the class. How similar or different were your ideas?

WRITING

a nomination for an award

6 A You read the following announcement on your school's social media page. What are people being asked to do?

> We're now accepting nominations for our annual 'Most Appreciated Teacher' award. In 200 words or less, we would like you to tell us who your nominee is and just what makes them so special.
>
> Submissions close on 23 April, with the announcement of the winner at the end-of-year speech on 15 May.

B Work in pairs and discuss the questions.

1 Have you ever nominated somebody for an award?
2 What type of information do you think people would give about their nomination for 'Most Appreciated Teacher'?
3 Which of the teachers you have had in your life would be deserving of such an award?

C Write your nomination for an award. Go to the Writing Bank.

▶▶ page 104 **WRITING BANK**

GRAMMAR

conditional forms

1 A Answer the questions using two types of conditional forms. The first word(s) is (are) given.

1 Which new language would you like to take up, given the opportunity?

  a If ....

  b Should ....

2 What learning experience would you have missed out on, without a good friend's advice?

  a But ....

  b If ....

3 In what way did an early teacher from your childhood have an influence on you?

  a If ....

  b Had ....

4 What do you now know as a result of watching or listening to a recent news report?

  a If it ....

  b But ....

B Work in pairs and compare your answers.

nominal relative clauses

2 A Complete each sentence with a relative pronoun.

What are your strategies for developing your English skills?

1 I take every opportunity to chat with .... I can, in English of course.

2 I speak quite slowly, as I need to think about .... I'm going to articulate my thoughts.

3 If I get stuck choosing between two grammatical forms, I simply go with .... is simpler.

4 .... I watch an English film, I try not to look at the subtitles.

5 If I don't know .... to say, I just ask a question and let the other person talk.

6 I just let the words come out of my mouth, ... they happen to do so, without over-thinking it.

7 If I hear an English person pronounce something differently to the way I pronounce it, I repeat .... has been said for practice.

B Work in pairs and discuss. To what extent are the statements in Ex 2A true for you?

VOCABULARY

3 Complete the collocations in bold with the words in the box.

> environment   excellence   initiative   mutual   path   potential

1 Teachers need to maintain a **nurturing** .... at school to ensure the best education for all children.

2 Without proper guidance and support, some students may not **fulfil their** .... and that is a shame.

3 We cannot all be geniuses, but if we **strive for** .... , that's the most we can do.

4 With so many job options it can be difficult to **find your own** ....

5 I learnt early on to **take the** .... and as a result I now run my own company successfully.

6 Good teachers create a classroom atmosphere where .... **respect** is established.

4 Choose the correct words to complete the sentences.

1 People with **fertile** / **intuitive** imaginations have the potential to become writers and artists.

2 I still believe that the most important thing you need if you want to be a sports success is **born** / **innate** talent.

3 I rarely get ideas completely **down from** / **out of** the blue, but need to sit and think a lot.

4 The screenwriter said that the idea for his new film was **lit** / **sparked** by watching a very old western.

5 It must be very hard to keep coming up with **latest** / **novel** ideas for new drama series.

6 The writer suddenly had a **flare** / **flash** of inspiration and decided how the story would end.

5 Complete the second sentence using the word given so that it has the same meaning as the first sentence. Use between four and six words.

1 The timing of the sessions means I can't go to extra tennis training.   IT

  If it wasn't for the timing of the sessions, I'd be able to go to extra tennis training.

2 We shouldn't worry too much about our mistakes, but let them go and move on.   HUNG

  It's important .... our mistakes, but let them go and move forward.

3 The belief of many educators is that looking at students' work throughout the year is fairer than final examinations.   CONTINUOUS

  Many educators .... fairer than final examinations for students.

4 Some parts of the story ring true, but I still don't believe the whole thing.   ELEMENT

  Although there's .... in the story, I still don't believe the whole thing.

5 When she didn't win the competition, it made her feel a failure and she never entered another.   KNOCKED

  Losing the competition .... and she never entered another.

6 Complete the blog post with one word in each gap.

I'm sitting in a Greek taverna with a phrase book and I'm trying to learn the numbers one to ten. I've been giving it a good [1] .... for half an hour now, but [2] .... I'm reading is going into my head and then straight out again. But [3] .... the fact that I have already learnt three other languages fluently, I [4] .... already have decided to throw in the [5] .... [6] .... said that anyone can learn anything at any age was wrong! If it [7] .... not for my stubbornness, I'd [8] .... tack and try learning the words for food … but I'll keep going, for now.

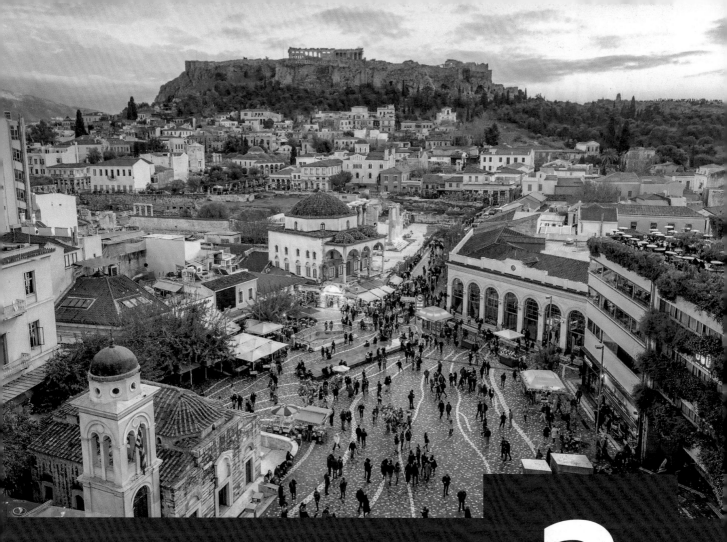

culture

2

VLOGS

Q: If you could live anywhere in the world, where would you choose and why?

1 ▶ Watch the video. How many people's choices do you agree with?

2 What other places do you think would be good places to live?

GSE LEARNING OBJECTIVES

2A READING | Read an article about Cities of Culture: describing the impact of an action; binomials

Pronunciation: schwa /ə/

Talk about applying to be 'City of Arts': advanced ways of comparing

2B LISTENING | Understand a radio interview about interpreting: summarising verbs; multi-word verbs for reporting

Pronunciation: using intonation to show contrasting opinions

Talk about translation apps: reporting

Write an informative summary for a careers brochure

2C HOW TO ... | maintain and develop interaction: conventions/cultural heritage

Pronunciation: expressing surprise and asking for reaction

2D BBC PROGRAMME | Understand a TV travel and cookery programme about food in the USA

Make a proposal for a new restaurant: describing food

Write a blog post about a food hotspot

2A Cities

GRAMMAR | advanced ways of comparing
VOCABULARY | describing the impact of an action; binomials
PRONUNCIATION | schwa /ə/

READING

1 A Work in pairs. Name as many capital cities as you can in one minute. Compare how many you got with the rest of the class.

B Work in pairs and discuss the questions.
1 What do you understand by the term 'Capital of Culture'?
2 Why do you think a city would want to become one?

2 A Read the first paragraph of *Do we need Cities of Culture?* and answer the questions.
1 What point is the writer trying to make?
2 How factual or serious do you think they are being?

B Read the rest of the article and decide whether the writer thinks Cities of Culture are beneficial or not.

C Read the article again and choose the correct answers.
1 The writer cites the Borough of Culture as an example of how the 'culture' awards might be
  a positive.   **b** negative.
2 Expos used to be an opportunity for countries
  a to exhibit their construction and technical skills.
  b to interact on a national scale.
3 The main aim of the 'City of Culture' idea is
  a to improve the accommodation in the area.
  b to improve people's lifestyles.
4 The writer mentions the enormous puppets
  a to illustrate an event's cultural legacy.
  b to highlight the ingenuity of artists.
5 Which of the following reflects the writer's general attitude in the article?
  a The idea of 'Cities of Culture' is basically flawed and cannot effect real change for a city.
  b The level of cultural legacy left following a city being a 'City of Culture' is predictable.
  c By attempting to spread the 'culture award' notion more widely, the overall impact may be lessened.
  d Being awarded 'City of Culture' status can be highly beneficial in the short term.

3 Work with a partner. Which of the sentences (a–d) in Question 5 in Ex 2C do you agree with? Why?

VOCABULARY

describing the impact of an action

4 A Look at the phrases in bold in the article. Are they being used to describe positive (P) or negative (N) effects?

B Complete the sentences with your own ideas.
1 .... would have tangible benefits for my town.
2 .... would be a great way of showcasing the positive things about where I live.
3 The building of a .... would be one way to raise the profile of this town.
4 .... would give everyone here a boost.
5 Investment is needed to facilitate the development of ....
6 I don't think .... would bring long-term benefits to our city.
7 The problem with lots of tourism is that you end up stuck with ....
8 .... has had a detrimental effect on the place where I live.
9 Having .... in my area can do more harm than good.

C Work in pairs and compare your ideas. How many of your ideas are the same?

D Learn and practise. Go to the Vocabulary Bank.

▶▶ page 137 **VOCABULARY BANK** binomials

Do we need Cities of Culture?

The phenomenon of 'Capitals of Culture' is a bit like one of those sets of Russian dolls, in that it's becoming progressively smaller and smaller. It started in 1851 with the Great Exhibition, when the cultures of the world convened in London. Over a hundred years later there were European Capitals of Culture and soon after that, UK Cities of Culture – like Hull. Next, London was divided into Boroughs of Culture, and shortly thereafter they announced a House of Culture on every street, and then a Capital Room of Culture within each house, until humans were all assigned the most cultural part of their bodies before accepting that they, and all things, were culture.

All right, the second half is yet to play out, but surely it was brought closer when the Mayor of London announced back in 2019 that Waltham Forest would become London's first 'Borough' of Culture. Are we perhaps going overboard in jumping on the 'Cultural Award' bandwagon?

Let's look at what else is coming up on the cultural map of the world. Deep breath. Over the next few years we will see, among others, European Capitals of Culture, UK Cities of Culture, World Expos, American Capitals of Culture and Arab Capitals of Culture, by and large most of them awarded annually. With this dizzying number of cultural capitals and expos across the planet, you have to wonder, does the practice of funnelling attention onto a single destination for one year still **have tangible benefits**?

To begin with: the good old-fashioned World Fairs, now known as expos. These pan-global events were set up with the aim of **showcasing the best of** the world's technology, industry and culture, with the host city typically erecting iconic buildings – like the Eiffel Tower in Paris (you couldn't get a structure any more iconic than that!), the Space Needle in Seattle, and the sadly burnt down Crystal Palace in London – to mark the event. The late Urso Chappell, a former world expo consultant, told *The New York Times* that an expo marked a certain 'coming of age' for a city. Such an award could aid a city's physical redevelopment as well as that nation's image abroad. On top of that, a world expo will typically bring thousands of new jobs (albeit temporary ones) and pump a fair whack of money into the pockets of restaurateurs, hoteliers, fridge magnet traders and so on.

Building on from the expo concept, the creators of City of Culture programmes have aimed to **raise the cultural profile** of a city by putting it in the world spotlight for a period, usually a year, and investing vast amounts of money to **give the cultural life of that city a boost**. First and foremost is the idea that this will **facilitate cultural development** and have an impact on the future life of that city, ensuring a lasting legacy and helping to embed culture into policymaking.

But is it definitely worth it? It is undeniable that the year in the spotlight does channel creativity, and tourists flock to see exhibitions, installations and events. Investment is there for building new venues, attracting new businesses, and designing thrilling cultural events, and the hope is that it will result in a sea-change in people's attitudes to culture and a year during which the city is vibrant and buzzing, tourism sky-rocketing and the economy and cultural life thriving. However, what happens if being City of Culture fails to **bring long-term benefits** to a city? What if the tourists simply stop coming and a city **ends up stuck with** museums and galleries it has no use for? Can being City of Culture actually start to **have a detrimental effect** when the news is announced that local people have been saddled with the costs of paying for the upkeep of these empty buildings? Can being the City of Culture actually **do more harm than good**, and can the positive effects be not so much a lasting legacy as a brief hurrah? The answer is, frustratingly, 'sometimes', but there are some brilliant success stories, too.

Liverpool (European Capital of Culture 2008) showed the world in 2018, with its tenth anniversary celebrations, that a remarkable legacy is indeed possible. Its creative culture has been amplified and there is a determination in the city to continue to thrive. Since 2008 it has changed physically, economically and culturally. And who could have failed to be impressed by the sight of the giant mechanical gold spider climbing a tower block, or be equally as astonished by giant puppets telling the story of Liverpool's Dream through the streets of the city a decade later?

It would appear that cultural legacies are continuing to be delivered in many places, while for others, the impact has been nothing like as strong as had been predicted. Unless an arts council continues to inject the money for projects related to music, visual arts, fashion, storytelling and everything else that is part and parcel of the creative culture, the vibrancy can disappear as quickly as it came. And as for the desire for ever more specific 'cultural awards', will this not simply make the significance of them so weak as to be almost meaningless?

GRAMMAR

advanced ways of comparing

5 Look at two different structures we use when comparing. Complete the examples in bold from the article (1–7) with the correct words.

Using *like/as*

1 ... the impact has been **nothing** .... **as strong as** had been predicted.

2 ... the vibrancy can disappear **as quickly** .... **it came**.

3 ... is **a bit** .... one of those sets of Russian dolls, ...

4 ... will this not simply make the significance of them **so weak** .... **to be** almost meaningless?

5 ... and can the positive effects be **not so much a lasting legacy** .... a brief hurrah?

6 ... or be **equally** .... **astonished** by giant puppets telling the story of Liverpool's Dream ...

Using *couldn't* + verb + *any (more)* + adverb/adjective

7 ... you couldn't get a structure **any more iconic** .... **that**!

6 A Match the sentence beginnings (1–7) with the endings (a–g).

1 Where I live is not so much a town

2 Living here is a bit

3 People leave here

4 In summer the weather gets so hot

5 Our capital city is nothing

6 You couldn't get a more fascinating

7 The weather in winter is equally as

a as quickly as they arrive.

b as to make going outside a terrifying prospect.

c like as big as I'd imagined it was going to be.

d as a large village.

e like experiencing the same day over and over again.

f nice as it is in summer.

g city than our capital.

B Work in pairs. Discuss whether or not the sentences in Ex 6A are true for you.

C Learn and practise. Go to the Grammar Bank.

▶▶ page 115 **GRAMMAR BANK**

PRONUNCIATION

7 A 🔊 **2.01 | schwa /ə/ |** Listen to the sentences (1–3). What vowel sound do the words in bold have in common?

1 It's not so much **an** investment in our future as a quick way of making cash.

2 We couldn't get a better opportunity to put ourselves on the map **than** this one.

3 The money will drain away **as** quickly **as** it comes.

B 🔊 **2.01 |** Listen again and repeat the sentences. Use the schwa /ə/ sound to help you say the sentences more quickly and naturally.

SPEAKING

8 A Your city has the opportunity to apply for the status of 'City of Arts' next year. People will be asked to vote on whether to apply or not. Work in pairs. Discuss the questions and make some notes.

1 What benefits would applying to be 'City of Arts' bring to the city?

2 What disadvantages might there be in being 'City of Arts'?

B Work in pairs. Turn to page 142 and compare your ideas. Add your own ideas to the sections for benefits and the possible negative effects.

C Swap partners. Discuss the pros and cons of applying to be 'City of Arts' next year. Student A: Try to persuade Student B that it is a good idea. Student B: Try to persuade Student A that it is not a good idea.

D Agree whether you will vote in favour of applying or against applying.

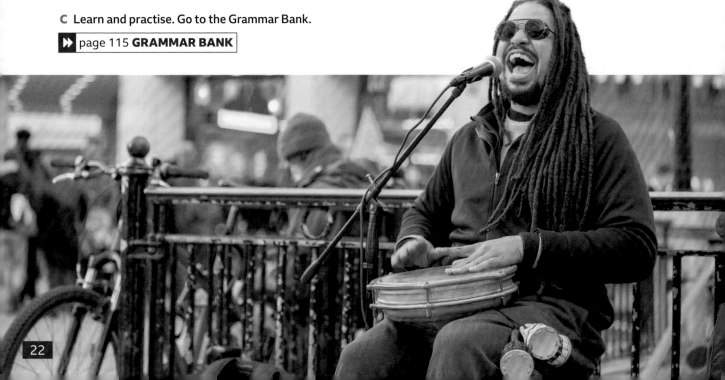

2B Lost in translation

GRAMMAR | reporting
VOCABULARY | summarising verbs; multi-word verbs for reporting
PRONUNCIATION | using intonation to show contrasting opinions

VOCABULARY

summarising verbs

1 Work in pairs and discuss the questions.

1 In what situations might people need a translator or an interpreter?
2 What do you think is meant by the phrase 'lost in translation'? Give some examples.

2 A Read the summary of a TV programme about translation. What challenges to effective translation are mentioned?

A fascinating programme yesterday evening **raised** the issues involved in translating, whether it be simultaneous interpretation for speakers or of the written word. One contributor to the programme **voiced** a concern that the intonation of an original utterance cannot be translated, which can open the door to misunderstanding. Ron Davis, a poet, **echoed** this point and was also insistent that certain types of writing, such as poetry, simply cannot be translated. According to Davis, whenever you 'translate' a poem from one language to another, you end up with two poems, because a poem is created through words, sound, rhythm and visuals. He **illustrated** his point by referring to poems that use line length to help impart meaning. Another guest, Anna Parton, a linguist, **called for** all translators to have a real awareness of the importance of cultural differences when translating. She **acknowledged** the difficulties that translators face and **accepted** that these may never be completely overcome. She **maintained** that it is often nearly impossible to find equivalent translations for words that express shades of meaning or concepts that differ from one culture to another. She **cited** the fact that the Irish language has thirty-two different words for the English word 'field', and **pondered** the difficulty of expressing all the feelings contained in the one Portuguese word 'saudade' – longing, nostalgia, hope, melancholy and emptiness. She went on to **question** whether training courses for translators and interpreters focus enough on this aspect of this specialised work. Viewers' posts following the programme **commented on** the valuable insights the programme offered.

B Work in pairs. Match the infinitive form of the verbs in bold in the summary in Ex 2A with their definitions 1–12.

1 express an opinion or attitude ....
2 agree with a statement ....
3 give something as an example ....
4 repeat another point or opinion ....
5 ask or wonder ....
6 ask for action ....
7 admit the existence of ....
8 express a firm belief ....
9 start to talk about a topic ....
10 clarify with an example ....
11 think carefully ....
12 give a reaction to something ....

C Choose the correct summarising verbs to complete the report.

Dubbing or subtitles: Which is best?

In the discussion a student [1]**raised / commented** the issue of dubbing in films and mentioned how disjointed this can make a film feel.

Another student [2]**echoed / illustrated** this concern, saying that her preference is always for subtitling. A third student [3]**voiced / accepted** that this reflected the views of most students but [4]**called for / questioned** the accuracy of subtitling and [5]**maintained / cited** that it often took viewers' attention away from the main action on the screen. Some students [6]**wondered / pondered** the degree of concentration required to follow subtitles, and one [7]**explained / illustrated** the point by mentioning falling asleep while watching a subtitled film the previous week.

D Work in pairs. Discuss the title of the report in Ex 2C. Then summarise your ideas using the alternative verbs not used in Ex 2C.

E Learn and practise. Go to the Vocabulary Bank.

>> page 137 **VOCABULARY BANK** multi-word verbs for reporting

LISTENING

3 A You are going to listen to a radio interview in which an interpreter is talking about simultaneous interpreting at international conferences. What problems might he mention?

B 🔊 **2.02 |** Listen to the interview and check if any of your ideas in Ex 3A are mentioned.

C 🔊 **2.02 |** Listen again and complete the sentences in your own words.

1 Alan begins by describing the source of most problems for interpreters as being a lack ....

2 According to Alan, the volume levels of the microphones mean that they are appropriate ....

3 Alan mentions a high-powered professor to illustrate ....

4 Alan prefers to summarise fast-paced speech rather ....

5 He believes that ideally .... However, it isn't always possible to do this.

6 He finishes by adding that his habit of predicting a speaker's thoughts and words also affects ....

D Complete the summaries of the interview with the correct form of verbs you found in Ex 2B. There may be more than one alternative.

1 Alan .... whether speakers ever consider the interpreters.

2 He .... concerns for the health of the interpreters and .... education for the speakers.

3 He .... one point by mentioning a particular incident.

4 He .... that there is no point in asking speakers to slow down and .... that there will inevitably be cultural differences.

5 He .... the issue of speakers using slang and .... his earlier point that speakers need to be educated.

6 He .... that most problems are fixable.

4 Work in pairs and discuss the questions.

1 Would you like to be a translator or an interpreter? Why/Why not?

2 What phrases and topics in your language or culture would be difficult to convey in English?

GRAMMAR

reporting

5 A Match the examples (1–4) from the summary in Ex 2A with the advice (a–d) on how to add variety to reporting.

1 He was insistent that certain types of writing, such as poetry, simply cannot be translated.

2 According to Davis, whenever you 'translate' a poem from one language to another, you end up with two poems.

3 She pondered the difficulty of expressing all the feelings contained in the one Portuguese word 'saudade'.

4 She maintained that it is often nearly impossible to find equivalent translations for words that express shades of meaning or concepts that differ from one culture to another.

a use a range of summarising verbs that carry the main meaning of the statement

b use adjectives instead of a reporting verb

c use nouns rather than clauses to follow the reporting verb

d use phrases to start the sentence

B Rewrite the statements in reported speech using the words given.

1 'There's no way that can be translated,' said Sarah.

Sarah was insistent ....

2 'Translating can be very problematic,' said John, and gave examples.

John pointed out that ....

3 'It's a really enjoyable job, in spite of the difficulties,' said Maire.

Maire maintained ....

4 'The variety of challenges makes the job interesting,' said David.

According ....

C Report the statements in as many ways as you can. Then compare your reactions to the statements with a partner.

1 The difference between interpreting and translating is interesting, but I would think that they require the same skills.

2 For me, it's the translating of certain cultural concepts that is tricky.

3 I agree completely and I think the fact that English has so many words for different types of rain is fascinating.

4 I wonder how people translate whole novels so quickly and easily. They must be completely bilingual, surely?

D Learn and practise. Go to the Grammar Bank.

▶▶ **page 116 GRAMMAR BANK**

What do you think of
translation apps?

1. How frequently do you use translation apps? What for?
2. What do you think are the main benefits of using translation apps?
3. Do you find that there are any drawbacks or limitations?
4. Why might translation apps sometimes produce an incorrect translation?
5. Are there certain situations or types of jobs where translation apps might be particularly useful?
6. With the wide availability of translation apps, do you think the jobs of translators or interpreters are at risk? Why/Why not?

PRONUNCIATION

6A 🔊 **2.03 | using intonation to show contrasting opinions** | Listen to the sentences (1–4). In which sentences is there a contrast of opinion? How do the speakers show this using their intonation?

1. John and Maya were critical of translation apps, but Tina felt differently.
2. Betina said most words can be translated accurately, but according to Juan there are lots of words that can't be.
3. Paul discussed the difficulty of real-time translation, and the group agreed with his views.
4. While most people agreed about the challenge of translating idiomatic language, Mo felt it wasn't such a big issue.

B Work in pairs. Take turns to read the sentences (1–4). Use intonation to help emphasise contrasts in opinion.

1. Natalie felt that mistranslation can have very dangerous consequences, but Mike found that a little dramatic.
2. Most of the group concluded that all translation will one day be automated, while Jake insisted that wouldn't be the case.
3. According to Dan, translated fiction can never be as good as the original, but JT said that with the right translation it could be even better.
4. Mika voiced concerns that interpreters sometimes work under too much pressure, but Joel replied that this situation is rapidly improving.

C Work in pairs. Discuss who you agree with in sentences 1–4 in Ex 6B.

SPEAKING

7A Work in pairs. Take turns to answer the the questions (1–6) in the survey above while your partner takes notes.

B Use your notes to summarise your partner's answers for the class, using summarising verbs and other means of reporting.

C Read the Future Skills box and do the task.

FUTURE SKILLS
Communication

When reporting information to others, it is important to organise your summary clearly so that listeners are not confused and can understand the main points. Try not to use long complex sentences or let sentences run into each other. Pause at points to allow the listener to take in the information.

Think about the summary you have just given in Ex 7B. How clear was the information? How might you have improved it?

WRITING

an informative summary

8A Work in pairs and discuss the questions.

1. What do you think the work of an interpreter for the deaf (a signer) entails?
2. Why do you think someone might want to become a signer?
3. What job opportunities do you think there might be for a signer?
4. What skills, qualifications and personal traits do you think are required for the work?

B Work in pairs and discuss the questions.

1. What do you think an informative summary is?
2. What sources could the writer use to find the relevant information to include in an informative summary?

C Write an informative summary. Go to the Writing Bank.

▶▶ page 104 **WRITING BANK**

2C The way we do it

HOW TO ... | maintain and develop interaction
VOCABULARY | conventions/cultural heritage
PRONUNCIATION | expressing surprise and asking for reaction

VOCABULARY

conventions/cultural heritage

1 Work in pairs. Is there anything you have learnt from another culture? Think about:

- attitudes to life.
- relationships.
- the arts.

2 A Read the posts from an online discussion board (A and B). Do you agree with either or both of the contributors? Why/Why not?

B Match the words and phrases in bold in the posts with their meanings (1–7).

1 fixed thinking about certain cultures and how they act ....
2 considered inappropriate ....
3 done often, therefore not unusual ....
4 originating from far in our past ....
5 unaffected by ....
6 existing for a long time ....
7 special to ....

C Complete the sentences with your own ideas. Then compare your answers with a partner.

1 An opinion that is stereotypical about people from my country is ....
2 A gesture of politeness, irrespective of culture, is ....
3 A way my perspective has been changed recently by reading a book or watching a film is ....
4 Some customs that are peculiar to my family include ....
5 An attitude that is commonplace in my country is ....
6 Something that used to be frowned upon in my country, but is no longer is ....
7 A deeply rooted tradition that I think is unlikely ever to change is ....

A   We've all got a **deeply rooted** cultural heritage which influences the customs and conventions that shape our lives. And we're all aware that our culture can be very different from others. What is **commonplace** in one country (for example, greeting by shaking hands) is inappropriate in another. There are, and there will always be, **long-standing** conventions that are **peculiar to** a certain culture, and unheard of, or even **frowned upon**, in others. However, as the world shrinks, and people are increasingly interacting with other nationalities, our conventions and customs are blurring or feeding into and being adopted by other cultures. In addition to this, advanced technology is bringing with it a sea-change in behaviour and convention, which is producing a culture all of its own. Who would ever have thought that it would be the norm to see people sharing a table but conducting various conversations simultaneously on their phones? And no one raising an eyebrow! Fascinating, isn't it? How far will cultures merge or adapt and change over the next few decades? That is going to be interesting.

B   As I see it, our culture shapes how we view the world (and our place in it), how we approach problems, the respect we show for others and a lot more that we just don't think about. And today, the need for understanding of other cultures and learning from them is becoming ever more important if we want to solve the global problems we are facing together, such as climate change. Exposure to different cultures helps us all to appreciate the diversity in the world. It helps us understand other people and makes us realise that there is more that links us than separates us. We start to challenge our way of thinking and view life from different perspectives. Our traditional way of approaching things isn't always the best way – and definitely not the only way! Learning from other cultures helps us to establish new ways of thinking and problem solving. Above all it minimises the notion of **stereotypical** behaviour and teaches us that, **irrespective of** our cultural heritage, we are all individuals, aren't we? Understanding other cultures will eventually reduce the fear that comes with not knowing, and can play an enormous part in reducing tensions between certain cultures that share the same space.

How to ...
maintain and develop interaction

3 A Work in pairs and discuss the questions.

1 How is respect for others shown in your culture?
2 Do you think that showing respect is part of a country's culture or a universal human trait? Why?

B Read the Future Skills box and do the task.

FUTURE SKILLS
Social responsibility

When interacting with people who have a different cultural background, it is important to respect social conventions to avoid causing direct or indirect offence.

Work in pairs and list social conventions in your culture that might be different in other countries or cultures. Would a failure to observe these conventions offend you?

C 🔊 **2.04 |** Listen to an extract from a radio programme discussing aspects of culture. How do the speakers' points of view differ? What do they agree on?

D 🔊 **2.05 |** Complete the phrases from the discussion with the correct words. Listen and check.

1 I'm not arguing ....
2 That's a .... point.
3 But .... respect has to be earned?
4 You're looking at things the wrong way ....
5 OK, I .... your point.
6 Fair ....
7 You .... a good point.
8 It's clear you both have .... here.
9 I think there's a .... in your argument.
10 I think I .... where you're coming from.

E Learn and practise. Go to the Grammar Bank.

▶▶ **page 117 GRAMMAR BANK**

PRONUNCIATION

4 A 🔊 **2.06 | expressing surprise and asking for reaction |** Look at the sentence from the discussion. Which word is stressed? Does the intonation fall or rise at the end? Listen and check.

But surely respect has to be earned?

B 🔊 **2.07 |** Practise saying the sentences expressing surprise and asking for reaction. Listen and check.

1 But surely it's the other way round?
2 But surely you can't really believe that?
3 But surely there's more to it than that?
4 But surely that's oversimplifying things?

SPEAKING

5 A Read the quotes (A and B). Choose one you would like to discuss and make notes to support your point of view. Think about your own culture, or other cultures that you know of. Consider:

- art.
- crafts.
- languages.
- family life.
- relationships.
- jobs.

> **A** It is inevitable that traditions and customs will disappear as the world moves forward. By insisting that we preserve the same attitudes and ways of behaving, we hinder the possible progress our society can make.

> **B** We should all stop looking at our cultures as separate from each other as that's what can lead to conflict and misunderstanding.

B Find a partner with the same point of view as yours. Work together and add to your notes.

C Find another student who holds the opposing point of view. Work in pairs and use your notes to discuss the issue. Express interest, agreement or disagreement.

D Report interesting points that arose during your discussion to the class. What is the general consensus?

MEDIATION SKILLS
analysing a fictional character

talk about a character and speculate on their motivation

▶▶ **page 146 MEDIATION BANK**

2D **BBC Food**
Flavours

VOCABULARY | describing food
SPEAKING | propose a new restaurant
WRITING | a blog post about a food hotspot

PREVIEW

1 Work in pairs. Discuss the questions.

   1 When you think of food from the USA, what do you imagine?

   2 Is there any American food that you like or dislike? Give examples.

2 Work in pairs. Read the programme information and questions 1–4. Which questions can you answer?

   1 Where do most immigrants to Los Angeles come from?

   2 Why might it be important for immigrants to the USA to make food from their original country?

   3 What is an 'Angelino'? What does it imply in relation to food?

   4 What do you understand by the 'American Dream'?

Nadiya's American Adventure

Nadiya Hussein, a well-known British TV chef, takes us on an extraordinary tour of the USA where she explores some of the most vibrant food cultures on earth. She travels around the country, which has one of the highest immigrant populations in the world, and treats us to glimpses of the 'culinary melting pot' that the USA has to offer. In this programme, Nadiya goes to Los Angeles, in California, where she learns about the influence of Latin American migration on Californian cuisine.

VIEW

3 ▶ Watch the BBC video clip and answer the questions in Ex 2.

4A Work in pairs. Look at the words and phrases in bold. Discuss which ones you know the meaning of and which ones you can guess.

   1 … they have brought with them their **unique cuisine**.

   2 This is a bit of an **assault on my senses**.

   3 This place is full of **intriguing smells**.

   4 This is the Guatemalan **take on** the stuffed chilli.

   5 … chefs using their heritage to **fuse flavours** …

   6 … **redefining** Californian cuisine.

   7 … **topped with** a Latin-inspired salsa.

   8 … to take flavours and ingredients from different places and **reinterpret it**.

B ▶ Watch the video again and listen out for the words and phrases from Ex 4A in context. Then work in pairs and discuss which of the phrases have become clearer.

VOCABULARY

describing food

5 A Think about your own experiences of food and eating and make brief notes on the topics (1–6).

1 an experience that was an assault on the senses
2 a food you tried that fused interesting flavours
3 a restaurant/food stall with intriguing smells
4 a modern take on a traditional dish
5 a dessert covered in your favourite topping
6 a unique cuisine you would be interested in trying

B Work in small groups. Talk about your experiences and share your ideas.

There's this street in my neighbourhood with pop-up food stalls every Saturday – talk about an assault on the senses! It makes me want to try everything.

SPEAKING

propose a new restaurant

6 A Work in pairs. You're going to propose a new restaurant for your area. Think about what type of restaurant might be fun, interesting and popular. Discuss:

1 what types of food your area already offers, and what it doesn't.
2 what new types of food might be popular with people in your area.
3 how you might adapt an existing cuisine to give it a modern twist.
4 what types of cuisine you could combine to make a 'fusion' restaurant.

B Decide what type of restaurant you're going to create and think of a name for it. Make a list of the features that would make it attractive to people. Use the vocabulary from Ex 4A to help you.

Japanese/Indian fusion = unique cuisine

C Pitch your restaurant idea to the class. Use the Key phrases to help you.

> ### KEY PHRASES
>
> What makes it such a unique concept is …
> People would jump at the chance to try …
> What we're aiming for is …
> Something that we're lacking round here is …
> We want to create a new take on (Italian cuisine).

D Vote to decide which of the restaurant ideas you would like to see in your area.

WRITING

a blog post about a food hotspot

7 A Look at the post on a city's social media page below. What do they want people to do?

> Bloggers – we're looking for your reviews of your favourite areas to go out for food! What kind of food can you find there? What makes it such a good experience? Is there anything unique about it? We'll be creating an interactive food map for our page, and if we like your review, we'll upload it to our map.
>
> ♡ 6   ⇄ 12   ♡ 1

B Work in pairs. Which areas, either in your country or abroad, would you choose to write about? Why?

C Write a blog post about a food hotspot. Go to the Writing Bank.

▶▶ page 105 **WRITING BANK**

GRAMMAR

advanced ways of comparing

1 A Choose the correct words to complete the sentences.

1 The actor's voice was so weak **so / as / like** to be almost completely inaudible.

2 The legacy of the award was **nothing like / as / like** as significant as we had been promised.

3 It wasn't **so / like / like as** much an exchange of views as a heated argument.

4 You **couldn't / shouldn't / wouldn't** get advice **any more / like as / so** unhelpful than that if you tried!

5 The outdoor performances continued **so / as / like as** long as was possible during the showery weather.

6 Interpreting is actually **like / more of / as much as** a summary than literal word-for-word translations.

B Choose three of the ways of comparing used in Ex 1A and write sentences that are true for you and where you are at the moment. Compare your sentences with a partner.

reporting

2 A Complete the second sentence using the word given so that it reports the direct speech in the first sentence. Use between four and six words.

1 'I have faith in the council's ability to address the development issues,' Ms Saunders said. CONFIDENT

Ms Saunders was .... the development issues.

2 'We submitted our application well before the deadline,' the council leader said. CLAIMED

The council leader .... application well before the deadline.

3 'It is extremely difficult to translate speeches delivered at speed,' David said. THE

David mentioned .... speeches delivered at speed.

4 'I feel that we've made the wrong decision,' Jonah said. OPINION

In .... the wrong decision.

B Work in pairs. Tell your partner two things that you've heard or been told today. Use two different ways to report this information.

VOCABULARY

3 A Match 1–6 with a–f to form collocations.

1	raise	**a**	the development
2	first and	**b**	the profile
3	detrimental	**c**	effect
4	make	**d**	more harm than good
5	facilitate	**e**	or break
6	do	**f**	foremost

B Complete the sentences with phrases from Ex 3A.

1 Good publicity can .... of an area and promote tourism.

2 Income from tourists can .... many small businesses.

3 A favourable majority in a council can .... of cultural establishments in the area.

4 Becoming a City of Culture can .... to the local economy.

5 An excess of tourists can have a .... on fragile ecosystems.

6 ...., we need to set a date for the carnival parade.

4 Rewrite the sections in bold in the reported statements using appropriate verbs in the box.

> call   cite   echo   fill   question   talk

1 During the literature lecture, the professor **gave the works of** many famous novelists **as examples** to clarify his main points.

2 My classmates **told me about** what I had missed at college.

3 Katya **persuaded me to go** to listen to a local folk group perform.

4 The writer **said that he had the same concerns as the presenter** that many local customs were disappearing.

5 In the discussion I **asked people** whether new words and slang expressions should be added to the dictionary.

6 The school governors **said they thought more classical writers should be** studied by students.

5 A Choose the correct options (A, B or C) to complete the text.

Culture shock

It can be a tremendous shock to the system, [1]............... of how well prepared you are. Going for the first time to a country where the culture is nothing [2]............... your own can be overwhelming. [3]............... to the autobiography of a famous traveller, his first trip abroad couldn't have been [4]............... more traumatic. His knowledge of the language was so limited [5]............... to be practically non-existent, he was vegan and found himself in a meat-loving country, and he had no knowledge of customs or traditions at all. However, although he [6]............... that culture shock is commonplace, he is [7]............... that it soon fades, and the [8]............... benefits that being immersed in another culture [9]............... are far more important than the initial cultural isolation.

	A	**B**	**C**
1	unconcerned	unrelated	irrespective
2	as	like	than
3	Matching	Regarding	According
4	any	some	that
5	so	like	as
6	comments	acknowledges	questions
7	insistent	expectant	assured
8	long-standing	long-held	long-term
9	brings	gets	raises

B 🔊 **R2.01** | Listen and check your answers.

working life 3

B|B|C

VLOGS

Q: What's the best or worst job you have ever had?

1 ▶ Watch the video. Have you had similar experiences to any of the speakers?

2 What other factors have made jobs good or bad for you?

GSE LEARNING OBJECTIVES

3A LISTENING | Understand a question-and-answer session on job hunting: collocations: job searching

Record a video résumé: modal verbs and phrases

Pronunciation: linking sounds in modal phrases

Write a cover email/letter

3B READING | Read an article and a blog post about remote working and studying: verb–noun collocations; metaphors

Pronunciation: word stress

Talk about solutions to problems with remote working: passives

3C HOW TO ... | check understanding by paraphrasing and summarising: collocations: politics; politics

Pronunciation: stress and intonation when paraphrasing

3D BBC STREET INTERVIEWS | Understand people talking about changing jobs

Talk about suggestions for a better workplace

Write a report on work experience

3A Get that job!

GRAMMAR | modal verbs and phrases
VOCABULARY | collocations: job searching
PRONUNCIATION | linking sounds in modal phrases

VOCABULARY

collocations: job searching

1 A Work in pairs and discuss the questions.

1 What would be your ideal job? Why?

2 How many different ways of finding a job can you think of?

B Share your ideas for question 2 in Ex 1A with the class. Who came up with the most ways of finding a job?

2 A Read the advice from a job seeker's website. Do you agree with the advice? Why/Why not?

B Look at the gaps in sentences 1–6. Predict which words complete the phrases in bold, then check your answers in the advice in Ex 2A.

1 What are the challenges involved in **identifying your strong _____ points** for a CV or job application?

2 What kind of information might _____ **a second look** in a job application?

3 What kind of job would _____ **to your particular strengths**?

4 What sort of things **can leave a problematic digital _____**?

5 What could _____ **a person's chance** of success in a job application?

6 Who would you use from your own network to help _____ **the word** about looking for a job?

C Work in pairs. Discuss your answers to the questions in Ex 2B.

Help! I need a job. Suggestions, please!

Finding a job can be confusing these days, and difficult. Research in the USA has shown that it can take between 100 and 200 job applications to get a job offer. There are many different ways of going about job searching and of course it depends on the job you're looking for. But perhaps the most important thing to remember is to be proactive – don't just sit back waiting for a job to drop in your lap, or just apply for one position and then wait and wait for a response that may never come. Use all the means available to you out there and above all, think creatively.

Here are a few suggestions to point you in the right direction.

Work on your CV: While different companies will have different forms to complete, keep your own CV up to date, with information that will warrant a second look. Tailor the CV to suit the job you're looking for.

Do a job search on dedicated job sites: This can be a useful starting point to see the type of jobs that are out there.

Find a professional recruiter: These guys are experts in their field and have built up networks that can find opportunities you would otherwise never encounter. They can help identify your strong selling points and play to your strengths.

Track down the right people: Do your own detective work, use professional networking platforms, find companies you'd like to work for and contact them directly. It's estimated that up to eighty-five percent of roles are filled via networking.

Use your immediate network: Spread the word amongst your colleagues, friends and even family – badger them for contacts and introductions.

Be wary of your online history: Leaving a problematic digital footprint could jeopardise your chances by negating the image you want to convey, so always be wary of what you post on social media.

And finally, set up alerts on search sites and keep a record of what you've done and what needs to be followed up. You'll get there!

LISTENING

3 A 🔊 **3.01 |** Listen to a question-and-answer session after a talk on job hunting. What four topics related to job recruitment are mentioned?

B 🔊 **3.01 |** Listen again and choose the correct options (a–c).

1 The expert mentions the everyday information we deal with to
  a contrast with the type of information we need to deal with at work.
  b illustrate a similar need for organising information at work.
  c emphasise how much more information we deal with at work.

2 Which is true, according to the expert?
  a Online communication skills are the most sought after in a potential employee.
  b Communication is all about listening.
  c Online interactions are just as important as face-to-face meetings.

3 The expert explains 'flexibility' as
  a the requirement to be available at any time.
  b a readiness to take on unscheduled tasks.
  c an ease at working either individually or in teams.

4 A point made about interviews is that
  a there is an underlying reason for seemingly strange requests.
  b interviewers can be influenced by the way an applicant speaks.
  c remote interviews benefit the recruiters more than the applicants.

C Work in pairs and think of two questions that you would ask the speaker if you were in the audience in Ex 3A. Join another pair and ask and answer your questions.

D Work in pairs and discuss the questions.

1 Which type of interview would you be most comfortable with: remote or face-to-face? Why?

2 Would you agree that face-to-face interviews favour certain people with regards to appearance and manner? Why/Why not?

3 Do you think it's true that recruiters tend to recruit people who are similar to themselves?

GRAMMAR

modal verbs and phrases

4 A 🔊 **3.02 |** Complete the sentences from the talk with the correct modal phrases in the box. Listen and check.

> a strong likelihood that   absolutely essential
> being able   inevitably it will   may well
> might be   need to be good
> obviously your responsibility

1 There's .... certain key phrases will come up in a job advertisement.

2 It's .... that you have the skills to enable you to manage large amounts of information efficiently.

3 .... to interact with people well is important on many levels.

4 You .... at getting people to want to listen to you.

5 It's .... to present yourself in the best possible way.

6 .... come out at some point.

7 You .... asked to take on a range of tasks.

8 In the future, recruiters .... be using voice analysis to learn more about the candidates.

B Which sentences in Ex 4A imply obligation/ necessity (O), possibility/probability (P) and ability (A)?

C Rewrite the sentences in Ex 4A using the phrases in the box. In some sentences more than one phrase may be possible.

> a requirement is   be crucial
> be expected that   be highly likely
> have an aptitude for   in all probability
> it's a given that   the odds are that
> there's a chance that   vital   will undoubtedly

D Learn and practise. Go to the Grammar Bank.

▶▶ page 118 **GRAMMAR BANK**

PRONUNCIATION

5 A | **linking sounds in modal phrases** | Look at the underlined words. How do you connect them when saying them aloud?

1 There's a <u>strong likelihood</u> that it will happen.
2 It's <u>absolutely essential</u> that we attend.
3 It's obviously <u>your responsibility</u> to get it done.
4 You <u>should always</u> be aware that others might see it differently.
5 <u>In all</u> probability, this will fail.

B 🔊 **3.03** | Listen and check. Then listen again and repeat the sentences.

C Complete the sentences with your own ideas. Work in pairs and compare your answers.

1 Before a job interview it is absolutely essential to …
2 When looking for a job, you should always …
3 In all probability, most people will experience …
4 When attending an interview, it's crucial that …
5 If I'm in an interview situation, there's a strong likelihood that …
6 In an interview, it's your responsibility to …

WRITING

a cover email/letter

6 A Work in pairs and discuss the questions.

1 What is a cover email or letter when applying for a job and what do you think should be included in one?
2 Should a cover email be written in formal or informal language?
3 Do you think employers place a lot of value on cover emails and letters? Why/Why not?

B Which of the following do you think should be given priority in a cover email/letter?

> availability experience
> general suitability interests
> personal skills qualifications

C Write a cover email. Go to the Writing Bank.

⏩ **page 106 WRITING BANK**

SPEAKING

record a video résumé

7 A What do you think a video résumé is? Read the blog post to check your ideas. What would your reaction be if you were asked to record one?

> Posted May 5 by Zephyr   • • •
>
> Hey – this morning I recorded my first video résumé and sent it off with the job application I mentioned yesterday. And it was nowhere as difficult as I'd thought it would be. They say sixty seconds is a good length so that's what I did. It was actually quite fun. It may seem a bit daunting, but honestly, it's a really good way to make your application stand out. The recruiter can see you, hear you and get a feel for your personality. And you can make an impact. So, what did I learn? It's vital that you write a script that will convey a good image of who you are and explain briefly why you're applying and would be the best person for the job. As all the advice says, I checked out the job description and made sure that my video addressed all the key points. Just remember to take the time to rehearse a few times beforehand so that you don't need to actually read the script. Sit comfortably – don't fidget – and speak naturally, clearly and slowly. Simple editing – like adding your name, a title and contact details is fine. And don't get TOO creative, with fancy images or sound, etc., unless of course you're applying for a job where that kind of creativity is required.

B Choose a job to apply for. This could be the same one that you wrote the cover email for, or one of the adverts you or other students wrote. Work in pairs and discuss what you would include in a video résumé.

C Plan your video résumé. Consider using these useful phrases:

- For a job like this it's essential that …
- Working in … will inevitably involve …
- One of my strengths is being able to …
- I definitely have the capability of/an aptitude for …
- I consider it vital that …
- In my opinion, a … needs to …
- It is obviously a …'s responsibility to …

D Read the Future Skills box and do the task.

> **FUTURE SKILLS**
> ## Interviewing
>
> An interview is your opportunity to showcase what you can do and that you are the right person for a job. You should always prepare well and pay attention to your appearance and manner. Maintain eye contact during a face-to-face interview and try to appear relaxed, as body language reveals a lot about a person.
>
> Work in pairs and practise introducing yourselves to each other as you would in an interview.

8 A Either record your video résumé and share it with your partner or the class, or deliver it face-to-face.

B Work in small groups and discuss the questions.

1 How difficult was it to make your video résumé?
2 How useful do you think video résumés are to an employer?

3B Going remote

GRAMMAR | passives
VOCABULARY | verb–noun collocations; metaphors
PRONUNCIATION | word stress

READING

1 Work in pairs and discuss the question. Give reasons and examples for your answers.

What are the challenges and benefits of remote working for both employers and employees, students and teachers? Think about:

- motivating staff/students.
- managing staff/students.
- working in large teams.
- technical issues.
- work hours.
- mentoring.

2 Look at the titles of the article below and the blog post on page 36 about remote work and study. What might you expect the texts to include? Which might be the more formal? Scan the texts to check your ideas.

A Video call fatigue

Your screen freezes. There is a weird echo. A dozen heads stare at you. There are the break-out rooms, the chat functions, the one-to-one meetings and at the end of the day you are exhausted even though you haven't moved from your work or study space. But what, exactly, is tiring us out? Is video chat harder?

Being on a video call requires more focus than a face-to-face chat, says Gianpiero Petriglieri, an associate professor who studies workplace development. But this applies equally well to online classes or learning situations for students. Video chats mean we need to work harder to process non-verbal cues like facial expressions, the tone and pitch of the voice and body language; paying more attention to these consumes a lot of energy. 'Our minds are together when our bodies feel we're not. That dissonance, which causes people to have conflicting feelings, is exhausting. You cannot relax into the conversation naturally,' he says. Rather than **strengthening bonds** between participants, it can do the opposite and **exacerbate divisions**. Relationships between team members can become strained.

The 'gallery view' of the video call is challenging for the brain, which has to work overtime to try to decode visuals of a whole range of people. We try to observe protocol and maintain eye contact with a camera rather than a face, we smile awkwardly, nod appropriately,

cover up any signs of boredom and try not to let our eyes drift to the real faces on the screen staring at us.

Silence is another challenge, he adds. 'Silence creates a natural rhythm in a real-life conversation. However, when it happens in a video call, you become anxious about the technology.' It also makes people feel uncomfortable. One study showed that delays on phone or conferencing systems shaped our views of people negatively: even delays of 1.2 seconds made people perceive the responder as less friendly or focused, or even **engendered distrust**. Indeed, sometimes people who were thought to have been listening intently were actually found to have been working on something else entirely at the same time!

What **aggravates the problem**, says Marissa Shuffler (associate professor at Clemson University), is that if we are physically on camera, we are very aware of being watched. 'When you're on a video conference, you know everybody's looking at you; you are on stage, so there comes the social pressure and feeling like you need to perform. Being performative is nerve-wracking and more stressful.' It's also very hard for people not to look at their own face if they can see it on screen, or not to be conscious of how they behave in front of the camera.

It has been suggested by experts that to **ease those stress levels** we may wish to consider going old-school – use emails, share files, have shorter, more personal calls. Or even use a phone – remember those?

B All good online, apart from ...

By Rebecca Hart
Published 19th May

It's now six months since I started my online course at university, and I must admit I love every minute of it. It's the flexibility – we can stream lectures when we want and arrange study calls with other students at times to suit us all. And – ahh – not having to waste time and money on commuting every day! Big plus. Weirdly, I'm getting a lot done. Before I moved to studying online, my assignment writing would be down to the wire – midnight the night before submission deadline! Now I seem much more organised somehow. I imagine that's down to having fewer distractions – not being tempted to spend ages in the café with friends and so on. Although my parents do need to be reminded not to bang on my door when I'm in an online class. I've heard people in jobs say that working remotely can be hard. They don't establish a proper routine and end up with work spilling into their home and social lives, which stresses them out. And I've got friends who say they feel isolated and miss being in a physical classroom and

getting immediate feedback that **boosts morale**. I can understand that, but for me it certainly works. Rather than having my workflow interrupted, I'm left alone to focus on what I'm doing, and there are always people I can reach out to when I need to. Also, I have a good social life when I'm not studying, which **alleviates any boredom** I might experience. If I had to pick out any drawbacks of studying online, I'd have to say that some of our online discussion classes can be a pain. It's often difficult to contribute or ask a question and on a bad day they can seem never-ending. Some people take it as a chance to catch up socially and unless the leader is quite disciplined, you sit there listening to people wittering on for ages and start to lose the plot. And afterwards, for some reason I feel drained – even though I haven't done a thing apart from look at a camera and make the odd comment! But for me, at least, the advantages outweigh the drawbacks and I'm really glad I chose this option.

3 A Read the texts again and answer the questions (1–8) in your own words.

1 Why do video chats or conferences consume more energy than face-to-face ones?

2 What does the word 'dissonance' in Text A paragraph 2 refer to?

3 What are 'video call protocols' and why is it sometimes difficult to observe them?

4 Are silences helpful during a video call? Why/Why not?

5 Why is being on camera sometimes stressful?

6 Why does the writer of Text B use 'ahh' near the beginning of paragraph 1?

7 What advantages to remote studying does the writer of Text B give?

8 What disadvantages are mentioned?

B Find colloquial ways of saying the following in Text B.

1 an advantage

2 because of

3 talking for a long time about something unimportant

4 occasional

C Make notes on questions 1 and 2. Work in pairs and compare your answers.

1 How do the styles of each text differ? Consider:
- vocabulary.
- grammatical structures.
- interaction with the reader.

2 What are the differences in structure of the two texts? Consider:
- paragraphing.
- sentence length and complexity.
- introductions and conclusions.

VOCABULARY

verb–noun collocations

4 A Scan the texts in Ex 2 again. Match the collocations in bold with the meanings (1–7).

1 reduce the amount of tension

2 makes you feel more valued

3 increases possible differences between people

4 makes a difficult situation worse

5 improves relationships

6 stops the monotony

7 created a feeling of suspicion

B Complete the questions with the correct form of the verbs you found in Ex 4A.

1 How has a difficult situation you've been in been .... recently?

2 How do you try to .... stress levels when you're feeling tense?

3 How might remote working .... distrust?

4 How do you .... boredom when you're not busy?

5 How can employers .... bonds between employees?

6 How has your morale recently been .... ?

C Work in pairs and discuss the questions. Share your ideas with the class.

1 How do you feel during video calls or online meetings?

2 Have you ever worked or studied remotely? Are there any points you would like to share that are not mentioned in Texts A and B?

D Learn and practise. Go to the Vocabulary Bank.

▶▶ page 138 **VOCABULARY BANK** metaphors

PRONUNCIATION

5 A | word stress | Look at the words in the box. How many syllables does each word have? If there is more than one syllable, where do you think the stress is?

> aggravate   alleviate   distrust   ease   engender
> exacerbate   isolation   morale   strengthen

B 🔊 **3.04** | Listen and check your answers to Ex 5A. Then listen again and repeat the words.

6 Work in pairs. Discuss the questions in Ex 4B.

GRAMMAR

passives

7 A Complete the sentences from the texts in Ex 2 with the appropriate passive form using the words in brackets.

1 Although my parents do need _____ (remind) not to bang on my door when I'm in an online class.

2 Rather than _____ (workflow / interrupt), I'm left alone to focus on what I'm doing, …

3 … sometimes people who were _____ (think / listen) intently were actually _____ (find / work) on something else entirely at the same time.

4 … we are very aware of _____ (watch).

5 It _____ (suggest) by experts that to ease those stress levels we may wish to consider going old-school.

B Which sentence in Ex 7A includes an agent (the person or thing doing the action)? Why do the other sentences NOT name the agent?

C Choose the correct words to complete the sentences. Discuss your reactions to the statements.

1 Employees should have the right **being allowed** / **to be allowed** to work from home if it is appropriate.

2 **Having been given** / **Being given** a start time for the call, people need to make sure they are punctual.

3 During trial periods working remotely, employees should be aware that their work is **monitoring** / **being monitored** closely by their line manager.

4 I **'ve been made** / **'m making** aware that a number of video meetings have **been cancelled** / **being cancelled** due to low attendance numbers. We need **have** / **to have** attendance at these meetings made mandatory.

5 If people **are found** / **were found** to be avoiding online meetings, they should **be** / **being** given a warning.

D Learn and practise. Go to the Grammar Bank.

⏩ page 119 **GRAMMAR BANK**

SPEAKING

8 A Work in groups of three. Discuss the problems with remote working that some employees have raised (1–4).

1 Video meetings are non-productive, take too long and involve technological issues.

2 It is difficult to develop a team spirit when most interaction is online.

3 Remote working blurs the line between home and work as colleagues and management can contact people at any time.

4 People feel isolated, unappreciated and stressed.

B Student A: Go to page 142. Student B: Go to page 143. Student C: Go to page 143. Read the suggestions for dealing with the problems in Ex 8A. Add more ideas to your list.

C Read the Future Skills box and do the task.

> ## FUTURE SKILLS
> ## Communication
>
> We often use the passive to distance ourselves from information and to avoid sounding too aggressive. The passive allows us to avoid mentioning an agent when it might be too direct or sensitive to do so. Soften the tone in discussions where you strongly disagree, e.g. 'It **has been pointed out** that people **have been excluded** from meetings.'
>
> Think about your general position in Ex 8B and how you might use the passive to soften your position.

D Discuss ideas for dealing with the problems in Ex 8A. Promote your ideas from Ex 8B, giving examples and challenging the other students' points.

9 Have a class discussion. What are your own views on the problems in Ex 8A? How do they differ from the views you presented in Ex 8D?

3C Tackling the real issues

HOW TO ... | check understanding by paraphrasing and summarising
VOCABULARY | collocations: politics; politics
PRONUNCIATION | stress and intonation when paraphrasing

VOCABULARY

collocations: politics

1 **Read the extract and answer the questions.**
   1 Where do you think you would hear or read this?
   2 Would you say that promises like this are believable?
   3 What skills and qualities do you think politicians should have?

> It's in our manifesto, and it will be a priority if we are elected by you, the public, to serve as the next government of this country. Addressing the pay gap between the public and private sectors is a matter of urgency. In this country, in these times, it is a scandal that there is such a difference. I promise this party will do its utmost to stand up for all workers' rights. You have my word.

2 A 🔊 **3.05 | Listen to an extract from a politician's campaign talk. Which inequalities is the politician addressing?**

B **Work in pairs. Check the meaning of the words in the box. Complete the sentences (1–5) with the correct form of the words.**

| allocate | bridge | eliminate | encourage |
| enforce | shape | stand | tackle |

   1 Our intention is to .... **the** gender pay **gap** by increasing higher-level work opportunities for women.
   2 A major policy of ours going forward will be to .... **more resources** to enable more rough sleepers to leave the streets.
   3 We realise that .... **discrimination** across the board will be a huge challenge, but we shall .... existing **regulations** and pass new laws.
   4 **Diversity** is to be .... in every area of life and we shall .... **inequalities** wherever we find them.
   5 Helping the environment is high on our agenda and our party will .... **up for** those who want to develop greener energy and .... further **policy** to fight climate change.

C 🔊 **3.06 | Listen and check your answers.**

3 A **Work in pairs and rank the promises in Ex 2B from most important (1) to least important (5). Give reasons to justify your opinions.**

   I would rank the promise about helping the environment as number 1. If we don't have a planet to live on, none of the other promises even matter.

B **Learn and practise. Go to the Vocabulary Bank.**

   ▶▶ page 138 **VOCABULARY BANK** politics

4 A **What is the 'gender pay gap'? Read the short article and check your ideas.**

What is the 'gender pay gap'?

Be aware that the gender pay gap is not the same as pay inequality. There is a law in place in some countries that makes it illegal for a man and a woman to be paid differently for doing the same job. The gender pay gap refers to the difference in pay between men and women overall and shows that because more men are appointed to higher positions than women, and more women do lower-paid part-time work, men's earnings are significantly higher on average.

B **Work in pairs and discuss the questions.**
   1 Why do you think the gender pay gap exists?
   2 Do you think there is a gender pay gap in your country?
   3 What could be done about a gender pay gap in a country where it exists?

How to ...
check understanding by paraphrasing and summarising

5 A 🔊 **3.07 |** Listen to a discussion on a radio show about a politician's promise. How do the guests' points of view differ?

B 🔊 **3.07 |** Listen again and complete the sentences from the discussion with the correct phrases.

1 So, in _____ , you're going to vote for her because of one election promise.

2 Not _____ . What _____ that she made a good speech.

3 So, what _____ that men and women don't have the same opportunities …

4 Absolutely. That's _____ .

5 Am _____ that you believe there's nothing more politicians can do … ?

6 OK, I'll _____ .

7 That's not _____ .

8 Please correct _____ , …

9 Let me _____ .

6 A 🔊 **3.08 |** Listen to one of the exchanges from the interview again. How does the woman check understanding?

1 by repeating the man's words back to him

2 by summarising the points in her own words

B Read some statements about gender equality in the workplace. How could you respond using paraphrasing to check your understanding?

> I believe that job stereotypes influence us from a very early age.

> So, in …

> I think women are limited in their job opportunities because they are less willing to negotiate higher salaries than men.

> So, what …

> More men would take paternity leave if the financial terms were better.

> Am I right … ?

C Learn and practise. Go to the Grammar Bank.

▶▶ page 120 **GRAMMAR BANK**

PRONUNCIATION

7 A 🔊 **3.09 | stress and intonation when paraphrasing |** Listen to the two sentences. Notice the stress and intonation of the introduction to the paraphrase. Is there a pause or not?

1 So, what you're basically saying is that men and women don't have the same opportunities to reach the high-salaried positions.

2 Correct me if I'm wrong, but it sounds like you're talking about a complete lack of progress.

B Practise saying the following sentences.

1 Let me rephrase that. Do you support equality or not?

2 Correct me if I'm wrong, but you seem to agree with the policy.

3 So, what you're saying is that we shouldn't worry about other people's situations.

SPEAKING

8 A Look at the statements (1–4). Decide whether you agree or disagree with each one.

1 Every company regardless of size should be obliged to offer childcare facilities on site.

2 Every business should be required to publish a summary of what it has done to protect the environment every year.

3 No company director should earn more than five times the salary of the company's lowest paid worker.

4 There should be the same number of students from low-income backgrounds as high-income backgrounds at top universities.

B Work in pairs. Find a statement that you have opposing views on. If you agree on everything, choose one to take opposing sides on.

C Note down points you can use in your discussion. Consider what your partner might say and be prepared to counter their views.

D Read the Future Skills box and answer the question.

FUTURE SKILLS
Communication

Be aware that people sometimes find certain issues difficult to discuss publicly or with people they do not know well. These include things like income, politics, heritage, religion, etc. This can be different from one culture to another. Be sensitive to other people and what they might not be comfortable talking about.

What other topics might some people be sensitive about?

E Have the discussion. Use collocations and language for paraphrasing where possible. Then, share your conclusions with the class.

MEDIATION SKILLS
showing sensitivity to other opinions and empathising
share and listen to viewpoints

▶▶ page 148 **MEDIATION BANK**

3D

B B C Street Interviews

Company culture

Hazel

VOCABULARY | workplace and work culture
SPEAKING | make suggestions for a better workplace
WRITING | a report on work experience

Michael

PREVIEW

1 **Work in pairs and discuss the questions.**

1 How many reasons can you think of for people to change careers or jobs?

2 Do you know anyone who really loves their job? Why do they like it so much?

3 Do you know anyone who is unsatisfied with their job? What issues do they have?

Q1: What would you look for in a company if you were changing careers?

Q2: If you had the chance to live comfortably and never work again, would you?

VIEW

2 A ▶ Watch the interviews. Note down the different things that the speakers say they would:

a look for in a new company.

b do if they never had to work again.

B Work in pairs and compare your notes. Which speaker do you most identify with? Why?

3 A Work in pairs. Look at the phrases from the interviews. Try to complete the phrases in bold.

1 I do like to look for a **corporate social** .... **policy** …

2 I have worked for a company before that .... **sustainability** …

3 … a company that had a **good, sound financial** .... …

4 … where … it's not like a .... **culture**, I guess, in the company.

5 I like being in places that are .... **based** …

6 … somewhere where I feel we have **shared** .... …

7 I enjoy the **social** .... of working …

8 It doesn't have to be work in terms of your **current** ....

B ▶ Watch the interviews again. Check your answers to Ex 3A.

VOCABULARY

workplace and work culture

4 A Complete the sentences with your own ideas.

1 If a company has a good, sound financial footing it can afford to …

2 In a company that has a toxic culture, employees might feel …

3 The social aspect of working is important because …

4 Working with colleagues with shared values can be important because …

5 If I stayed in my current field of work all my life, …

6 What I don't like are companies which prioritise …

B Work in pairs and compare your ideas. How far do you agree with each other?

Sagar

Adeleke

B B C

Nick

Kirsty

SPEAKING

make suggestions for a better workplace

5 A Work in pairs. Look at the list of suggestions for encouraging teamwork and a positive culture at your company. Discuss the suggestions, adding your own comments, and add another suggestion.

- A system where employees can anonymously submit concerns or suggestions.
  Yes OK, but just how anonymous would it be?
  They'd just be ignored!

- 'Away Days' with physical and mental challenges to encourage teamwork.
  For example?
  Not everyone likes physical activity!

- Unlimited annual leave as long as deadlines and expectations are met.
  Amazing, but how realistic is this?
  We'd end up never taking any leave.

- New space for employees to relax and socialise together.
  I'd rather socialise outside of work, thank you!
  It'd just become a meeting room.

- Fewer video calls and more face-to-face meetings.
  Great idea!
  Some of us work from home though.

- ....

B Work in small groups. Present your opinions and comments on the suggestions you discussed in Ex 5A, giving examples and justifying your ideas. Use the Key phrases to help you.

KEY PHRASES

In terms of … , I'd go for something like …
For me, … is crucial because …
No one wants …
Can you see any value in … ?
But not everyone's comfortable with …
I completely go along with whoever wrote …

C In your group, prioritise three suggestions for the company. Present your group's suggestions to the class.

WRITING

a report on work experience

6 A Read the notice on a college website. What type of jobs or work might people write about?

Reports wanted!

Have you had a part-time job or other holiday employment? If your answer is yes, then we want to hear from you.

Our jobs page is compiling information and guidance for students looking for holiday employment. We would like to hear about your experiences. What job did you choose? What were your expectations? Did the reality of the experience live up to your expectations? What advice would you give other students considering work experience?

Please submit a report to the email address below, and help other students make informed choices.

B Work in pairs and discuss the questions.

1 Have you ever had a part-time job or a holiday job as a student? Why/Why not?
2 What do you think are the benefits and drawbacks for students having holiday jobs?
3 What kind of information would be useful to include in the report for the website?

C Write a report on work experience. Go to the Writing Bank.

▶▶ page 107 **WRITING BANK**

GRAMMAR

modal verbs and phrases

1 A Complete the text with the words in the box.

> bound   essential   expected   inevitably
> likelihood   requirement   responsibility
> unlikely   well

MY WORST JOB

Young as I am, I'm a realist, and I know it's absolutely
¹............. for people to have humility when starting out in
the working world. I knew my first job after university was
²............. to be difficult and lacking in personal rewards.
I accepted that it may ³............. be my ⁴............. to carry
out menial tasks. But it was a lot worse than I'd foreseen.
First of all, we were regularly ⁵............. to work twelve-hour
shifts; at the interview they had said this was highly
⁶............. except during holiday periods. Secondly, I was
translating documents from English to French, Spanish
and Italian – and the original ⁷............. was only for
Spanish. All this ⁸............. led to me quitting and starting
again, thankfully in a job that was more rewarding. If I had
stayed, I think there would have been a strong ⁹.............
that my long-term health would have been affected.

B Tell your partner about a bad work experience
that you, or someone you know, has had.

passives

2 Rewrite the sentences using the passive.

1 You need to have rewritten this report by the
end of the day.
This report ....

2 People think that Sam was working for a
competitor at the same time as working for us.
Sam ....

3 Placing too much pressure on employees can
affect their productivity.
Being ....

4 They didn't shortlist my brother after the
interview, and this knocked his confidence.
Not to ....

5 Someone needs to inform prospective
employees about possible promotion paths
within the company.
Prospective ....

6 They say that the present owner's great-
grandfather founded the company.
The company ....

VOCABULARY

3 A Choose the correct words to complete the sentence starters.
Then finish them with your own ideas.

1 For me a job advert that would **benefit** / **warrant** a
second look would ....

2 The best way for me to spread **a** / **the** word if I were
looking for a job would be ....

3 An example of leaving a problematic digital **footprint** /
footstep is ....

4 Identifying my strong **sales** / **selling** points is hard, but I
would say that ....

5 Something that would **risk** / **jeopardise** your chances in a
job interview is ....

6 If I were to **play** / **work** to my strengths when searching
for a job, I would ....

B Work in pairs. Compare your sentences and comment on
what your partner has written.

4 A Complete the questions with the correct form of the verbs in
the box.

> alleviate   allocate   ease   encourage   enforce
> strengthen

1 What can help .... bonds between classmates or work
colleagues?

2 What do you do to .... boredom in the evenings?

3 What helps you to .... stress levels after a hard day at
college or work?

4 How can companies .... diversity in the workplace?

5 What additional resources do you think should be ....
to your college or workplace?

6 Do you think that regulations at your college or
workplace could be better .... ? Why/Why not?

B Work in pairs and discuss the questions in Ex 4A.

5 Complete the second sentence using the word given so that
it has a similar meaning to the first sentence. Use between
four and six words.

1 I am careful about keeping my work and free time
separate. SPILL
I am careful that my work .... my free time.

2 We know that's it's necessary for us to put in lots of hours
to prepare for the exams. GIVEN
It's .... have to put in a lot of hours to prepare for the
exams.

3 The mood amongst staff has already improved thanks to
the new manager. MORALE
The new manager has .... staff.

4 I think it's unlikely that I shall get a job before
June. ODDS
I would say that regarding my getting a job before June,
.... quite low.

5 The student representative promised to voice the
demands of his classmates. STAND
The student representative promised to ....

6 Students can benefit from doing some travelling between
finishing their studies and starting work. BRIDGE
Doing some travelling is a good way .... between
finishing their studies and starting work.

humanity 4

VLOGS

Q: What human characteristics are the most important?

1  Watch the video. Did anyone's answer surprise you?

2 Would you add any other important characteristics to those described by the people?

4A Pioneers

GRAMMAR | verb patterns
VOCABULARY | verb–noun collocations; adverb–adjective collocations
PRONUNCIATION | syllable stress in verb–noun collocations

READING

1 A Work in pairs and discuss the questions.

1 How have technological advances affected your life? Think about travel, education and entertainment.

2 What technological breakthroughs do the photos show and what impact have they had? Can you name any pioneers in these fields?

3 Do you think technological changes like these are always for the better?

4 Why do you think humanity continues to seek more knowledge and progress?

B Look at the title of the article. What do you think it's about? Read the article quickly to check your ideas. How are the two pioneers and their projects similar and different?

2 A Read the article again. Work in pairs and discuss the question.

Why does the writer mention the following?

1 children's questions   5 Jacques Cousteau
2 volcanic craters   6 370 square metres
3 Tesla, Inc.   7 Columbus
4 SpaceX

B Do you agree with the writer's conclusion that 'the world definitely needs them both'? Why/Why not?

VOCABULARY

verb–noun collocations

3 A Match the collocations in bold in the article with their meanings (1–8).

1 achieve an ambition
2 benefit progress
3 bring in some money
4 understand things that intrigue you
5 try to do something you have always wanted
6 give you the encouragement
7 support a plan
8 exploring beyond what is known

B Complete the questions with the correct form of the verbs in bold in the article. Answer the questions.

1 How do you usually .... your curiosity about things that intrigue you?

2 What .... your motivation to follow a particular career or education path?

3 Is there a particular dream you would like to .... ?

4 Which pioneer from your country's history is famous for .... the limits? What did they do and how valuable was it?

5 What advice would you give to somebody who wanted to .... an ambition?

6 If you could .... funding for a project in your local area, what would it be?

7 Do you often .... online projects or campaigns? Why/Why not?

8 How important do you think it is for pioneers to .... science in their endeavours?

C Work in pairs. Write a comment in response to the article in Ex 1B, using one or more verb–noun collocations. Share your comment with the class.

Heights and depths

Limits? What limits? It is at the heart of being human – or at least, that is what we are told – to push boundaries as far as we can, to try to see round the next corner, to work out just what it is that makes us tick and why. We begin questioning as children, asking 'Why?', and the need to go further and deeper, expanding our world and our knowledge, **fuels the motivation** of those scientists and explorers who never stop asking 'Why? How? What if … ?' History is full of examples of those pioneers and trailblazers whose persistence has changed our lives, the majority of whom made many sacrifices and whose main motivation was to answer the unanswerable and to help society move forward.

So, what is left to be explored in our physical world? Pioneers have conquered mountains, blazed trails through jungles, scaled volcanic craters and filled in the map of the world with as much detail as is currently possible. Yet, there is still scope for more. Pushing these limits requires passion, determination, vision and … funding. Whether the **research projects** necessary to make the next breakthrough **are backed** by government, well-funded private enterprise or alternatively are solo projects in the hands of 'mini-pioneers', humankind will never stop trying to find answers to questions it may not even have asked yet. Two of today's pioneers, the well-known entrepreneur Elon Musk, and Fabien Cousteau, an aquanaut, are **pushing the limits** in very different directions: upwards to the stars, and downwards to the ocean floor.

Elon Musk is a household name for a variety of reasons. We associate his name with Tesla, Inc., artificial intelligence and hyperloop tunnels (a revolutionary form of public and city-to-city transport). But perhaps he is best known for his SpaceX project, founded in 2002 to develop space transport and send rockets to Mars. While government-sponsored space agencies and research are limited in what they can achieve by the huge costs involved, Musk has had the financial freedom to **pursue his ambitions** and indulge his vision. Working closely with space agencies, he has significantly helped further the possibilities of space transport. SpaceX, a commercially successful company, acts as a space taxi service, taking astronauts to and from the International Space Station. In recent years, SpaceX has offered the service to space tourists, too – who pay handsomely for the experience – and its rockets are reusable. This privately funded research has brought the possibility of accessible space tourism ever closer, and in doing

so, appears to have made the idea of reaching further into space to visit, explore and perhaps establish bases on other planets such as Mars a startlingly realistic prospect.

Another man with **a big dream** that he is hoping to **have realised** before too long is Fabien Cousteau. Unlike Musk, he is not looking to the stars and beyond, but downwards to the vast ocean depths that have yet to be explored – shockingly, humans have only charted five percent of the Earth's oceans. Cousteau is an aquanaut and, also unlike Musk, without the necessary money to invest. He is endeavouring to **raise funding** from universities and research departments to establish a 'Space Station of the Seas'. Following in the footsteps of his famous grandfather Jacques Cousteau in the 1960s, Fabien's project, Proteus, involves building an expandable station of about 370 square metres, at a depth of 180 metres below the surface. It will provide a base where aquanauts can live and conduct research from for long periods of time. At the moment, a major obstacle to ocean research is the limited time that aquanauts can spend underwater; their bodies risk being deprived of oxygen after a limited time period. Proteus will change that, being an underwater base that they can return to and stock up on oxygen. The station will allow scientists to explore the oceans and research climate change, new drugs, sustainable food production and many, many more things that will have the potential to change lives. Unlike Musk's endeavours in space, building and operating the habitat for its first three years will cost a mere $150 million – a drop in the ocean compared with the multi-billions of dollars required to send tourists up into space, but of equal scientific worth. It is quite remarkable to be following the paths of two very different pioneers, the one pushing upwards, the other pushing down.

Unquestionably, breaking new scientific ground in whatever direction requires funding. The first explorers, like Columbus, are known to have been backed by royal benefactors. Today the funding is in the hands of governments and research departments, but it also depends on the investment of companies that can turn a profit while at the same time **serving science** and progress. While large-scale exploration projects of the future will involve the big players looking for a return on their investments, there will always be the need for individuals with a big dream, and to **satisfy humankind's constant curiosity** and thirst for knowledge, the world definitely needs them both.

PRONUNCIATION

4 A 🔊 **4.01 | syllable stress in verb–noun collocations |** Which syllable in these collocations is given the main stress? Listen and check.

1 What **fuelled** your **motivation**?

2 If you could **pursue** an **ambition**, what would it be?

B 🔊 **4.02 |** Mark the syllables in the words in bold (1–5) given the main stress. Listen, check and repeat.

1 It's important to **satisfy your curiosity**.

2 What worthwhile local projects in your area need to **raise funding**?

3 How important do you think it is for pioneers to **serve science** in their endeavours?

4 Many people want to **realise a dream** although not all succeed.

5 Have you found anybody to **back your project**?

C Learn and practise. Go to the Vocabulary Bank.

⏩ **page 138 VOCABULARY BANK** adverb–adjective collocations

GRAMMAR

verb patterns

5 A Complete the sentences with the correct forms of the verbs in the box. Then check your answers in the article.

> back   build   deprive   explore
> follow   make

1 … in doing so, appears _____ the idea of reaching further into space … a startlingly realistic prospect.

2 … but downwards to the vast ocean depths that have yet _____ .

3 … Fabien's project, Proteus, involves _____ an expandable station of about 370 square metres …

4 … their bodies risk _____ of oxygen after a limited time period.

5 It is quite remarkable _____ the paths of two very different pioneers …

6 The first explorers, like Columbus, are known _____ by royal benefactors.

B Which sentences in Ex 5A are examples of the following?

a an infinitive passive form

b a gerund passive form

c an infinitive active form

d a gerund active form

6 A Complete the forum chat with the correct form of the verbs in brackets.

> **MA** **Maura22**   Comment | Share | Like
>
> Going forward, I'd definitely say we need urgent investment [1]_____ (make) in order to protect and restore areas of the environment known [2]_____ (suffer) significantly from the effects of climate change. That's where I'd get the big companies to put their money. Like the new coral reefs they're building in an attempt [3]_____ (revitalise) the dying coral.

> **AI** **Aiden46**   Comment | Share | Like
>
> What's in it for them? They can't risk [4]_____ (upset) shareholders!

> **MA** **Maura22**   Comment | Share | Like
>
> You're right, I suppose. Shareholders also need a return on their investment. But perhaps they could justify [5]_____ (back) people like Cousteau if they could then allow these centres [6]_____ (rent) to research facilities, a bit like SpaceX charging to transport astronauts?

> **AI** **Aiden46**   Comment | Share | Like
>
> But those companies usually want [7]_____ (go after) the high-profile ventures. I see that Musk is aiming [8]_____ (solve) the traffic congestion problem in big cities. Special transport tunnels or something?

> **MA** **Maura22**   Comment | Share | Like
>
> Yes, he expects us all [9]_____ (speed) through transit loops in the future. I can't really see it [10]_____ (happen) myself though.

B Work in pairs and discuss. How likely is it that we will see the results of initiatives like those mentioned in Ex 6A within a few years?

C Learn and practise. Go to the Grammar Bank.

⏩ **page 121 GRAMMAR BANK**

SPEAKING

7 A Work in pairs. Discuss points for and against the statement.

> Investment into further space research should be limited until problems on Earth have been solved.

B Student A: You will argue in favour of the statement. Go to page 142. Student B: You will argue against the statement. Go to page 143.

C Read the Future Skills box and do the task.

FUTURE SKILLS
Critical thinking

In a debate, we need to understand the opposing point of view so that we can respond and counter it effectively.

Think about the opposing view in the debate. What arguments might be made? How would you counter them?

D Work in small groups with other students on the same side. Plan your debate. When you are ready, have the debate with a group from the opposing side.

4B Community

GRAMMAR | continuous and perfect aspects
VOCABULARY | collocations: needing and giving; adjectives to describe people
PRONUNCIATION | stress in collocations featuring verbs with 'weak' meanings

LISTENING

1 A Read about some acts of kindness. Would you or anyone you know have done the same?

Was queuing at the checkout today and having to choose which items to put back because I'd forgotten my debit card and didn't have quite enough cash on me. Woman behind me smiled and paid the difference. Made my day. What a star! Thank you – whoever …

 6   12   1   ✉

Was on the train home the other day, completely shattered after a heavy day's work, resting my head against the window frame, trying to get comfortable and have a snooze. I was dozing off when the lady next to me pushed a rolled-up cardigan behind my neck to make me more comfortable. What a kind thing to do!

 9   18   6   ✉

B Work in pairs and discuss the questions.
   1 When did you last help a stranger?
   2 When were you last helped by a stranger?
   3 Do you find it easy to ask for help if you need it?

2 A 🔊 **4.03** | Listen to a radio programme about an unusual charity organisation. What does it do?

B 🔊 **4.03** | Listen again and choose the correct answers (a, b or c).
   1 Helen Carter is
      a a radio presenter.
      b a donator to charity.
      c a reviewer.
   2 52 Lives' main focus is on
      a raising funding for large-scale projects to help people.
      b finding homes for people who have nowhere to live.
      c bringing people's problems to the attention of people who can help.
   3 Jaime Thurston started the project when
      a she met a woman who was having financial problems.
      b she learnt of a woman's plight while doing something quite different.
      c she started volunteering in the community.
   4 What is the philosophy behind the website?
      a Showing and receiving kindness benefits all involved.
      b It is better to give than to receive.
      c People in general lack compassion and need encouragement.

C Work in pairs and discuss the questions.
   1 How is 52 Lives similar or different to other charity organisations you know?
   2 Would a programme like this one work in your country or home environment?
   3 What sort of problems might arise? How could they be solved?

VOCABULARY

collocations: needing and giving

3 Choose the correct words to complete the questions.

1 What is the best way to **pass / spread** the word about how to help vulnerable people?

2 What should people do if they find it hard to **make / do** ends meet?

3 Why do you think it is that some people are not prepared to give others a **caring / helping** hand?

4 What knock-on effect can losing a job **make / have** on a person?

5 Do you think it's inevitable that most people will have periods in their life when they go **through / over** a rough patch?

6 What do you do if you wake up in the morning and feel unable to **enter / face** the day?

4 Learn and practise. Go to the Vocabulary Bank.

▶▶ page 138 **VOCABULARY BANK** adjectives to describe people

PRONUNCIATION

5A | stress in collocations featuring verbs with 'weak' meanings | Look at the phrases in bold in sentences 1–3. What carries the most meaning, the verbs or the nouns? Do you think the verbs will be stressed? Why/Why not?

1 People will always be grateful when you **give them a helping hand**.

2 It can **have** a serious **knock-on effect**.

3 We all **go through rough patches**; things do get better.

B 🔊 4.04 | Listen and check. Then listen again and repeat the sentences.

6A Work in pairs and discuss the questions in Ex 3.

B Do you agree with the statements (1–3)? Discuss why/why not and give examples.

1 Giving a helping hand to those less fortunate rewards the giver more than the receiver.

2 A compassionate society can be measured by how it treats its most vulnerable citizens.

3 Looking out for others, through donating or some form of volunteering, should be made compulsory.

GRAMMAR

continuous and perfect aspects

7A 🔊 4.05 | Complete the sentences from the interview with the correct form of the verbs. Listen and check.

1 I _____ (sit) here, and I _____ (wonder) what on earth this amazing woman is going to do next!

2 Jaime Thurston _____ (work) on the project for nine years.

3 I'd heard about this website a while back and I _____ (mean) to check it out.

4 She _____ (think) about doing some volunteering for a while.

B Match the sentences in Ex 7A with the reasons the verb forms are used.

a to emphasise a time period that started in the past and will be ongoing at a point in the future

b to make a past situation immediate and dramatic

c to emphasise the length of an action or intention before a point in the past

C Work in pairs. Imagine a story that could go on the 52 Lives website. Make notes about the person's situation.

Lucas needs help with … , but he lacks …

Lucas is …ing at the moment, and he's finding it …

He's been …ing for several years. Before that, he'd been …ing.

D Swap partners and tell your new partner the story. What help do you think could be given?

E Learn and practise. Go to the Grammar Bank.

▶▶ page 122 **GRAMMAR BANK**

SPEAKING

8A Work in pairs. Read the advert and discuss how an app might be able to help people in need. Share your ideas with the class.

> ↪ ⋯
>
> ### Make a difference: Design an app!
>
> We are looking for apps that can help people in need in our community.
>
> Enter our competition and YOUR app might make all the difference to someone's life.
>
> _____
>
> **See more** ⌄

B Choose one of the ideas for an app to help people in need. Think about what it could include. Answer these questions.

1 What would the purpose of the app be?

2 How would the app work?

3 What useful features could the app include?

4 What would you call the app?

C Compare your app with those of other pairs. Vote on the most useful and best-designed app.

WRITING

an informal review of a product or service

9 A You are going to read a review of an app called 'Realise your dreams'. Work in pairs and discuss what you think this app might do.

B Read the review of the app and choose the best title for the review. Give reasons for your choice.

1 Can dreams come true?
2 A realistic approach to realising a dream
3 The real cost of fulfilling a dream

C How does this app differ from others? Would you try it? Why/Why not?

10 A Answer the questions.

1 Who would read this review?
2 Where might you find this review?
3 Is the style formal or informal?
4 What is the aim of the review?
5 How does the review initially engage the reader?

B Find examples of the following in the review.

1 contractions
2 personalisation
3 missing words
4 colloquialisms

C Look at the structure of the review. In which paragraphs (A, B, C or D) does the writer do the following? Sometimes more than one answer is possible.

1 summarise
2 recommend
3 engage
4 compare
5 expand
6 explain

11 A Work in pairs. Think about an app that you have found helpful or choose one of the apps that were designed in Ex 8C. Make some notes on what you would include in a review.

B Write your review.

C Swap your review with your partner. Comment on how informal your reviews are and how they might be improved.

< Featured

Realise your dreams

Version: 1.0
Release date: 07 April
Price: Annual subscription €55 or monthly €8
Available: All major app providers

★★★★★ by Jonah_Ng1   1 day ago

A: Analyse your dreams

What a brilliant idea! This app does a load more than it appears. Realise your dreams, on the surface, is an app that encourages people to make known their wishes and offers advice from genuine psychologists on how to achieve those all-elusive dreams. We're asked to type in exactly what we're wishing for. The app then analyses what we've written and tries to make us reflect on our dreams by making us prioritise and question ourselves. And who knows, you might be as lucky as one recent user, whose dream was seen by a celebrity chef and she was offered work experience in his kitchen!

B: Realise your dreams

Tips on how to realise our dreams are personalised and we are given realistic targets and step-by-step mini goals to work on. Unlike many apps like this, it doesn't sidestep the issues with 'wise old owl' generalities but tries to help us work out for ourselves what we need to do. In doing so, we might realise that our dreams are just impossible, or (and you never know!) how achievable they might be.

C: User-friendly and realistic

Whether we're looking for a new career direction, new learning opportunities or trying to rediscover the dreams from our childhood, this app helps in plenty of ways. It's straightforward, super user-friendly and the advice really tries to keep people grounded and realistic in their hopes and dreams.

D: Worth the investment

There are so many apps out there that claim to make our dreams come true, but 'Realise your dreams' seems to be in a league of its own. It's clearly been designed by developers with the help of psychologists, and the approach is both positive and helpful, not fobbing users off with hackneyed comments. Pricey, but definitely worth the money! My app of the month.

4C Economies

HOW TO ... | present survey results
VOCABULARY | money and economy
PRONUNCIATION | chunking language

VOCABULARY

money and economy

1 A Work in pairs. What do you think is meant by the terms 'sharing economy' and 'circular economy'? Go to page 142 and check your ideas.

B Decide if these businesses (1–6) are examples of the 'sharing economy' or the 'circular economy'.

1 We convert animal waste to fertiliser and natural gas using solar-powered greenhouses.

2 Who needs a car when you can call us anywhere, anytime and get your lift?

3 Buy furniture manufactured using recycled raw materials here.

4 You're only a few clicks away from finding a spare room or apartment from a few days to a few months.

5 Fancy changing your work location? Rent a desk in our co-working space whenever you need it.

6 Mail us your old clothes and we'll turn them into new fashion items. Zero waste is the way forward.

2 Read the article and complete the collocations in bold with the words in the box.

collaborative   driven   economy   finite
incentives   investment   loyalty   model
on-demand   online   terms   zero-

The future way to do business?

Once a game-changing movement, the so-called **sharing** [1]_____ has long since become a recognised **business** [2]_____ . Also referred to as [3]_____ **consumption**, another term that emphasises the 'sharing' element, businesses that fall under these **umbrella** [4]_____ came into existence once [5]_____ **transactions** became the norm. Yet, however these businesses brand themselves, they are still essentially **profit**-[6]_____ .

As many businesses don't actually involve sharing, the term 'access economy' came into use, focusing more on the notion that the provider offers [7]_____ **access** to a product or service – for a price. More recently the term 'circular' economy has become ever more familiar, as businesses are coming to terms with the potentially enormous profits that could accompany shifting focus to a [8]_____ **waste** goal, with continual recycling, reusing and remanufacturing. It incorporates the idea of **aligning** [9]_____ for customers, businesses and the planet, and is based on the assumption that this will **drive customer** [10]_____ in the future.

[11]_____ **opportunities** in the sectors of building, fashion, food, transport and plastic packaging will move away from consuming [12]_____ **resources** towards continual recycling. Is this a realistic vision of how economies will work in the future? Many hope it is.

How to ...
present survey results

3 A Answer the questions in the survey on the sharing economy. Work in pairs and compare your answers.

Your thoughts:
the sharing economy

1 What sharing-economy businesses have you used?
2 How often have you used it/them?
3 Have you been happy with the service(s)?
4 Do you think they give value for money?
5 Which sharing-economy businesses would you like to find out more about?
6 Which would you like to try?
7 Which would you never use?

B 🔊 **4.06** | Listen to an extract from a presentation of the survey results and answer the questions.

1 Which survey questions are mentioned?
2 What did the speakers find interesting? What examples do they give?
3 What do they conclude about human nature?

4 A 🔊 **4.07** | A second survey was carried out with questions about the circular economy. Complete the phrases in a report on the results with the correct words. Listen and check.

1 **On the** _____, people expressed a curiosity about how effective the businesses were in significantly reducing waste.
2 **To** _____ **one example**, people who were interested in sustainable fashion wondered how many times fashion items could be recycled.
3 **Our** _____ **was simply that** people were interested in the difference between the claims and the actual reality of these business models.
4 **Their interest** _____ **reflected** a genuine concern to help protect the planet's finite resources.
5 **Another** _____ **of this is** the number of people who asked for more information about second-hand furniture outlets and clothes-swap websites.
6 _____ **speaking though**, there was limited interest in trying out services that had no proven track record in sustainability and seemed to be profit-driven rather than eco-friendly.
7 **The** _____ **seems to be that** people favour businesses that persuade us that they are really committed to a truly circular economy.
8 **One might** _____ **that** this way of approaching services will continue to attract consumers and marks a radical shift in the way we will spend money in the future and why.

B Which phrases (1–8) in Ex 4A relate to a) generalising, b) exemplifying or c) speculating?

C Learn and practise. Go to the Grammar Bank.

▶▶ page 123 **GRAMMAR BANK**

PRONUNCIATION

5 A 🔊 **4.08** | **chunking language** | Read and listen to the sentences. Mark the natural pauses as you hear them. Listen again and repeat.

1 To cite one example, businesses which sold upcycled furniture reported a significant increase in customer interest.
2 Generally speaking though, the cost and effort that goes into upcycling tends to lead to very small profit margins.

B 🔊 **4.07** | Look at sentences 1–8 in Ex 4A again. Mark where you think the natural pauses would occur. Listen again, check and repeat.

SPEAKING

6 A Work in pairs. Write survey questions based on one of the businesses in Ex 1B, or another business you can think of. Think about the points below.

• people's experience of such a business
• their attitude to businesses like this
• opinions on the future of the business

B Ask other students to complete your survey. Make notes on their answers.

C Work with your original partner and compare your notes.

7 A Read the Future Skills box and do the task.

FUTURE SKILLS
Communication

When presenting information to a group, we may refer to notes, but we should not just read them with our heads down. It is important to make eye contact with the audience to maintain interest and check understanding.

Work in pairs and organise your notes by key points so that they are easy to refer to.

B Present your survey results to the class.

MEDIATION SKILLS
describing a process diagram

explain a complex diagram

▶▶ page 150 **MEDIATION BANK**

4D BBC Documentary

Extinction

VOCABULARY | extinction
SPEAKING | plan a documentary introduction
WRITING | an opinion essay

PREVIEW

1 A Read the programme information below. Work in pairs and answer the questions.

1 How many endangered animals can you name in two minutes?

2 Do you know the names of any animals that have become extinct?

B Do the quiz. Compare your answers with a partner.

Circle the correct answers.

1 What percentage of vertebrate mammals has been lost since 1970?

  a 20% **b** 40% **c** 60%

2 How many animals and plant species face extinction today?

  a 500,000 **b** 1 million **c** 2 million

3 How much faster are we losing animal species than the natural evolutionary rate?

  a ten times faster **b** fifty times faster
  c a hundred times faster

4 How many northern white rhinos are left on the planet?

  a 2 **b** 22 **c** 42

VIEW

2 A ▶ Watch the BBC video clip and check your answers to Ex 1B.

B Work in pairs and discuss the questions.

1 Why should we be concerned about the loss of biodiversity?

2 How do we know the current extent of biodiversity loss?

3 Species have become extinct at various stages in history. Why is what is happening today different?

4 What is tragic about the state of the northern white rhinos?

C ▶ Watch the video again. Check your answers to Ex 2B.

Extinction: The Facts

This documentary film explores the extent of the dangers facing numerous species on our planet and the consequences for humanity unless this mass extinction is halted or reversed. Featuring the natural historian, Sir David Attenborough, and other academic experts, this film is a stark warning for humanity to deal with the problems it has created.

VOCABULARY

extinction

3A Complete the collocations in bold from the video with the words in the box.

> brink   global   grave   pooled   seemingly
> set   taken   unprecedented

1 Our planet is home to **a**   **infinite** variety of species.

2 The evidence is that unless **immediate action is**   , …

3 … this crisis has   **impacts** for us all.

4 Many of these wonders seem   **to disappear** forever.

5 This is the first time there's been a   **assessment** …

6 All the **evidence has been**   **together**.

7 We're losing biodiversity at a **rate** that is truly   …

8 … were pushed to **the**   **of extinction** by habitat loss and hunting.

B Complete the sentences with your own ideas.

1 The **grave impacts** on humanity would include …

2 We should **take immediate action** such as …

3 Something happening at an **unprecedented rate** that most people are aware of is …

4 An animal that is **set to disappear**, which I would miss greatly, is …

5 In my opinion, the likelihood of all nations acting on the results of this **global assessment** is …

C Work in pairs. Compare your ideas in Ex 3B.

SPEAKING

plan a documentary introduction

4A Work in pairs. Imagine you are working on a wildlife documentary in fifty years' time. Think about what you will include. Discuss:

- what wildlife might remain (in the wild, in captivity, in conservation programmes).
- which animals and plants might have become extinct and why.
- which animals are now endangered.
- which species may have come back from extinction.
- how the future looks.

B Plan the introduction to the documentary with your partner. Think about the music, images and video shots you will use. Make notes on what the voiceover will say. Use the Key phrases to help you.

> ### KEY PHRASES
>
> We could kick it off with …
> To start with, how about …
> I'd say we need to include …
> Thinking about the current state of things, I'd imagine …
> I think it's pretty safe to say that …
> It's hard to say for certain, but I'd think the likelihood of …
> Nothing's written in stone, but it's more than likely that …

C Share your plan for the documentary introduction with the class. Have a vote on which introductions would be most appealing.

WRITING

an opinion essay

5A You are going to write an essay on the topic of extinction. Read the essay question below with your partner. How far do you agree or disagree with the statement?

> 'The time for "humanity first" is over – perhaps we would do the rest of the species on the planet a favour if we became extinct ourselves.'

B Write an opinion essay about extinction. Go to the Writing Bank.

▶▶ page 107 **WRITING BANK**

GRAMMAR

verb patterns

1 A Complete these sentences with your own ideas by adding a verb phrase in the correct form.

1 In the near future, the world risks <u>being threatened by rising sea levels</u> .

2 Being a pioneer involves ....

3 Early pioneers in my country are known ....

4 A friend of mine has recently taken up ....

5 In my opinion, large companies are not justified in ....

6 As a child I would love ....

7 To help protect the environment we need to avoid ....

8 In recent months the economy appears ....

B Work in pairs and compare your sentences.

continuous and perfect aspects

2 A Work in pairs. Discuss the difference in meaning (if any) between each pair of sentences (a and b).

1 a So, I'm waiting there at the bus stop and I'm thinking about …

b So, I was waiting there at the bus stop and I was thinking about …

2 a By the end of this year, I'll have been living …

b By the end of this year, I'll have lived …

3 a A year from now my lifestyle will have changed completely, specifically …

b A year from now I'll be living in a completely different way, specifically …

4 a I'd been studying for most of my life, so adjusting to a full-time job …

b I've been studying for most of my life, so adjusting to a full-time job …

5 a I was planning on studying another language, but …

b I'd planned to study another language, but …

6 a This time a year ago, I was planning to …

b This time next year, I'm planning to …

B Complete one sentence in each pair. Then compare your answers with a partner.

VOCABULARY

3 Complete the article with the correct form of the verbs in the box.

> back   fuel   push   raise   realise   satisfy   talk

If we're ¹ .... about people ² .... the limits, surely there is no better example than Nirmal Purja, the Nepalese climber who conquered all fourteen of the world's 8,000-metre-tall mountains within seven months, setting a magnificent record. According to Nirmal, his motivation was ³ .... by the enormity of the challenge and the desire to show that nothing is impossible. He maintains that ⁴ .... this dream was not down to a need for self-glory or financial gain, but as a pioneer, representing not just his nation, but humanity in general. ⁵ .... the funding for such a project was not easy – ⁶ .... a project that risky cannot have been attractive for any sponsor, but Nirmal succeeded on all fronts. If you are wondering how he did it, ⁷ .... your curiosity by reading about his exploits on his website. They are quite breathtaking!

4 Choose the correct words to complete the sentences.

1 It is hoped that the number of people using food banks will be **importantly** / **significantly** reduced by the new benefit scheme.

2 The risks that some explorers take are **wildly** / **ludicrously** high, but these are exceptional people.

3 Sharing and collaboration can have **tactile** / **tangible** benefits for the whole of society.

4 People who are going **over** / **through** a rough patch can approach the charity for assistance at any time.

5 The new company's business **shape** / **model** is ambitious.

6 Fossil fuels are a **limited** / **finite** resource and will one day run out.

5 A Choose the correct options (A–C) to complete the text.

One of the most successful projects of recent years aimed at ¹ .... the lives of people living on or below the bread line has been The Big Issue Foundation. Homeless people or those desperately trying to ² .... ends meet have become mini entrepreneurs, selling magazines which have been compiled by people just like themselves. The project has brought many out of poverty, restored their self-esteem and enabled them to ³ .... each day with a brighter outlook. People who buy these magazines are not donating to charity but are involved in a transaction which has the knock-on ⁴ .... of both raising the profile of the homeless (through the articles in the magazine) and helping each vendor on a financial and life-affirming journey. Thousands of vendors are known to ⁵ .... benefitted from the scheme and the lives they live now are infinitely ⁶ .... to sleeping rough and not knowing where the next meal is coming from.

1 A improve	**B** improving	**C** to improve
2 A do	**B** make	**C** allow
3 A look	**B** involve	**C** face
4 A effect	**B** affect	**C** influence
5 A be	**B** having	**C** have
6 A better	**B** preferable	**C** improved

B 🔊 **R4.01 |** Listen and check your answers.

influence 5

B B C

VLOGS

Q: Who's the most famous person you've ever met?

1 ▶ Watch the video. Who had the most interesting story?

2 Based on the stories, how does meeting a famous person affect most people?

GSE LEARNING OBJECTIVES

5A READING | Read a blog post about the influence of accents: collocations: first impressions; adjectives and adjectival endings

Pronunciation: stress while giving emphasis

Talk about positive and negative first impressions: giving emphasis: inversion, clefting, tailing, fronting

5B LISTENING | Understand a radio programme about a fake news story: spreading misinformation

Talk about fake news: participle clauses

Pronunciation: intonation in participle clauses

Write a report about raising awareness and fact checking

5C HOW TO ... | use persuasive techniques in presentations: persuasion; adjectives to describe presentations

Pronunciation: intonation: being persuasive

5D BBC STREET INTERVIEWS | Understand people talking about people who influence them

Talk about types of influence: role models

Write a contribution for a website

5A First impressions

GRAMMAR | giving emphasis: inversion, clefting, tailing, fronting
VOCABULARY | collocations: first impressions;
adjectives and adjectival endings
PRONUNCIATION | stress while giving emphasis

READING

1 Work in pairs and discuss the questions.

  1 Tell your partner about the last time you met somebody new. What was your first impression of this person? Why?

  2 Would you say that your first impressions of a person generally turn out to be correct?

  3 What things can contribute to a person's initial impression of someone?

  4 What kind of things might people guess about a person from their accent?

2 A Read the blog post about accents and their influence and check your ideas for question 4 in Ex 1.

  B Read the blog post again and answer the questions.

  1 Why does the writer use the word 'fortunately' in paragraph 1?

  2 What do the two questions at the end of paragraph 2 tell us about the writer's attitude towards accents having a 'social value'?

  3 Why does the writer use the word 'blurring' when talking about accents in paragraph 3?

  4 Why did the writer's acquaintance feel horrified by an action of her child?

  5 What is the writer's attitude to a classmate who faked an accent?

  6 What is implied by the phrase 'cashing in' in the final paragraph?

  7 How has the writer's attitude to the way he speaks changed over the years?

VOCABULARY

collocations: first impressions

3 Look at the collocations in bold in the blog post. Which words in the collocations can be replaced by the words a–g?

  a long-term ....
  e assessing ....

  b characteristics ....
  f assumptions ....

  c convey ....
  g connection ....

  d an effect ....
  h spoil ....

It's not what you say, it's …

I remember as a child desperately wanting to have an accent. My parents had moved several times when I was young, and I ended up with no significant accent at all. For a while it made me feel different, almost bereft. In my mind an accent was a sign of belonging – to a place, a community. My parents were unperturbed. At that time having a regional accent made getting some jobs more difficult, and they saw it as a benefit. Fortunately, times have changed, and accents are welcomed with open arms, employers eagerly bending over backwards to show how well they are accommodating the need for diversity.

It is curious, though, how bereft I still feel at times. My cousins live in Essex, and all speak strong Estuary English. When I visit, I know they consider me 'posh' because I speak in a different way, but that's what accents do, isn't it? They tell you all sorts of things about the speaker and can **have a bearing on** future relationships and an influence over how that person is perceived, be it rightly or wrongly. At first meetings when we are **sizing up** the other person, the unfavourable impression created by an accent that we are suspicious of can **have a lasting effect**. And by 'suspicious of' I'm referring to the fact that in addition to showing where people are from, some accents carry a form of social value, which can **lead to problematic preconceptions**. Is a person with an accent from a public school privileged and pompous? Does this accent command instant respect or irritate us? On most occasions we need to be aware of prejudice and look beyond an accent. The way a person speaks should not **taint our impression of them**.

It's perhaps this concern about my lack of obvious accent that has led to my fascination with accents. What I find quite remarkable is the range of accents existing in some shape or form in the UK – upwards of forty, would you believe – with some accents changing within a few hundred metres of each other. One reason for this is the influence of successive invading peoples, another is the isolation of communities, which allowed accents to develop in different areas. Today, with people relocating and travelling much more widely than before, many accents are blurring.

However, the accent someone uses still tells us a lot about that person. And sometimes what it tells us is about how far people consciously, or subconsciously, want to relate to those they are speaking to, **establishing an immediate rapport**. Or not. Have you ever noticed how children's accents can change depending on who they are interacting with? An associate of mine told me about her horror when her very young daughter appeared to be mocking a shopkeeper once when buying sweets. The child took the bag, opened her mouth and out came a perfect imitation of the shopkeeper's accent. But this was not done on purpose. Apparently, this is common, as all we want to do as children is to adapt and 'fit in' with a group. So important is this need to conform that children will even subconsciously **adopt** speech **mannerisms** of those around them. And contrarily, we can emphasise our own accents when we wish to establish a difference between ourselves and the other speaker, for whatever reason. Even more interesting, in my mind, is the fact that some people consciously change accents to **project a certain image**. I remember a schoolmate who was from London, who used to put on an American accent, presumably because he wanted to sound 'cool'. He didn't.

Whatever the reason for the way we accent our speech, the fact remains that it is a powerful indicator of who we are and subconsciously is often thought to be an indicator of personality, too. Currently, companies are cashing in on the influence that certain UK accents can have on listeners (particularly on the phone or in advertisements). According to a recent YouGov poll, it's the Scottish accent that is top of the list (after the Queen's English) when it comes to being perceived as trustworthy and reassuring. Manchester accents are considered creative and industrious, and a Yorkshire one wise and honest. I suppose I have finally come to terms with my lack of clear accent, but I have to admit that I still experience a little tug of envy when I meet someone whose voice immediately takes me to a particular part of the UK.

4 Read the post and comments about first impressions. Complete them with the correct form of the collocations from the blog post in Ex 2A.

What's your impression?

¹ _____ quickly when we first meet them is part of our make-up as human beings. In about seven seconds, we have already formed an opinion from visual and vocal cues that the person is relaying as to whether we might like, dislike or be wary of them, and whether we'll ² _____ or not. This dates back to when we had to infer from a person's appearance or the ³ _____ whether they were a danger, and that instinctive reaction is still with us. This initial impression can ⁴ _____ and determine how a relationship develops in the long-term. So, what influences you when you first meet someone?

Comments ...

AJ ♥12 💬13 ↗

In my opinion, the best way to make a favourable impression on someone is by being confident but not over-confident. If someone talks too loudly or tells me too much about themself at a first meeting, trying to ⁵ _____ , it can definitely lead to a bad first impression.

Keyops17 ♥19 💬21 ↗

For me it's all about body language. It tells us how interested that person is in having a conversation with us or if they'd rather be somewhere else! In my case that ⁶ _____ whether I want to continue a conversation or not!

RayTheLima ♥4 💬2 ↗

Oh, it's all about the eyes. If someone doesn't actually look me in the eye, I assume the person's not that honest. Perhaps they're fine and just have little confidence? We're told things like this can ⁷ _____ , but I can't help it!

5 A Work in pairs. Tell your partner about:
1 someone who likes to project a certain image, for example, a celebrity.
2 someone who has problematic preconceptions.
3 what features have a bearing on your first impressions of people.
4 someone you established an immediate rapport with.
5 how long it takes you to size people up.

B Learn and practise. Go to the Vocabulary Bank.

▶▶ page 139 **VOCABULARY BANK** adjectives and adjectival endings

6 🔊 **5.01** | Listen to the three posts in Ex 4 and discuss the questions in pairs.
1 Do you recognise the accents? How are they different?
2 Can you hear many different accents in your country? Which accent is used by the largest number of people?

GRAMMAR

giving emphasis: inversion, clefting, tailing, fronting

7 A Identify what information is being emphasised in these sentences from the blog post in Ex 2A.

1 So important is this need to conform that children will even subconsciously adopt speech mannerisms of those around them.

2 It is curious, though, how bereft I still feel at times.

3 … all we want to do as children is to adapt and 'fit in' with a group.

4 … it's the Scottish accent that is top of the list (after the Queen's English) when it comes to being perceived as trustworthy and reassuring, …

5 … what it tells us is about how far people consciously, or subconsciously, want to relate to those they are speaking to …

6 The child took the bag, opened her mouth and out came a perfect imitation of the shopkeeper's accent.

B Rewrite the sentences in Ex 7A without the emphasis.

1 This need to conform is so important that children will even subconsciously adopt speech mannerisms of those around them.

C Work in pairs. Rewrite the statements starting with the words given. Can you think of an alternative way to use emphasis for each sentence?

1 An accent doesn't always give an indication of the speaker's true origins.
   What an accent ....

2 I'm fascinated by the way actors can move seamlessly from one accent to another.
   It's ....

3 To speak a foreign language with no trace of an accent is extremely difficult.
   It's speaking ....

4 Speaking in public requires nothing more than a strong voice and confidence.
   All that ....

5 I find it so hard to follow subtitles that I often give up watching foreign films.
   So hard ....

D Work in pairs. Discuss how far you agree or disagree with the statements in Ex 7C.

E Learn and practise. Go to the Grammar Bank.

▶▶ page 124 **GRAMMAR BANK**

PRONUNCIATION

8 A | **stress while giving emphasis** | Look at the underlined words in the sentences (1–4). Which of the words do you think will be more stressed when the sentence is read aloud?

1 It's a person's accent that tells others whether they can be trusted or not.

2 What disturbs me is when people have really weird facial expressions.

3 What I love is when people make eye contact with you when they're talking to you.

4 It's the way people walk that tells me the most about them.

B 🔊 **5.02** | Listen and check. Listen again and repeat the sentences with the same stress.

C Work in pairs. Discuss which of the sentences are also true for you, and give reasons.

SPEAKING

9 A Work in pairs. Discuss how the things in the box might both negatively and positively influence people in a first meeting. Can you add any others?

> body language   clothes   facial expressions
> mannerisms   posture   sense of humour

B Share your ideas with the class and reach a consensus about which might have the strongest influence.

What's important is …

It's what someone says rather than how they say it that is most important.

It isn't the clothes they wear, it's how they wear them that has an effect.

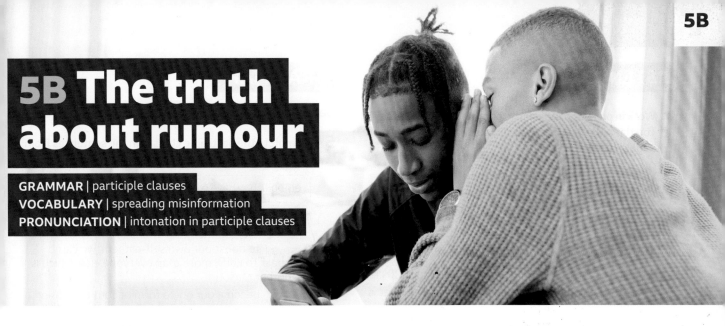

5B The truth about rumour

GRAMMAR | participle clauses
VOCABULARY | spreading misinformation
PRONUNCIATION | intonation in participle clauses

VOCABULARY

spreading misinformation

1 Answer the questions. Work in pairs and compare and discuss your answers.

1 How far do you agree or disagree with the quotes?

a 'I share posts and stories online all the time. I see something interesting, amusing or incredible and I pass it on. It's good to share!'

b 'I like reading what others share online, but I don't often share myself. I'm pretty concerned about my digital footprint.'

c 'I share from time to time, but always check out if a story is fake or true.'

2 Can you usually distinguish misinformation from true information? How?

2 A Read about the BBC Radio programme and answer the questions.

1 Why do people spread rumours?

2 What damage can rumours do?

B Match the collocations in bold in the BBC Radio programme information with the definitions (1–8).

1 adding extra information to make something more interesting

2 there are numerous ideas and reasons

3 alter details

4 make someone feel more important

5 a story is stopped or shown to be untrue

6 a story gets more and more detail and attention

7 spread quickly and widely online

8 persuading people to think differently

C Complete the questions with the correct form of verbs from the collocations in Ex 2B. Then discuss the questions with a partner.

1 Do you ever .... the details of an experience when you are telling someone about it?

2 Can you think of any news stories in your country that have .... recently?

3 What can people do to .... their self-esteem?

4 If there is a rumour going around that you know to be untrue, how would you .... it?

5 What stories have .... viral recently?

6 How can public opinion be .... by politicians? Can you think of any examples?

Whispers 🅱🅱🅲

Is spreading a rumour human nature? If so, why do we do it? Experts say that there are many reasons why we pass on unverified information, **embellishing the details** as we do. It appears that rumours can be started consciously to turn people against others we are perhaps jealous of. Wanting to **boost our own self-esteem**, we can appear to know more than everyone else, which is another reason. Rumours can also circulate as a way of people trying to deal with an unknown situation, to make sense of something unknown. The impact of rumours can vary, from having a devastating effect on individuals to **swaying public opinion** and changing the course of politics. In the past, rumours were spread by word of mouth, but today, having become our go-to form of communication, social media allows misinformation to spread like wildfire with one click. Often started as a joke, stories can **go viral** immediately. But it is not only the gullible who repost, retweet and **distort information**. Much of the misinformation that surfaces on social media is plausible, with fake pictures and outraged headlines. Having perhaps simply skimmed the information, we share it and **the story escalates**. Conspiracy **theories abound** and so susceptible are we to some misinformation that we may continue to believe it long after **the rumour has been quashed**. In 'Whispers', part of the BBC's *The Digital Human* series, we hear first-hand about how one famous rumour was started.

LISTENING

3 A Work in pairs and look at the photo below. What do you think the news story associated with the photo might have been about?

B 🔊 **5.03 |** Listen to the first section of the BBC Radio programme 'Whispers' and check your ideas in Ex 3A.

C 🔊 **5.03 |** Listen again and answer the questions.
1 What happens in a children's game of 'whispers'?
2 Why does rumour have a 'bad rep'?
3 What real news event happened in London in 2011?
4 What is the double meaning of this line: 'The tiger is on the loose'?
5 What do Twiggy and Ty decide to do?
6 What happens to the tiger story?
7 Why was the picture important?

4 A 🔊 **5.04 |** Do you think Twiggy regretted starting the rumour? Why/Why not? Listen and check.

B 🔊 **5.04 |** Listen again and answer the questions.
1 According to Twiggy, why did the story go on for as long as it did?
2 What criticism did some people make of Twiggy's actions?

C Complete the colloquialisms in the sentences from the programme with the words in the box.

| bad rep   fanned the flames   flared up   kicked off |
| lit the fire   out and about   word out there |

1 But rumour has a .... It's not always untrue.
2 Because that is what happened in August 2011. Just at the time the London riots ....
3 Twiggy and his following on social media ...., getting the .... initially, but then the design of Twitter ....
4 But just as quickly as it ...., fellow Twitter users began questioning the 'truthiness' of the rumour.
5 I still heard people at parties and .... talking about it.

D Work in pairs. Student A: You think Twiggy was wrong to spread the rumour. Student B: You think he was right. Think of points to support your viewpoint and have a discussion.

GRAMMAR

participle clauses

5 A Complete the participle clauses in the sentences from Ex 2A with the correct form of the verbs in the box.

| embellish   have (x2)   start   want |

1 ... we pass on unverified information, ... the details as we do.
2 .... to boost our own self-esteem, we can appear to know more than everyone else, which is another reason.
3 .... become our go-to form of communication, social media allows misinformation to spread like wildfire ...
4 Often .... as a joke, stories can go viral immediately.
5 .... perhaps simply skimmed the information, we share it and the story escalates.

B Complete rules with the words in the box.

| before   reason   the same time as |

1 Participle clauses can describe an action that happens at .... the main action.
2 Participle clauses can describe an action that happens .... the main action.
3 Participle clauses can give background or extra information, or a .... for the main action.

C Learn and practise. Go to the Grammar Bank.

➡ page 125 **GRAMMAR BANK**

PRONUNCIATION

6 A 🔊 **5.05 | intonation in participle clauses |** Listen to the sentences. On which part of the sentence does the intonation rise then fall? On which does it just fall?
1 Having shared the story, I instantly felt bad.
2 Knowing what I do now, I wish I hadn't reposted it.
3 Being a smart person, I always check the sources before I share news posts online.
4 Having seen stories like that before, I was wary about it.

B 🔊 **5.05 |** Listen again and repeat the sentences.

C Complete the sentences with your own ideas. Read your endings to a partner. Guess which starters they used.
1 Having listened to the interview extract, I ....
2 Shared with me by a friend, the post ....
3 Having been advised the story was fake, I ....
4 Knowing more about fake news now, ...
5 I shared the story, hoping ....
6 Having gained enormous numbers of users, video-sharing sites ....

SPEAKING

7A Work in pairs. Think of a recent fake news story you have heard about. Consider areas such as:
- celebrities • medicine • politics • entertainment

B Work in pairs and discuss the questions.
- How and why do you think the story you thought of in Ex 7A was started?
- How and why might it have spread?
- How do you think those who shared it felt afterwards?

C Work in pairs or small groups. Discuss what needs to change or be changed to prevent the spread of misinformation online. Whose responsibility is it?

WRITING

a report

8A Work in pairs and discuss. In which situations do people write reports?

B Read the request and discuss what you might include under the headings of 'positive effects' and 'negative effects'. Share your ideas with the class.

We would like you to write a report about the positive and negative effects of social media on interpersonal relationships for the University Governing Council. Include recommendations as to how negative effects could be minimised.

9A Read the report. What do you notice about its style and organisation?

B Match the phrases (1–10) in bold in the report with the phrases with the same meaning in the box.

a clear consensus   a negligible number
a substantial percentage   commonly cited
concerning   in light of the above   it will go on to
major   surprisingly large   this report will present
to improve the situation

10A Work in pairs. Student A: Read the report request below. Student B: Go to page 142 and read the report request. Write some survey questions to ask.

A report is needed about students' use of different social media platforms and websites. In particular, we would like information about sharing potential misinformation and recommendations on how to encourage awareness and fact checking.

B Use your survey questions to gather information from the rest of the class. Make notes on the answers.

C Write your report using the information you gathered in Ex 10B. Try to use phrases from Ex 9A and 9B.

REPORT:
Effects of social media

INTRODUCTION

[1]**The aim of this report is** to summarise the positive and negative effects of social media on interpersonal relationships, based on the findings of a survey of 100 university students. [2]**The final section will** offer recommendations on ways people could change their use of social media [3]**to minimise any negative effects**.

POSITIVE EFFECTS

[4]**A significant proportion** of people interviewed indicated a positive effect of social media on their relationships. The most [5]**frequently mentioned** reason was that social media makes it easy to keep up to date with people without the need to communicate by email or phone. There was [6]**widespread agreement** that social media apps are convenient tools for making contact with friends on a daily basis and that it was helpful to base exchanges on common topics such as a viral video. [7]**A few people** commented on the advantages of a closed group of friends or colleagues to keep communication private.

NEGATIVE EFFECTS

There was, however, a [8]**significant** disagreement regarding the negative effects. While a few respondents mentioned an over-dependence on technology, an [9]**overwhelming** number felt that this was not an issue. A surprising percentage did express a concern that constant online checking could affect face-to-face interactions, and that being online for many hours at a time often created fatigue. A [10]**worrying** number of students, albeit a minority, raised the point that they (or friends) often felt demoralised because of comparison with others on social media.

RECOMMENDATIONS

[11]**After considering these points**, I recommend that students should be advised to:
- be more selective about which 'friends' to follow.
- be more aware of the amount of time spent on social media, and limit this where necessary.
- switch phones to 'mute' when meeting in person.
- give themselves some periods in the day when phones are switched off.

I believe that on balance the effects of social media on interpersonal relationships are positive and that if active users follow some of the recommendations, they are less likely to experience the negative effects.

5C Try it out

HOW TO ... | use persuasive techniques in presentations
VOCABULARY | persuasion; adjectives to describe presentations
PRONUNCIATION | intonation: being persuasive

VOCABULARY

persuasion

1 A Read the first part of an article. Work in pairs and discuss the final two questions.

A virtually perfect presentation

So, you have to give a presentation to your colleagues, or your boss or your class. You need to sell an idea, advertise a product or simply **bring them round to your way of thinking** about an issue. But the presentation isn't face-to-face. You're working remotely and the presentation will be online. How different will it be? What do you need to consider?

B Read the rest of the article to check your ideas.

C Work in pairs and discuss the questions.
1 When you are in online meetings, do you have a real or virtual background? Why?
2 What problems can people encounter in online meetings?

2 A Replace the phrases in bold in 1–7 with the correct form of the phrases in bold from the texts in Ex 1A and Ex 1B.
1 A colleague **made a great effort** to convince her boss that she would be the best candidate for promotion.
2 It was difficult to **work out how he felt about** the news.
3 A good speaker will **command the attention and respect of everyone there immediately** when they start speaking.
4 Sometimes I think **people get the impression that I'm** far more intellectual than I really am!
5 It's quite a skill to **persuade people to think the same as you do**.
6 The speaker couldn't **make people trust him**.
7 A schoolmate used to **make herself look more studious** by wearing large, serious-looking glasses.

B Work in pairs and discuss the questions.
1 How do you think you can 'own the room' effectively?
2 When there's a disagreement, how do you usually bring people round to your way of thinking?
3 Have you ever consciously bolstered your image by altering your appearance for a certain situation?

C Learn and practise. Go to the Vocabulary Bank.

▶▶ page 139 **VOCABULARY BANK** adjectives to describe presentations

With an increase in remote working, one of the first things we need to deal with is whether **we come across as** professional or friendly on screen and that involves being aware – super aware – of our location! Our audience will be getting a peek into our homes. Do we want them to see a messy desk, untidy shelves or personal items strewn around the room? If it's a serious, professional call, then we have to consider how professional our background is, and also be aware that whatever background we choose to present will reveal a lot about ourselves. Some people **go to extraordinary lengths** to try to create the perfect backdrop. Certain second-hand book retailers are reporting dramatic increases in sales to those who want to present tidy shelves full of worthy book collections to **bolster their serious, studious, academic image**. Others are utilising virtual background options, so that they may appear to be on a tropical beach, by a harbour or even in a popular TV or film setting. The location can be serious or fun – just remember that it says a lot about your professionalism, your interests and your sense of humour.

Background sorted, now think about how you personally come across. Unlike physical meetings and presentations, an online setting means you can't monitor people's body language to **gauge their reactions**. You need to work harder to **own the room** and **convince people of your credibility**. So, whether you're giving your presentation from outer space or your own (tidied!) room, remember to frame yourself well for the camera, don't intimidate and appear too pushy by leaning forward or slouching in your chair. Use facial expressions and gestures wisely, avoid distraction that comes with too much fiddling or fidgeting and amplify that smile! It shows confidence and implies that you know what you're talking about!

How to ...

use persuasive techniques in presentations

3 A 🔊 **5.06 |** Listen to a short presentation about escape rooms and answer the questions.

1 Would you like to try an escape room?
2 What do you understand about how one works?
3 What kind of person do you think an escape room suits?

B 🔊 **5.06 |** Work in pairs and try to complete the sentences. The number of missing words is given in brackets. Then listen again and check.

1 It's _____ this huge 3D puzzle. (1)
2 You've got to communicate a lot with the others, _____ 'Why do you think we got this piece of paper?' (1)
3 But you can't panic, _____ get out and stop working as a team. (2, 2)
4 If you succeed, it's great, you did it as a team and you feel really good about it. _____, well that's a shame, but you did it as a team and you _____ . (3, 6)
5 And who does it suit? Well, it suits people who like doing hands-on work, _____ looking around and taking it all in, trying to connect the dots, and most of all it suits _____ working in a team. (3,3)
6 The thing is, it's _____, it's _____, but it's not _____ . (1, 1, 1)
7 Not only will you have a unique, exciting experience, _____ share an experience that you'll be talking about for years. I guarantee it. (4)

C Look again at the sentences in Ex 3B and decide what kind of language is being used to be persuasive.

D How many examples of the techniques for being persuasive (a–f) can you find in Ex 3B?

a direct speech   d repetition
b simile or metaphor e rhetorical question
c negative inversion f the rule of three

E Learn and practise. Go to the Grammar Bank.

▶▶ page 126 **GRAMMAR BANK**

PRONUNCIATION

4 🔊 **5.07 | intonation: being persuasive |** Listen to sentences 3 and 7 in Ex 3B. Say the sentences with the recording, paying attention to the rising intonation when something is unfinished and the fall when it is finished. What is the pattern?

5 A Look at this sentence from the presentation. What do you notice about the adjectives used?

The thing is, it's cooperative, it's collaborative, but it's not competitive.

B Think of adjectives to complete the sentences (1–5). Compare your sentences with a partner and practise reading them with the correct intonation.

1 As a speaker I'm self-confident, systematic and _____ .
2 People like me because I'm generous and _____ although sometimes rather juvenile.
3 My contributions in discussions are realistic, responsible and _____ .
4 When I'm trying to make someone change their mind, I'm patient and _____ without being _____ .
5 When I talk about my achievements, I think I come across as confident, _____ and _____ .

SPEAKING

a presentation

6 A Work in pairs. Choose an experience or a product that you feel positive about and prepare to give a presentation aimed at persuading others to try it out. Use the following structure and note down points to talk about.

- Introduce the topic: **I'd like to tell you about ... ; What I'd like to talk about is ...**
- Go into a short description: **So what is ... ?**
- Include some examples: **Just to give you an example ...**
- Wrap up the description: **So that's how X works.**
- Give your final pitch: **In short, ... ; To sum up ...**

B Decide where you can use persuasive techniques in your presentation.

C Swap pairs. Practise giving the presentation to each other, imagining you are online. Use relevant posture, facial expressions and gestures.

D Give your presentation to the class and listen to other students' presentations. Which experience or product would you most like to try out? Why?

MEDIATION SKILLS
describing the techniques used in advertising
give opinions about a course of action

▶▶ page 152 **MEDIATION BANK**

Role models

Rory

VOCABULARY | role models
SPEAKING | discussing types of influence
WRITING | a contribution for a website

PREVIEW

1 A Work in pairs. Discuss who or what has influenced the following in your life.

- the foods you like/dislike
- the opinions you hold
- the clothes you wear
- your preferences in music
- your hopes and dreams
- your personality

My father never liked seafood and I just have this thing about seafood myself, even though I've never tried it.

B Add two more areas of people's lives that can be influenced by external factors.

Perhaps growing up in a big city has had a part to play in my dislike for trips to the countryside – I can't imagine not having shops or facilities just round the corner.

BBC

Q1: In what areas of your life are you influenced by others?

Q2: Who has had the biggest influence on your life?

VIEW

2 A ▶ Watch the interviews. Do the speakers mention any of the influences you discussed in Ex 1? What other influences do they mention?

B Answer the questions. Work in pairs and compare your answers.

1 Which speaker mentions a negative aspect of influence?

2 Which speakers were/are influenced by the following people and in what ways?

> family   friends   politicians   teachers

C ▶ Watch the interviews again and check your answers.

D Work in pairs. How similar or different are you to the people in the interviews?

VOCABULARY

role models

3 A Work in pairs. Discuss the meaning of the words and phrases in bold in the sentences (1–9).

1 I am not **susceptible** to flattery.

2 Most people are concerned about how they **present themselves** to others.

3 What are your plans **career-wise**?

4 My brother **went down the same path** as my cousin and studied economics.

5 Most people have a person **they aspire to** be like.

6 A role model is often someone whose **work ethic you want to replicate**.

7 I admire the way my sister **handles herself** in difficult situations.

8 My friend's mother is very welcoming and always **has an open house**.

9 It's good to learn from your friends' strengths and **build them into your character**.

B Complete the sentences with the name of a person you know. Work in pairs and explain why you have named this person.

1 Someone who always has an open house is …

2 Someone whose work ethic I would like to replicate is …

3 The person I most aspire to be like is …

4 Career-wise, someone who I think will certainly succeed is …

5 Someone who is very susceptible to advertising is …

Mohammed

Zoe

Jane

Magda

Philo

SPEAKING

discussing types of influence

4A You are going to take part in a group discussion about the ways in which people can influence us. Work in pairs and note down positive and negative influences that these people can have in our lives.

> celebrities   contacts on social media
> family members   friends   influencers
> politicians   salespeople   teachers

B Work in small groups. Discuss the relative value of these people's influence and reach a consensus on which two might affect our lives the most positively and which two the most negatively. Use the Key phrases to help you.

KEY PHRASES

I would say that … has/have a huge impact on …
The influence of … is quite subtle really …
People are often quite unaware of …
The people who really shape our lives are …
There's a difference between exerting influence and exerting control …
It's all quite subconscious really …

WRITING

a contribution for a website

5A You are going to write a contribution to a website about celebrities who have used their influence well. First, think of some celebrities you admire.

B Work in pairs. Tell your partner about the celebrities you chose in Ex 5A. Explain why you admire them and how they have used their position to make a positive impact. Think about:

- charity work.
- philanthropic donations.
- promoting healthy lifestyles.
- raising awareness of global issues.
- setting a positive example in terms of character and behaviour.

C Work in pairs and choose a celebrity to write about. Note down points you would include about them.

D Write a contribution for a website. Go to the Writing Bank.

▶▶ page 108 **WRITING BANK**

GRAMMAR

giving emphasis

1 A Complete the answers to the questions with your own ideas.

1 Which famous person do you consider to be a good role model today? Why?
- The person _____ .
- It's because of _____ .

2 Which aspects of English pronunciation do you find most difficult?
- It's the _____ .
- What is _____ .

3 What interests you about accents and their influence?
- What fascinates me _____ .
- It's interesting how _____ .

4 What do you usually notice first when you meet someone for the first time?
- The thing I _____ .
- It's their _____ .

5 What have you done this week that you've never done before?
- Never _____ .
- Something _____ .

6 Can you explain why you like the work of a particular actor?
- The reason _____ .
- What I _____ .

B Work in pairs and compare your answers to Ex 1A.

participle clauses

2 A Choose the correct words to complete the sentences.

1 Every summer you can find me **lain** / **lying** on a beach, **sip** / **sipping** iced tea, **having watched** / **watching** the clouds go by. But sometimes I'd rather be _____ .

2 **Having** / **Having been** read up about identifying fake news, I think I'm quite good at differentiating between the real and false now, but I still _____ .

3 Every now and then, **being fed** / **fed up** with life and **frustrated** / **frustrating** by not finding my niche, I just feel like moving somewhere far away. For example, I'd love to _____ .

4 Never **have** / **having** been the sort of person to stick out in a crowd, sometimes I surprise myself when I start talking in class. When it happens, I feel _____ .

5 I tend to be cautious and think carefully before acting, **informed** / **informing** by careful reflection rather than emotional impulse. But sometimes I wish _____ .

6 If I want something, I keep pushing till I get it, never **put** / **putting** off by obstacles and the negativity of others. People think I'm _____ .

B Complete the sentences in Ex 2A with your own ideas. The sentences do not need to be true for you. Then compare your sentences with a partner's.

VOCABULARY

3 Complete the sentences with the correct form of the verbs in the box.

> adopt   boost   distort   embellish   establish
> go   have (x2)   project   quash   size   sway

1 In my opinion, we shouldn't let other people's ideas _____ our own opinions and _____ a bearing on our decisions.

2 Instead of taking time to _____ someone up when meeting them, you should try to _____ an immediate rapport with them.

3 Some people _____ certain mannerisms because they want to _____ a certain image.

4 Praise from the right person can _____ our self-esteem and _____ a lasting effect on our confidence.

5 People who _____ details of a story that they're retelling can subconsciously _____ information.

6 A rumour that _____ viral a few weeks ago has finally been _____ , but it is still circulating on some platforms.

4 Choose the correct words to complete the sentences.

1 The local parliamentary candidates have been out and **around** / **about** today persuading people to vote for them.

2 A big row has **knocked** / **kicked** off about plans to demolish a local landmark.

3 A statue was graffitied overnight in the local park and theories **flourish** / **abound** regarding who was responsible.

4 There is a lot of local opposition to the new recycling scheme, but **successful** / **successive** councils have generally gone ahead with unpopular plans in the past.

5 If you're looking to raise a lot of money with your challenge, you need to get the **word** / **thoughts** out there.

5 Complete the blog post about a presentation with one word in each gap.

A persuasive speaker
Posted by Y. Washizu | 10.26

I attended an amazing presentation last Friday. It was given by a representative of a film company that is trying to sell the college the idea of making a reality show set here. Of course, there has been a lot of resistance to the potential intrusion the show might bring, but this guy was brilliant and [1]_____ across as really sincere. He didn't go to extraordinary [2]_____ with lots of slides and handouts, but he definitely [3]_____ the room. He was able to [4]_____ reactions immediately and his clear but soft-spoken voice giving honest explanations [5]_____ people of his credibility and [6]_____ many opponents round to his way of thinking. In [7]_____ , his pitch was so good that I am sure the college is going to go for the idea.

classics 6

VLOGS

Q: Are new things always better than old things?

1 ▶ Watch the video. What's the consensus on whether new things are better than old ones?

2 What's the oldest thing you possess and why do you still have it?

GSE **LEARNING OBJECTIVES**

6A READING | Read an article about classics: describing literature; describing books and films

Talk about books or films you think should become classics: narrative tenses review

Pronunciation: intonation to show surprise/interest

Write a review of a book or film

6B LISTENING | Understand a radio discussion about poetry and song: reacting to poetry and song

Pronunciation: intonation to show contrast

Talk about and agree on a playlist for space: adverbials

6C HOW TO … | tell an anecdote: adjective–noun collocations: travel

Pronunciation: informal phrases when telling anecdotes

6D BBC PROGRAMME | Understand a TV programme about everyday design miracles

Talk about selecting classic designs: innovation

Write an account of an exhibition

6A Hidden gems

GRAMMAR | narrative tenses review
VOCABULARY | describing literature; describing books and films
PRONUNCIATION | intonation to show surprise/interest

READING

1 A Work in pairs and answer the questions.

1 What makes a book a classic?

2 What are your top three classics? Why do you think they have become classics?

3 What do you think is meant by a 'cult classic'?

B Read the article about classics and compare your ideas.

C Read the article again and answer the questions.

1 Why are these works mentioned in the article?

A Study in Scarlet   Macbeth   Frankenstein   Gormenghast

2 Work in pairs. Discuss the meanings of the words and phrases (a–e). Then decide why the writer has used them in the article.

a trite (Paragraph 1)   d colouring (Paragraph 2)

b worthy (Paragraph 1)   e hip (Paragraph 3)

c finding an echo (Paragraph 2)

D Scan the article again and choose the correct option (a, b or c).

1 The writer mentions crime thrillers as an example of a book genre that

a can never become a classic.

b is sometimes as difficult to read as some classics.

c we may feel guilty about reading.

2 According to the writer, cult classics

a endure equally as long as classics.

b are loved mainly by critics.

c attract followings for a variety of reasons.

3 The writer's own classic, *The Gormenghast Trilogy*, appeals to him because

a it is better written than other Gothic novels.

b he immediately gets caught up in the story.

c he identifies with the character of the protagonist.

E Work in pairs and answer the questions.

1 Read the statement. Do you agree or disagree? Why?

'Classic books have earned their status and should never lose it.'

2 Are there any classics you do not like? Why?

3 What book(s) should become classics? Why?

VOCABULARY

describing literature

2 A Replace the words and phrases in bold in the comments (1–8) with the correct form of the words and phrases from the article in the box.

address   breaking new ground
devoted following   plunged into   resonates with
revolved around   seen through the eyes of
set against the backdrop of

RT A future classic?   Comment | Like

I love the book *Elizabeth is Missing*, where the world is ¹**described by** an older lady with dementia. The reader is ²**thrown into** a confusing world, as the heroine tries to find her missing friend. The book certainly ³**explores new themes** and is a superb piece of writing, ⁴**appealing to** anyone who loves good mystery and clever plotting. The book has a ⁵**lot of loyal fans** and could well become a classic.

DA Great book and film   Comment | Like

My 'own' classic is *Never Let Me Go*, by Kazuo Ishiguro, which is magnificent! The story is ⁶**situated in** what seems to be a traditional boarding school and ⁷**concerns** the lives of a group of friends. However, the reader slowly realises that the school is something else entirely. The novel progresses and ⁸**deals with** universal ethical issues that may soon affect each of us. The film is something else, too.

B Work in pairs. Tell your partner about a book or film that:

1 is seen through the eyes of an unusual narrator.

2 is set against an interesting backdrop.

3 addresses some important ethical issues.

4 resonates with young people today.

5 plunges the reader/viewer into a completely different world.

C Learn and practise. Go to the Vocabulary Bank.

▶▶ page 140 **VOCABULARY BANK** describing books and films

Classic or cult classic?

Reporter Tim Morgan outlines what, in his opinion, separates classics from cult classics and tells us about his own favourite.

What makes a book a classic? The standard reply of 'it stands the test of time' is too trite, trips too easily off the tongue, yet surely it holds an element of truth. Or does it? An unfortunately common idea of what constitutes a classic book is that of a mammoth tome, difficult to wade through unless you are an academic with an insatiable love of the written word. It conjures up an idea of being 'worthy' literature that is on your school reading list or one that everyone tells you that you *should* read, unlike that crime thriller you've just thoroughly enjoyed. The truth is probably that if that crime thriller stands the test of time – in that it will still be enjoyed in fifty years' time, still engage the reader, and still have something to say to them – then it may well become a classic. It may even be on a reading list somewhere. Think Arthur Conan Doyle's *A Study in Scarlet*, with the eccentric investigator Sherlock Holmes and his sidekick Dr Watson.

Perhaps an important point to make here is that classics come in all shapes and sizes and genres. *Alice in Wonderland* by Lewis Carroll, although published over 150 years ago, still resonates with new generations of children. Shakespeare's stories, breaking new ground at the time, still address universal issues today, as testified to by numerous novels and films retelling and reinterpreting his plays – most recently Nordic noir writer Jo Nesbø's version of *Macbeth* and Margaret Atwood's novel *Hag-seed*, which is based on *The Tempest*. Mary Shelley's *Frankenstein* still reaches out to us, finding an echo in our tussle with right and wrong, and Charles Dickens' characters and stories set against the backdrop of Victorian city life still make us think about attitudes to poverty and class. This is because the truths dealt with in a true classic are always relevant no matter the generation. They are books that influence us in some way, colouring or clarifying our understanding of the world.

And then there are the cult classics, the ones that have not made it to full classic status, for whatever reason, but still have a devoted following. They are books that have either been dismissed by the mainstream critics or, conversely, loved by critics and ignored by the mainstream reading public. Some age badly; they became fashionable because they revolved around protagonists who were involved in a subculture of the time, or a topic that appeared to be 'hip', only for their popularity to wane as society moved on and the books have no more to say to readers. Then there are the ones whose reputation carries them forward through the generations. I am thinking here of books such as *The Hitchhiker's Guide to the Galaxy* (Douglas Adams) or *Catch-22* (Joseph Heller) among many, many others that started out as cult books, popular among a small, loyal but enthusiastic following, but which, with time, were seen as inspirational and have now become true classics.

Each of us will have our 'own' classic, or cult classic, a book that has affected us personally in some way. For me, it is the cult classic *The Gormenghast Trilogy* by Mervyn Peake. The books are sometimes referred to as the first 'fantastical' novels, written a few years before Tolkien's *The Lord of The Rings*, but have never achieved full classic status, perhaps because of being overshadowed by the popularity of Tolkien's fantasy novels and its niche attraction to individuals fascinated by the language and surreal world created by Peake. In my opinion, *Gormenghast* is the superior work, more Gothic than fantasy, with its bleak vision – no elves or dragons. Its main character is the huge castle of the title, which sprawls over the whole book, stifling the lives of the eccentric characters that live within its walls.

The first time I read the trilogy was at university and, as with many cult classics, I heard about it by word of mouth. On my literature course I'd been fed a diet of underwhelming books described as 'classics' and I was feeling rather disenchanted with fiction. I remember the day I opened the first book, *Titus Groan*. I'd been reading something heavy and obscure – it might even have been *Moby Dick* – and I was yearning for some relief from the complex prose. From the first page, I was hooked. *Moby Dick* took a back seat as I plunged into the world of Gormenghast, seen through the eyes of the young heir Titus Groan. What catapults this trilogy from a cult classic to a true classic for me, apart from Peake's evocative descriptive abilities, is the universal message delivered in the final book. Titus escapes Gormenghast's confines and goes out into the modern world, but realises that the new world will be ultimately as stifling. A sombre but timeless truth, in my opinion. Will it ever be widely accepted as a true classic? I hope so. It's up there with the best. Only time will tell.

So, that's my take on the classic vs cult classic question. How wide, how far does a book's appeal stretch? Are the themes timeless or limited to a certain cultural context? What's your opinion? And does your favourite cult or classic still have something to say to the world?

GRAMMAR

narrative tenses review

3 A Complete the sentences from the article in Ex 1B with the correct form of the verbs in brackets.

1 The first time I _____ (read) the trilogy was at university …

2 On my literature course I _____ (feed) a diet of underwhelming books described as 'classics'…

3 … I _____ (feel) rather disenchanted with fiction.

4 I _____ (read) something heavy and obscure – it might even have been *Moby Dick* …

5 … I _____ (yearn) for some relief from the complex prose.

6 Titus _____ (escape) Gormenghast's confines and _____ (go) out into the modern world, …

B Match the examples of narrative tenses in Ex 3A (1–6) with the rules (a–e).

a describing a dramatic action, or sequences of actions when retelling a story

b describing a passive situation before a point of time in the past

c describing a situation in progress at a point of time in the past

d describing a continuous action up to point of time in the past

e describing a single, completed action in the past

C Learn and practise. Go to the Grammar Bank.

▶▶ page 127 **GRAMMAR BANK**

PRONUNCIATION

4 A 🔊 **6.01 | intonation to show surprise/interest |** Listen to someone describing the plot of a film. Underline the parts of the plot that they think are interesting or surprising. How do they use stress and intonation to show this?

The thing is, they all think he's just a petty criminal, but actually, he's the criminal mastermind. He's there the whole time, answering the police officers' questions, asking for coffee, pretending just to be this very average crook who walks with a limp and is very low on confidence. Then when they let him go, we suddenly see he doesn't walk with a limp at all. He's been playing with the police all along.

B Work in pairs. Take turns to briefly summarise the plot of a film you like. Use intonation and stress to emphasise interesting or surprising elements of the story.

SPEAKING

5 A Prepare to give a presentation on either a book or a film that you like, but which is not widely known. Think about these questions.

1 Does it deserve to be a classic, and if so, why?

2 Why is it not well known already?

3 What's the basic plot?

4 What are the selling points of the book or film?

5 What kind of people might it appeal to?

B Work in small groups. Deliver your presentation to the group.

C Discuss the different presentations and decide which film or book the majority of you would like to read or watch.

D Work in pairs. Discuss which films or books from today will become classics in the future and why. Share your ideas with the class.

WRITING

a review

6 A Work in pairs and discuss the questions.

1 Do you ever read reviews about books or films? Have you ever posted one?

2 How useful do you think reviews can be? Why?

B What kind of information do you think should be included in a review?

C Write a review. Go to the Writing Bank.

▶▶ page 109 **WRITING BANK**

6B Words and music

GRAMMAR | adverbials
VOCABULARY | reacting to poetry and song
PRONUNCIATION | intonation to show contrast

SPEAKING

1 Work in pairs. Think about the types of topics that songs and poetry often deal with. How many can you list in one minute? Compare your ideas with the class.

2 A 🔊 **6.02** | Look at the first line of the poem. What do you think the poem might be about? Listen and check your ideas.

B Read the poem. Underline any phrases or lines that you find interesting. Then work in pairs and compare the parts you have underlined. Explain why they interest you.

C Work in pairs and answer the questions.

1 What type of friends does the writer refer to using the metaphor of books?

2 Why does the writer use the following phrases?
  a assembled by chronology and theme
  b I'm glad for their messy intrusion
  c covers
  d some are half read
  e small talk of an introduction

The Bookcase

Friendship is a bookcase,
Packed with stories which impact my own.
Rows of friends lined neatly to attention,
Assembled by chronology and theme,
Index the stages of my life,
School, university, work, travel,
Fiction of hopes and dreams, non-fiction.
Some are stacked in disorderly piles,
Shoved in the gaps between shelves.
I'm not sure how they got there
But I'm glad for their messy intrusion.

Many books are read regularly,
I dip into new chapters,
Scan pages
Or am drawn in by engrossing details,
Tales of romance, adventure, comedy, drama, tragedy.
A few have attractive covers
And in haste are added to the shelf
But, after a closer look,
Contain narratives less captivating than they first
    seemed.
Some are the reverse,
Unsuspecting appearance,
They leave lasting impressions and bring
    unexpected joy.
And some are half read,
No fault of their own,
But time and distance have placed them out of
    sight, for now.

My favourite books
Are the ones I open to the last page I was reading.
No need to start with the small talk of an introduction,
Just re-join the conversation from where we left off
Even if it's been weeks, months, years
Since well-thumbed pages were last turned.
The characters of these loved stories
Are so familiar,
I sometimes feel as if I wrote them myself.

LISTENING

3 A Work in pairs and answer the questions.

1 Is a song more powerful for you than a poem? Why/Why not?
2 Tell your partner about a song that you associate with a particular memory.

B Read a blog post about the effect of songs. In pairs, discuss your answer to the final question posed in the blog post.

Posted June 22 by Cassie   ● ● ●

They say music talks to our soul. I'm not quite sure about that, but it certainly has an amazingly powerful effect on us. And combine music with lyrics, and there's a time machine that can transport us back without warning to random points in the past – beautiful moments, painful moments, life-changing moments – whatever. Sometimes it's nostalgia – a yearning for a happy, sometimes more innocent time. Then, there are relationships. Songs can remind us of a loved one before we lost them for whatever reason, or a romance before it turned sour. And there are other associations. Cat Stevens' classic *Father and Son* is a beautiful, poetic and haunting song that talks to us about the despair caused by the generation gap. But for me it will always be associated with the final scene of the film *Guardians of the Galaxy 2* – a space funeral with the song highlighting a father-son relationship, albeit not a biological one. I'm a sucker for emotionally charged moments! So, which songs take you back in time and why? I'd love to know.

---

4 A 🔊 6.03 | Listen to a radio discussion about poetry and song. What are the two main questions the presenter asks her guests' opinion on?

B 🔊 6.03 | Listen again and choose the correct answer (a or b).

1 Why do you think Andy is relieved to hear about the first question?
  a He doesn't know the answer.
  b It's not the old, often-asked question.
2 Andy feels that poetry is not popular with many people because at school
  a they're taught poems that are difficult to understand.
  b the poems have no relevance to modern life.
3 According to Kate, what misguided ideas do many people have about poetry?
  a They have to follow strict rules.
  b They must communicate something to the reader.
4 Why does Kate mention Japanese haiku?
  a as an example of a short yet effective poem
  b as an example of poetry anyone can write
5 In Andy's opinion, how can writing poetry help people?
  a It can serve as a form of relaxation.
  b It can help people express themselves.
6 The guests compare two song versions to illustrate what point?
  a how universal poetry is
  b how performance is part of the poetry

C In pairs, discuss how far you agree with the guests' responses to the two main questions.

VOCABULARY

reacting to poetry and song

5 A Match adjectives in the box with the definitions (1–8).

> confrontational   emotionally charged
> melancholic   melodic   poignant
> punchy   rousing   simplistic

1 exciting, making people ready for action
2 causing a sharp feeling of sadness
3 angry, looking for an argument
4 powerful, effective, exciting, often short and sharp
5 pleasant to listen to
6 full of passion and feeling
7 seeming very basic, not giving a true picture
8 indulgent, sad

B Choose the correct words to complete the messages.

< Chat   📞 🎥 📶

I've just checked out the song that everyone's going on about. I know people rate it highly, but it ¹**is / does** nothing for me, I'm afraid.

Really? I ²**find / believe** it haunting. The solo female voice raises the hairs on my neck! I particularly love the metaphors – they ³**raise / conjure** up images of wild, windswept countryside. And I can ⁴**identify / personalise** with the singer's heartache. It ⁵**runs / takes** me back to a time I was feeling exactly the same. Oh, it's so sad.

We DO ⁶**relate / favour** to different songs. I much prefer listening to songs that ⁷**increase / lift** my mood, rather than ⁸**reduce / leave** me to tears. I get stressed out enough without listening to people warbling about love and loss! Give me a good, rousing, upbeat song any day.

C Choose four adjectives from Ex 5A and name four different songs, one for each adjective. Explain your choices using phrases from Ex 5B. Compare your ideas with your partner.

GRAMMAR

adverbials

6 A Complete the sentences from the radio discussion (1–6) with the adverbials in the box. Check your answers in the audioscript on page 166.

> quite (x2)   really   relatively   strictly   to be honest

1 ...., I think it's down to poetry being misrepresented …

2 … classical poets who adhere .... to certain rhyme schemes and rhythms.

3 It can be .... intimidating.

4 … another version, more emotionally charged, will be .... moving and poignant …

5 … while the original uses harmonies, is purely melodic and .... melancholic, …

6 .... brilliant.

B Which of the adjectives in the box are gradable (G) and which are ungradable (U)?

> deafening   deceptive   interesting   fascinating
> furious   hilarious   incredible   loud   painful
> pleasant   special   thrilling   unique

C Add examples from Ex 6A to the rules below.

1 Sentence adverbials often come at the beginning of a sentence and show the speaker's attitude to a statement. They can be connected to:
  a surprise, e.g. *difficult as it is to believe*, or
  b other emotions, e.g. *to my amusement*, ...

2 Adverbs can intensify (strengthen) or modify (weaken) meaning:
  a Ungradable adjectives use a strong intensifier, e.g. *totally inadequate*.
  b Gradable adjectives can be modified, e.g. *relatively quiet*, or intensified, e.g. *terribly happy*.
  c *Quite* has different uses:
    quite + gradable adjective = modifies, e.g. *quite energetic*, ...
    quite + ungradable adjective = intensifies, e.g. *quite incredible*, ...

3 Many adverbs collocate strongly:
  a with adjectives, e.g. *highly successful*.
  b with verbs, e.g. *thoroughly recommend*, ...

D Choose the option which is NOT correct.

1 In my opinion, the song is **fairly / utterly / quite** enchanting and will appeal to a wide range of people.

2 Well, I suppose it's **relatively / quite / really** appealing, but I'd far prefer something less confrontational.

3 **Amazingly / To be honest / Unintentionally**, I actually enjoyed this new version. It's very different to the original.

4 I would **thoroughly / widely / definitely** recommend the album to anyone who likes hard rock.

5 **Utterly / Unfortunately / Sad to say**, the recording is highly controversial and had to be dropped from radio stations.

6 For me, the lyrics are **overly / pretty / totally** simplistic and **rather / a bit / absolutely** boring.

E Learn and practise. Go to the Grammar Bank.

▶▶ page 128 **GRAMMAR BANK**

PRONUNCIATION

7 A 🔊 6.04 | **intonation to show contrast** | Mark where you think the intonation pattern is on these sentences. Listen and check.

1 There are those who love poetry and those who don't.

2 A poem can be deceptively simplistic or linguistically complex.

3 It doesn't matter whether it's upbeat or slow, hard rock or gentle folk.

B Repeat the examples in Ex 7A. Then write two similar sentences with contrasts and swap with a partner to practise.

SPEAKING

8 A Work in pairs. Discuss two or three songs that have had a significant impact on you for some reason.

Explain:
- how you react when you hear the song.
- why it has such an impact on you.

B Work in small groups. Tell the group about the songs you discussed in Ex 8A.

9 A You are going to compile a playlist of five songs that will be sent into space to illustrate a snapshot of humanity. Discuss which songs from those in Ex 8B you would include and why.

The songs should:
- represent different genres.
- represent diverse singers and songwriters.
- convey a range of emotions.
- include a range of messages.

B Share your final list with other groups. Discuss and choose a final list of five songs.

6C Classic journeys

HOW TO... | tell an anecdote
VOCABULARY | adjective–noun collocations: travel
PRONUNCIATION | informal phrases when telling anecdotes

VOCABULARY

adjective–noun collocations: travel

1 A Work in pairs and discuss the questions.

1 Have you ever been on a long journey by bike, car, motorcycle, train, boat or on foot? What was it like?

2 Which well-known journeys would you like to go on?

3 Have you ever seen any films involving a journey that you would like to go on?

B Read about three classic journeys. Which appeals to you the most and which the least? Why?

2 A Cover the texts and work in pairs. Which adjectives described the words in the box?

> cuisine   culture   diners   dining   forests   hills
> journey   mountains   views   villages

B Check your ideas in the text. Underline the adjective–noun collocations.

C Replace the words in bold with an adjective from Ex 2B.

1 From the top of the Burj Khalifa you can see **wide and impressive** views of Dubai.

2 In Mexico it's possible to visit some beautifully **well-kept and looked after** Mayan temples.

3 We like staying with locals to experience **genuine, traditional** Thai cooking.

4 I love the **typical** thatched cottages in the English countryside that you cannot find anywhere else.

5 The **original native** people in parts of New Zealand have significant land rights.

6 You can see the **tall and impressive** Cliffs of Moher as you approach Ireland from the Atlantic.

7 A visitor must see the **luxurious** Victoria and Albert Museum in London.

D Change the sentences in Ex 2C to give examples from your country or other places around the world. Add any extra adverbs and adjectives that fit.

E Learn and practise. Go to the Vocabulary Bank.

> ▶▶ page 140 **VOCABULARY BANK** adjective–noun collocations: travel

Route 66

A 3,940-km three-week car ride from Chicago to Los Angeles, USA. The original road no longer exists in its entirety, but highways link the remaining parts.

What makes it special? The wide open road, the quintessential small-town diners with their original jukeboxes intact, the authentic cuisine featuring the eclectic mix of Deep South Cajun and Mexican dishes, museums in towns en route celebrating the indigenous culture, the amazing diversity of people and places, all ending up with a couple of nights in Los Angeles to unwind at the end of this road trip to end all road trips.

Walk the Nakasendo Trail

A legendary journey – a five-day walk along sections of the Nakasendo Trail in Japan. This was originally a 534-km ancient feudal route that linked Kyoto and Tokyo.

What makes it special? The fellow walkers you meet, the scenery on the way and the chance to take time out from your everyday life. Pass through undulating hills, soaring mountains, primeval forests and enjoy panoramic views on your way. Sample the local hospitality by night and visit exquisitely preserved villages and historical buildings by day. It's the epitome of walking holidays.

Take the Orient Express

An eight-night rail journey from Istanbul through Bucharest, Budapest and on to Paris, retracing the route of the original Orient Express.

What makes it special? The vibrant bustle of the Grand Bazaar, the idyllic cruise along the Danube and the opulent dining on the famous blue-and-gold carriages. Wonder at Klimt frescoes and ornate stained glass in the fairy-tale surroundings of Peles Castle. Soak in a picturesque sunset at Lake Balaton, a contender for one of the most beautiful and tranquil lakes in the world. If you love train journeys, it's the trip of a lifetime.

How to ...
tell an anecdote

3 A Work in pairs. Imagine you are going on an Orient Express trip. Discuss the questions.

1 Why are you travelling?
2 Who might you meet?
3 How would you communicate?
4 What problems might there be?

B 🔊 **6.05** | Listen to a podcast about a traveller's experiences. Did any of your ideas come up?

4 A 🔊 **6.06** | Work in pairs and try to complete these extracts. The number of words is in brackets. Then listen and check.

1 Some friends who had done it _____, 'Yeah, it's amazing, but it's quite expensive.' (2)
2 Fairly typical situation for a traveller in an exotic context, you know _____ ? (3)
3 It was really nice, _____ relaxed, like 'we're all in this together and let's just enjoy it'. (2)
4 Funny, I don't remember much about him now, but I remember understanding quite a lot about his family, his kids, his house, job, _____ . (3)
5 … for example on the first evening I think _____, he pulled out this huge, homemade cake … (2)
6 _____ guy I know got really excited when I mentioned we'd be going to Lake Balaton. (1)
7 I noticed that _____ kid kept looking at me. (1)
8 Stupid thing to do, maybe, but _____ moments when you just kind of go with the flow. (5)

B Use the extracts in Ex 4A to complete the categories.

Informal reported speech
1 Use _____ instead of *says/said* when reporting direct speech.

Informal use of determiners
2 Use _____ and _____ instead of *a/an* in a neutral way.

Vague language
3 Use expressions such as: _____ *like that, I think*, _____ + adjective.

Other informal expressions to involve the listener
4 Use adjectives such as *Strange*, _____ or _____ at the beginning of a sentence.
5 Use expressions such as *You know what* _____ and *It was one of* _____ to show shared experience.

C Read these sentences. Which words have been missed out?

1 Fairly typical situation for a traveller in an exotic context.
2 Stupid thing to do, maybe.

5 A Rephrase the anecdote to make it more informal, using ellipsis (missing out words) and informal phrases.

> I've just got back from a sailing holiday around the Greek islands. The weather was brilliant and the water was crystal clear. I went with a guy called Juan who I'd met last summer at a regatta. He said at the time, 'We must do the Greek islands together one day!' We swam a lot and had barbecues on the beach and other similar things. I got a bit sunburnt on the deck, but it is just something that often happens when you're out on the water with the salt spray. I'm sure you understand. It is more or less expected. Juan had an encounter with a jellyfish when he jumped in without looking – I think it was on the third day. It's a stupid thing to do, but a guy on the beach said, 'You should be grateful it wasn't a Portuguese man o' war!' We checked the water every time we went for a dip after that.

B Imagine what happened in Ex 5A when Juan jumped into the water, and the series of events that followed. Use present tenses to describe what happened, to make the action more dramatic.

C Learn and practise. Go to the Grammar Bank.

⏩ page 129 **GRAMMAR BANK**

PRONUNCIATION

6 A 🔊 **6.07** | **informal phrases when telling anecdotes** | Read the sentences and look at the phrases in bold. Would you say them faster, at the same speed or more slowly than the rest of the sentence? Listen and check.

1 I asked my friend about his trip, and **he was like**, 'Wow – it was amazing!'
2 The lake was like a huge mirror, **you know what I mean**?
3 We had all the basics – bread, coffee, milk, **stuff like that**.

B 🔊 **6.07** | Work in pairs. Listen again and repeat the sentences.

SPEAKING

7 A Think of something interesting or unusual that happened to you or a friend while travelling. Alternatively, invent your own story. Make notes on these questions.

- Where were you?
- When was it?
- Who were you with?
- What happened?
- How did you feel?

B Work in pairs. Practise telling the anecdote to your partner, using your notes. Try to use language from Ex 4B and Ex 4C. Change partners and tell it to your new partner, without your notes.

C Share your partner's anecdote with the class and choose the most unusual, funniest or most interesting anecdote.

MEDIATION SKILLS
referring to multiple sources
process and report a range of opinions

⏩ page 154 **MEDIATION BANK**

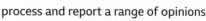
Speak anywhere Go to the interactive speaking practice 75

6D B B C Documentary
Design classics

VOCABULARY | innovation
SPEAKING | selecting classic designs
WRITING | an account of an exhibition

PREVIEW

1 A Read the programme information below. Work in pairs. Discuss how the development of the forms of transport in the box changed people's lives over time. Which do you think had the biggest impact on people's daily lives?

> bicycles   cars   planes   trains

B Work in pairs. Which of the forms of transport in Ex 1A do you think:

- was the most innovative in terms of design?
- has remained the least unchanged since its inception?
- has a design that will remain relatively unchanged in the future?

Everyday Miracles

In this documentary series, Professor Mark Miodownik looks at items of everyday life that we take for granted. There is design magic everywhere, from sofas to scanners. He shows us how these commonplace things developed from first designs and makes us wonder how on earth we could ever have managed without them.

VIEW

2 A ▶ Watch the BBC video clip. Match the different bicycles (1–3) with the adjectives in the box that Mark uses to describe them. Can you think of synonyms for the adjectives?

> cumbersome   hopeless   ingenious   revolutionary   sturdy

1 the Laufsmachine   **2** the Boneshaker   **3** the modern bicycle

B Work in pairs and answer the questions.

1 What does Mark find strange about bicycles?
2 What developments happened in 1886 and 1888? Which was the more important? Why?
3 What challenge does Mark organise? Who wins? Why?

C ▶ Watch the video again and check your answers for Ex 2B.

VOCABULARY

innovation

3 A Work in pairs. Discuss the meanings of the phrases in bold.

1 ... which all **came about** relatively recently, ...
2 It was this man, Baron Karl von Drais, who **set the ball rolling** ...
3 It was nearly half a century before that **was bettered**.
4 ... this was **the cutting edge** of bicycle design.
5 But it was still **far removed from** the modern bicycle.
6 ... to turn iron into high-strength steel **on a massive scale**.
7 ... and **launched a new era** of tools and machinery.
8 But the **best was yet to come**, the bicycle tyre.

B Work in pairs and discuss the questions.

1 What's the most cutting-edge piece of equipment you own?
2 Is there anything in your house that's far removed from what was in your grandparents' house?
3 In your opinion, what classic design will never be bettered?
4 Is there any product you think should not be available on a massive scale? Why?

SPEAKING

selecting classic designs

4 A Work in pairs. A new museum of design classics has asked for suggestions from the public on what to include. Think of an example of a design classic for each item in the box.

> car   computer   fashion item
> item of furniture   phone   toy or game

Remember those flip phones? I think they're quite classic.

B Work with another pair and compare your choices. Discuss your different suggestions and make a final selection of three designs to include in the museum. Use the Key phrases to help you.

KEY PHRASES

For me, this represents the cutting-edge style of the era …

It's a simple design, but it launched a new era of …

This simply has to go in because of its …

No collection would be complete without …

The … was far removed from anything that came before it.

This will remain a classic forever, so it's earned a place.

C Report your final selection to the class and explain why you have chosen your designs.

WRITING

an account of an exhibition

5 A Work in pairs. Have you been to an exhibition recently, or are there any that you would like to go to? Share your ideas.

B Look at the introduction taken from a tourist information website. How do new exhibitions differ from traditional displays?

These days, exhibitions are often far removed from the static, often boring museum displays of items on walls, on stands or behind glass. There has been a boom in temporary exhibitions that use space in existing galleries and in pop-up exhibitions that exploit unused spaces in public areas, such as empty stores and shop fronts. The trend today is to push the limits of the immersive experience and design areas that provide an all-encompassing, often sensory experience for the visitor. However, the very nature of 'temporary' and 'pop-up' is that we might blink and miss them!

Read some readers' accounts of 'Exhibitions I missed', and 'Exhibitions I got to experience'. Feel free to post your own.

C Write an account of an exhibition. Go to the Writing Bank.

▶▶ page 110 **WRITING BANK**

narrative tenses review

1 Complete the blog post with the correct form of the verbs in brackets.

Last night, I ¹_____ (watch) game shows all evening and ²_____ (fancy) something a bit different, so I channel ³_____ (hop) for a few minutes. While I ⁴_____ (check) out the film channel, I came across a biographical film I ⁵_____ (not see) called *The Man Who Knew Infinity*. I can tell you – it's excellent! It ⁶_____ (tell) the story of a young Indian mathematician called Ramanujan who ⁷_____ (attempt) to get university professors of mathematics to help publish his theories but ⁸_____ (fail). Finally, his genius ⁹_____ (recognise) by G. H. Hardy, a famous mathematician at the University of Cambridge, and Ramanujan ¹⁰_____ (go) to England to study and work with the professor. I ¹¹_____ (not tell) you the ending – but believe me, I ¹²_____ (have) tears in my eyes!

adverbials

2 A Read the comments about a poem. Add the adverbials in the box in suitable places in the comments.

> perfectly   utterly   vitally

1 I love the way he conveys the basic and important notion that giving is receiving, all in a short turn of words. This poem captures my feelings.

> distinctly   inextricably   quite

2 I remember my mum reading this poem to me when I was young, so I get a feeling of nostalgia when reading it that is connected to my past.

> instantly   unsurprisingly   vaguely

3 The first line of the poem evokes a sense of liberation that I once felt when I travelled, when I was younger. Perhaps I find it hard to see all the queuing at airports and sitting in seats with no leg room as even resembling that sort of travel the poem describes.

> painfully   sad to say   totally

4 I don't have the life experience to understand this poem. I've never really travelled, and I feel aware that I am ill-equipped to respond to it in any positive way.

B Write a short comment about a poem, book or film using three of the adverbials from Ex 2A. Work in pairs and compare your comments.

3 A Complete the extracts from book reviews (1–6) with the correct form of the verbs in the box. There are two verbs you do not need.

> break   conjure   describe   identify
> make   revolve   set   take

1 This debut thriller by F. G. Harris _____ new ground by having a most unusual narrator.

2 The opening of the story _____ up images of a grim society ruled by unemotional machines.

3 Anyone who has been through a recent trauma will _____ with the protagonist of this novel.

4 The novella _____ us back to our childhood summers, when the days were long and sunny and filled with fun.

5 The plot _____ around the attempts of a young climber to conquer Mount Everest, and a competitor who wants him to fail.

6 Most of the action in this historical novel is _____ against the backdrop of the English Civil War.

B Tell your partner which of the books or stories in Ex 3A you would prefer to read. Why?

4 Complete the sentences with the correct form of the words in capitals.

1 We had a _____ view from our hotel window. PANORAMA

2 The guitarist in the café was playing a song that was simple but _____ . MELODY

3 In the office there were paintings of _____ mountains and undulating hills. SOAR

4 I have a collection of albums by heavy metal bands, some of which record music that is very _____ . CONFRONT

5 Some people will choose to listen to _____ music when they're feeling sad. MELANCHOLY

6 The _____ reggae singer, Bob Marley, died in 1981. LEGEND

5 Complete the second sentence so that it has the same meaning as the first sentence, using the word given. Use between four and six words.

1 When we came out of the theatre, the streets were wet. RAINING
It was obvious that it _____ we had been in the theatre.

2 It is quite incredible, but the book was written when the author was only fifteen years old. IS
Difficult _____ , the book was written when the author was only fifteen years old.

3 I recommend that anyone who enjoys a good laugh should watch this film. THOROUGHLY
I would _____ anyone who enjoys a good laugh.

4 The critics say that the songs are full of emotion and claim that it is the singer's best album to date. CHARGED
The critics describe _____ and claim that it is the singer's best album to date.

5 Books that deal with problems that can affect anyone at any time will probably go on to become classics. ISSUES
Books that address _____ to go on to become classics.

6 The story is narrated by a dog, and it is hilarious. SEEN
The story is _____ a dog, and it is hilarious.

choice

7

VLOGS

Q: What important decisions will you need to make over the next decade?

1 ▶ Watch the video. How many of the decisions mentioned will you also have to make?

2 Which of the decisions the people mention seem the most difficult?

7A Decisions, decisions!

GRAMMAR | omitting words
VOCABULARY | idioms for choices; connotation
PRONUNCIATION: word stress in idiomatic phrases

READING

1 **Work in pairs and discuss the questions.**

1 In one minute, list what decisions you made yesterday, or this week, both small and large.

2 Would you say you are a decisive or an indecisive person? Give examples.

3 What's more important – the 'big' decisions we make infrequently or the hundreds of small decisions we make every day?

2 A **Read the article. How does the title relate to the content?**

B **Read the article again and the comments. Answer the questions.**

1 Why does the writer give examples of different choices in the first paragraph?

2 What main point does Helmstetter want to make in his book?

3 How does the writer of the article suggest that not everyone agrees with Helmstetter's points?

4 What is Andy2002's main criticism of the book?

5 How has Carl34 changed his attitude to people who tend to sit on the fence?

C **Find examples of the following in the comments about the article.**

1 a colloquial use of *so* (What effect does its use have?)

2 a colloquial way of saying *I understand*

3 two colloquial ways of reporting speech

4 a colloquial way of expressing *This is only my opinion*, or *I'm open to contradiction*

D **How far do you agree with the three comments?**

VOCABULARY

idioms for choices

3 A **Replace the phrases in bold in the sentences (1–6) with the correct form of the phrases in bold in the article and comments.**

1 I don't have much respect for people who **refuse to make decisions or give their opinion**.

2 We **have too many options** with online streaming for series and films to watch, so it's more difficult to decide on one.

3 If I'm sure I'm right, I will definitely **insist that my opinion or choice is right**.

4 In a group decision, I tend to **avoid conflict in a decision** and go with the majority.

5 If I'm really **unable to decide** (x2) about something, I **give myself more time to think about it**, or ask a friend for advice.

6 Once I've made a decision, I go with it and ignore any **reservations** I might have. No regrets, that's the way forward.

B **Complete the messages (1–6) with the correct words or phrases from the article and comments in Ex 3A.**

1 Don't ....! Make a decision.

2 I'm in .... I really don't know what to do. Can you help?

3 Just take .... and agree to everything. It'll be easier in the long run.

4 Did you see the menu I sent through? We're .... ! Amazing.

5 At work today I'm going to .... and refuse to accept the salary increase they're offering. Am I right?

6 I heard you've decided to take a year out from studying. Are you having .... , though?

C **Learn and practise. Go to the Vocabulary Bank.**

⏩ page 141 **VOCABULARY BANK** connotation

Cheese or chicken sandwich? …
I'm afraid I'm going to have to mull that over.

Decisions come in all shapes and sizes, and from the moment we wake up until we close our eyes at night, our brains are constantly confronted with choices. These may range from almost **subconscious** decisions, 'One or two pieces of toast for breakfast?' to those requiring more mental input such as what to wear if it's cold or raining or sunny. And then again, there are those decisions that require even more weighing up because they have potentially more impact, 'Should I post a particular image on social media?', 'Should I comment on the post I've just read?', 'How will others react, what does my decision say about me?' And once you've made that decision, there are the **second thoughts** you might have and the regret that you didn't **sleep on it**. Decision making can be a minefield. No wonder it has led to such a lot of research.

I recently came across this self-help book, written over thirty years ago, which has a particularly interesting slant on decision making. It's called *Choices: Discover your 100 Most Important Life Choices* and it's by a social psychologist called Dr Shad Helmstetter – apparently he was really successful at the time. In this book he invites everyone to reflect on the decisions we make, positing the theory that everyday choices are the ones that have the greatest impact on our lives and indeed on who we are, rather than the 'biggies' such as career/partner/home-related ones. Helmstetter's list, which ranges from decisions about 'Your posture' to 'Who you spend most of your time with' or 'How you spend your holidays', is good news for those of us who agonise over making decisions (and I include myself here!). People judged negatively for putting off making simple decisions will be relieved to hear that in Helmstetter's

eyes, every decision we make has significance, so it's totally reasonable to approach each one seriously.

Clearly, there are today those who may debate his conclusions, but the list in his book is engaging in itself. By looking at such a range of different examples of everyday decisions, we see that many have consequences of far greater significance than we might have thought at the time. This reminds us that, in fact, we are the ones in control of our destinies. It's not only actions such as what time we go to bed or how often we lie that are under our control, but also how much patience we have, what makes us angry and even how happy we are.

If you consider the degree to which self-reflection has become the norm these days, Helmstetter could be seen as something of a pioneer in making the notion of 'it's the little things that matter' so fashionable. This is all the more remarkable given that his book hasn't been updated since its first publication, and yet remains a go-to book for many looking for focus and motivation. A really interesting read.

So, in the spirit of Helmstetter, but with a little updating for a new generation, let us know what you think these day-to-day decisions say about you.

- How often you check social media
- How often you make your own meals
- If you try to fix a broken appliance
- How many hours you work each day
- How often you see your friends face-to-face

Comments

Andy2002

Fascinating, but I beg to differ. I'm not sure the decision not to fix something was particularly impactful for me, or am I missing something? What really drained my decision-making energy recently was **umming and ahhing** about whether or not to spend a year travelling before going to uni. The 'Should I?', 'Shouldn't I?' went back and forth in my mind for ages. Then having decided to do it, it turned into 'Should I have?', 'Shouldn't I have?', 'Should I cancel?', 'Shouldn't I cancel?' Now that decision-making process was exhausting!

Brenda71

Well, as somebody who's actually read *Choices* I'd like to point out a glaring omission. He doesn't seem to consider 'decision-fatigue' as a reason for having difficulty in making decisions. They say that everyone's brain has a limit to the number of decisions it makes every day (big and small, simple or when we**'re spoilt for choice**) and that we sometimes have problems when we reach that limit. I can so identify with that. What seems quick and easy to decide first thing in the morning becomes a really long and drawn-out tussle at the end of the day and you're **in a quandary** over the simplest choices. I can't be the only one who thinks like this.

Carl34

I'd always seen it as a sort of weakness, the not being able to make decisions or choices – particularly with regard to people who can't figure out where they stand on issues and end up **sitting on the fence**. You know, the guys who go, 'Well yes, I think you've got a point', but then, 'But yes, I can see there's a case for … too!' Used to really bug me and I'd be like, 'For goodness' sake, stop dithering!' Also, those who **take the path of least resistance** and just let others decide for them. But now get that ambivalence can actually be a strength. Rather than **digging our heels in**, maybe we should be open to being swayed by other opinions? Just saying.

PRONUNCIATION

4 A 🔊 **7.01 | word stress in idiomatic phrases |** Listen to the phrases and underline the syllable which carries the main stress.

1 umming and ahhing
2 spoilt for choice
3 in a quandary
4 sit on the fence
5 dig your heels in
6 take the path of least resistance

B Read the sentences (1–6) aloud. Try to put the stress on the correct syllable of the idiomatic phrases.

1 I was umming and ahhing about it for hours.
2 I was absolutely spoilt for choice.
3 I was in a quandary, so I called my best friend.
4 I used to sit on the fence when I was younger.
5 If you don't dig your heels in, they'll walk all over you.
6 Taking the path of least resistance makes you look weak.

C Work in pairs. Discuss how far you agree or disagree with the statements in Ex 3A.

GRAMMAR

omitting words

5 A We often leave words or clauses out of sentences, especially in colloquial language. Match the sentences from the text on page 81 (1–5) with the types of omission (a–e).

1 I'm not sure the decision not to fix something was particularly impactful for me …
2 People judged negatively for putting off making simple decisions …
3 But now get that ambivalence can actually be a strength.
4 Fascinating, but I beg to differ.
5 … he invites everyone to reflect on the decisions we make, …

a omission of relative pronoun
b omission of *that* in a clause
c omission of pronoun and auxiliary
d omission of relative pronoun and auxiliary verb
e omission of pronoun

B Rewrite the sentences in Ex 5A adding in the words that have been left out.

C Which words could be omitted in these sentences?

1 Most people who I've spoken to about the book completely agree with me.
2 I don't see how he'll manage this.
3 It's a good point, but I can't really see it working.
4 The decision that I most agree with is the third on the list.
5 Decisions that have been made cannot be unmade.

D Complete the conversations with your own ideas. Then compare your answers with a partner.

1 A: I think we should never make decisions without thinking carefully.
   B: Interesting idea, but _____ .
2 A: People worry too much about making decisions. They should just decide and forget about it.
   B: Not sure about that. I think _____ .

E Learn and practise. Go to the Grammar Bank.

▶▶ **page 130 GRAMMAR BANK**

SPEAKING

6 A Look at some more life choices inspired by Helmstetter's book *Choices: Discover your 100 Most Important Life Choices* below. Make brief notes in answer to the questions.

1 Which of the items below do you think you can make a choice about? Which do you think are not really within your control?
2 Regarding the items that you can control, what choices can you actually make? How big an effect can that have on your life?

- What you worry about most
- How healthy your lifestyle is
- What you think about when you go to bed at night
- How often you try something new
- How good a friend you are
- How you react when you lose something
- Who you message most often
- Where you spend your free time
- What you complain about most

B Read the Future Skills box and do the task.

FUTURE SKILLS
Teamwork

When tasked with reaching a decision, it is important to work as a team and listen and consider the suggestions and comments from the group. Everyone needs to be able to make their own contribution and you should be willing for your own opinion to be swayed.

Work in pairs. Tell each other about a time your opinion was influenced by another person's suggestion or comment.

C Work in small groups. Discuss the questions in Ex 6A. Think about how you answered the following question in Ex 1 and decide whether or not you would like to change it.

What's more important – the 'big' decisions we make infrequently or the hundreds of small decisions we make every day?

7B Online or offline?

GRAMMAR | prepositional phrases
VOCABULARY | ways of reading; idioms: books and reading
PRONUNCIATION | stress in phrasal verbs and dependent prepositions

LISTENING

1 A Work in pairs and discuss the questions.

  1 What sort of things do you choose to read in your free time?

  2 What proportion of your reading is on screen versus print? What is your preference? Why?

  3 Which do you think is a better choice for concentration and comprehension, print or e-books?

B 🔊 **7.02** | Listen to an extract from a radio chat show and check if any of the points you made in Ex 1A are mentioned.

C 🔊 **7.02** | Listen again and answer the questions.

  1 What issues have been discussed so far on the programme this week?

  2 What perceived advantages to both print and online reading are mentioned?

  3 What is Tara's opinion about why print and e-books are read?

  4 What does Tara say about concentration and comprehension when reading online?

  5 What examples does Tara give of the ways in which online reading may develop in the future?

  6 What example does Tara give to support her opinion that print will never completely disappear?

D Work in pairs and discuss the questions.

  1 How far do you agree with Tara about the future of the printed book? Why?

  2 Some people say that we don't get as emotional when reading an e-book. Do you think this is true?

  3 Some people say that those who resist reading digitally are 'dinosaurs' who fear that the world that they know is disappearing. How far would you agree or disagree?

  4 What advantages would you say there are to reading online?

VOCABULARY

ways of reading

2 A Work in pairs. Read the survey questions and guess what's true for your partner. Then discuss what's true for both of you.

You can't judge a book ...

1 Before going on holiday do you:

  a **pore over** maps to get as familiar as possible with the place?

  b **flick through** a guidebook to check out the highlights?

  c **peruse** some online reviews to get some ideas?

2 When you write something for college or work, do you:

  a **scrutinise** it for errors, checking down to the last letter and punctuation?

  b **cast a quick eye over** it to check there aren't any glaring mistakes?

  c not read it through again?

3 If you had an upcoming job interview, would you:

  a **read up on** the company to show you know all about their operations?

  b **dip into** any literature you can find about the company, just to catch key points?

  c keep any questions you have to ask in the interview?

4 If you're reading a long book and parts of it are a bit heavy-going, do you:

  a **plough through** to the end because you've already invested time and money in it?

  b **skip to** the end to find out what happens?

  c **skim** the boring parts to get to more interesting action?

B Look at the words and phrases in bold in Ex 2A. Which refer to:

  1 quick or shallow reading?

  2 slow, careful or deep reading?

C Work in pairs. For each word or phrase in bold in Ex 2A, think of one example of something that you read in that way.

D Learn and practise. Go to the Vocabulary Bank.

> ⏩ page 141 **VOCABULARY BANK** idioms: books and reading

GRAMMAR

prepositional phrases

3 A Complete the extracts from the radio show with the correct prepositions.

1 There have been several issues _____ for discussion …

2 We've even touched _____ virtual holidays and sports experiences versus the real thing.

3 Will the printed book or newspaper ever totally become a thing _____ the past?

4 The resilience of the print market is indicative _____ the value people still place _____ traditional books.

5 There is no great likelihood _____ screen reading taking _____ completely.

6 It isn't down to a clear preference _____ one over the other …

7 … which will have long-term implications _____ all of us.

8 They're all _____ the hands of those visionaries of the present and the future.

B Match the extracts (1–8) in Ex 3A with the types of language (a–e). More than one extract is possible in some cases.

a prepositions that depend on a verb

b prepositions that depend on a noun

c prepositions that are part of an idiomatic phrase

d prepositions that depend on an adjective

e phrasal verbs

C Complete the comments with the prepositions in the box and the correct form of the verbs in brackets. Do you agree with the comments?

| against   at   for   from   in   with |

1 Students often react _____ (force) to read certain books at school.

2 I completely understand people who have an obsession _____ (read) non-fiction.

3 Children should be encouraged to set aside time _____ (read) for pleasure.

4 I think people who read a lot are more accomplished _____ (express) themselves because they have a wider vocabulary.

5 If older people read a lot, it can protect cognitive function _____ (decline).

6 Reading before bedtime is said to aid people _____ (get) ready for sleep.

D Learn and practise. Go to the Grammar Bank.

▶▶ page 131 **GRAMMAR BANK**

PRONUNCIATION

4 A 🔊 **7.03 | stress in phrasal verbs and dependent prepositions |** Listen to the sentences. Underline the stress in the words in bold.

1 I don't **obsess about** whether I read online or offline, I just like reading.

2 I was resistant to getting an e-reader for years, then I **gave in** and bought one. I love it.

3 If we don't **set** time **aside** to read for pleasure, we'll eventually lose the skill to do it.

4 I believe that reading regularly can **protect** people **against** certain illnesses.

5 If you **skip to** the end of a book, you're cheating.

6 I don't **comment on** other people's taste in fiction, and I expect them not to comment on mine.

B Read the sentences in Ex 4A again and answer the questions.

1 Which of the words in bold are:
   a phrasal verbs (where the preposition/adverb changes the meaning of the verb)?
   b verbs with dependent prepositions (where the verb's meaning stays the same)?

2 What do you notice about the stress patterns of the two types of verbs?

C Work in pairs. Tell your partner which of the sentences in Ex 4A are true for you.

SPEAKING

5 A Work in pairs. What do you think are the benefits of reading for pleasure? List your ideas and share your thoughts with the class.

B Work in small groups. You're going to take part in a campaign called 'Read a little every day'. Think of ways you could encourage people to read more for pleasure, either in print or digitally. Consider:

- the reasons why people might not read often.
- habits you might encourage to counteract these issues (e.g. try to dip into a book every day if you've only got a little time).
- real-world events (e.g. meeting famous authors) for people to attend to encourage their reading.
- how technology could encourage more readers (e.g. reminders to take a few minutes to read up on something).

People just don't have the time to drop what they're doing and plough through the latest best-selling novel.

Perhaps an app could give summaries of popular books for busy people to cast a quick eye over to see what they find interesting?

C Present your ideas to the class. Then choose the best ideas from each group to make a final proposal.

Should we take the 'hand' out of handwriting?

Micah Lyles
12 April, 11.37 GMT

Remember learning to write at school? I can still feel the pen or pencil in my hand and recall how I angled my elbow as I laboriously drew the loops for 'l's, crossed my 't's and tried to make my letters the same size. We spent hours in class practising and perfecting our handwriting until it became automatic and, like driving, we no longer had to focus on the individual actions, but on the content – or the road ahead. But where does the skill of handwriting stand today? Now that keyboards and typing are our main tools for written communication, do we still need handwriting, or need to learn it? In Finland, joined-up (cursive) handwriting classes have been dropped from the curriculum, and other countries are following suit. Are they right?

Supporters point out that the skill of automatic typing is faster to acquire than that of handwriting. This means that more time in schools would be released to focus on other subjects. And it must be said that yes, the average person no longer uses handwriting very much. Even signatures are pretty much obsolete – they can be done online, or quickly scrawled. No finesse is needed. Note taking can be done on tablets, shopping lists recorded on phones. In addition to this, handwriting can be notoriously difficult to read – I'm guilty of almost total illegibility here!

Obviously, many disagree with the move. They maintain that handwriting improves our fine motor skills and according to experts, it can also stimulate visual recognition and memory retention. I have to say, personally, that I have a fondness for handwriting. There is something about creating words with a pen on paper that helps me in several ways. I do remember things better, and as I often hear other authors say, it is almost part of the creative process. Ideas come as the words appear from my pen. But perhaps that's just me. I did love those old handwriting lessons though. 😊 Did you?

WRITING

a blog post

6 A Work in pairs and discuss the questions.

1 When was the last time you wrote a letter?
2 What things do you write by hand?
3 How do you feel when you receive something handwritten?

B Read the title of the blog post. What do you expect it to be about? Read the blog post and check.

C Read the tips for writing a good blog post (1–8). Find an example of each in the blog post.

1 Use a catchy or intriguing title to invite people to read it.
2 Speak directly to the reader from the start.
3 Develop the article or blog post so that paragraphs flow naturally and logically.
4 Use a lively and informal style, with ellipsis and informal punctuation.
5 Include some interesting facts.
6 Give personal views and examples.
7 Add humour where possible.
8 Leave the reader with something to reflect on.

7 A You are going to write a blog post about how your language is or isn't changing. Work in pairs and discuss the questions.

1 Should the rules of a language remain fixed and 'correct', or change with time?
2 Are there many differences in the way your language is spoken and written?
3 How is texting different from standard written language?
4 Do you think texting affects (or will affect) people's normal writing?

B Decide on an interesting focus for the blog post and make a plan. Think of a title, your introductory paragraph and how the blog post will develop and finish. Write the blog post and share it with the class.

7C Urban animals

HOW TO ... | hedge an opinion and express reservations
VOCABULARY | collocations: discussing issues
PRONUNCIATION | intonation when hedging and expressing reservations

VOCABULARY

collocations: discussing issues

1 A Work in pairs and discuss the questions.

1 Have animals that usually live in the wild started to live in urban areas in your country? If so, which animals?

2 Would you consider it a pleasure or a problem to have wild animals living near you? Why?

3 Why do you think some animals have started to share urban spaces with humans?

4 Do you think any action should be taken to either protect these animals or clear areas of them? Why?

B Read the article. Does the writer share your point of view about question 4 in Ex 1A?

C Complete the sentences with the correct collocations in bold from the article.

1 Hunting is an issue that is .... with strong opinions held by people on both sides of the argument.

2 Laws designed to deal with animal cruelty are not always .... in this country, and the perpetrators go free.

3 People are .... over whether wild animals should ever be culled, with some thinking it's necessary to maintain a balance in nature and others thinking it is cruel.

4 Some people who get dogs are .... to what the care and cost of looking after them entails, and as a result abandon them sooner or later.

5 Animal welfare groups are always looking for volunteers to get .... in helping, often as assistants at rescue centres.

6 It is .... that pets sold on the black market will have no registration papers, because the sales are illegal.

D Work in pairs. Complete the sentences with your own ideas and discuss your ideas with your partner.

1 A hotly debated topic I have discussed recently is ...

2 Something I've heard about recently that is patently obvious is ...

3 Something that society is deeply divided over is ...

4 Something I would like to get actively involved in is ...

5 A law I think should be strictly enforced is ...

6 Something I used to be completely oblivious to was ...

Is that a wolf in my garden?

When she looked out of her kitchen window and saw a lone wolf rummaging through the rubbish bin just outside her back door, Camila Soto did a double-take and then a quick mental check. 'Where are the kids? That was my first thought.' Once she realised her son and daughter were upstairs playing, she quickly phoned the police. 'They were like, "Oh, another one, OK just stay inside", clearly unwilling to become **actively involved**. I had no idea that this was actually so common.'

Reports like this make the news, but wolves are far from being the only wild animals to be sighted in urban areas. As a result of our encroachment on the countryside and destruction of habitats, many species that previously lived in the wild are living cheek by jowl with humans, although many people are **completely oblivious** to this fact. And it is not only the easy availability of food that is encouraging this movement. One successful adaptor to urban life is the peregrine falcon, attracted by our tall city buildings. Interestingly, the fastest bird on the planet has adapted to hunting in the cities by targeting their prey at night, instead of during the daylight hours, using the artificial lighting. Urban animals are getting smarter.

However, some animals are more commonly seen. Coyotes in New York, wild boar in Berlin and foxes in London are just a few examples and animals like these are causing a degree of controversy. The number of London foxes in particular is rocketing and has become quite an emotive issue. To some people they are cuddly, cute creatures with their bushy tails and bright eyes, welcomed into gardens and encouraged with food. To others they are pests that ravage rubbish bins and pose a potential danger, coming close to and even inside houses uninvited.

What to do about these urban invaders is **hotly debated**. People are **deeply divided**. Should they be culled or protected, hunted or welcomed? Many believe that we need to share our space with nature and not seek to dominate it, and that it is possible to live side by side with these animals. Others want the animals banished from urban areas or at the very least, controlled with laws that can be **strictly enforced**. My personal view would be that it is a situation we need to live with; whatever we do will never eliminate the problem. And while seeing a lone wolf is probably a frightening situation, unless newly urbanised animals prove to be a real danger, then we should seek solutions that involve living in harmony with them. It is **patently obvious** that our actions have brought so many species to the brink of extinction, with numbers dwindling year on year, so surely we need to rethink our attitudes?

How to ...
hedge an opinion and express reservations

2 A 🔊 **7.04** | Listen to two friends discussing the problem of rocketing wolf populations. Summarise their general opinions about the topic.

B 🔊 **7.04** | Listen again. Work in pairs. Student A: Note the main points the man makes. Student B: Note the main points the woman makes. Compare your notes.

C Complete the phrases from the conversation (1–6).

1 Well, I _____ say …
2 Well, _____ it's just me, but …
3 I'm no _____, but I think …
4 There are some _____ that I agree with, but …
5 The idea has a lot _____ for it, but …
6 _____, you've got to have some sort of control, but …

D Learn and practise. Go to the Grammar Bank.

⏩ page 132 **GRAMMAR BANK**

PRONUNCIATION

3 A 🔊 **7.05** | intonation when hedging and expressing reservations | Look at the extracts from the conversation. Mark where you think the intonation rises, where it falls, and where there is a brief pause. Listen and check.

1 The idea has a lot going for it, but they'd need to be controlled.
2 Well, maybe it's just me, but the danger always feels exaggerated.
3 Well, I'm no expert, but I think the risk needs to be properly assessed.

B Work in pairs and discuss the statements (1–3). Use phrases from Ex 2C to give opinions and express reservations.

1 People should be fined if they actively encourage foxes and other wild animals in their gardens.
2 Animal theft should be treated more severely in law.
3 Hunting animals for pleasure should be banned.

SPEAKING

4 A Work in pairs. Choose one of the statements in Ex 3B. Student A: Defend the statement. Student B: Oppose the statement. Make notes and consider points your partner might make.

B Have the discussion. Support your opinion with reasons and examples.

C Summarise your discussion for the class. Take a vote on who presented the best arguments for and against.

MEDIATION SKILLS
taking notes
identify what is relevant in a talk

⏩ page 156 **MEDIATION BANK**

7D BBC Street Interviews
Too much choice?

Dylan   Tori

VOCABULARY | making choices
SPEAKING | prioritising essential items
WRITING | a newspaper opinion piece

Sagar

PREVIEW

1 Work in pairs and answer the questions.

1 Can you think of daily situations where we have so much choice that it is difficult to make a decision?

2 Do you think we make better choices when we have longer to think about it? Why?

3 Would you say we tend to make better choices when we are older? Why/Why not?

Q1: Do you think you can ever have too much choice?

Q2: Tell me about a time you made a right or wrong choice.

VIEW

2 A ▶ Watch the first part of the interviews. Do the people think having a lot of choice is good or bad? What reasons do they give?

B ▶ Watch the second part of the interviews and answer the questions. What examples do people give for:

1 making the right choice?
2 making the wrong choice?
3 saying there is no wrong choice?

C ▶ Watch the interviews again. Check your answers for Ex 2A and 2B.

VOCABULARY

making choices

3 A Complete the phrases from the interviews with the words in the box.

> chopping   indecisive   investigate   limitations
> narrow   overwhelmed   restricted   variables

1 It's up to you to .... what are the right choices.
2 … I would find myself .... and changing what I want.
3 If there is fewer options, then I can .... it down easier.
4 … you make your own .... …
5 I think that's a question for people who are ....
6 I feel .... if I have no choice.
7 I tend to become .... when there are too many options.
8 There are too many ....

B Think about your own life and make brief notes on each of the following situations, and what you decided to do in the end.

1 a time you felt restricted because of lack of choice
2 an occasion when too many options overwhelmed you
3 whether you ever put your own limitations on options
4 a decision where you were easily able to narrow down the options
5 a time when you kept chopping and changing your mind
6 an occasion where you carefully investigated all the options

C Work in pairs. Compare your answers to Ex 3B and give examples and reasons to clarify what you mean. What was your decision in each of the situations?

I really wanted to study Spanish at school, but they only offered French and German, so I was quite restricted. In the end I just went with French and then I finally took up Spanish at university.

Jane

Duncan

B B C

Catherine

Sky

Michael

WRITING

a newspaper opinion piece

5 A Work in pairs. Read the request on a newspaper opinion page. In what ways do you think our choices in life might be overly controlled by other people or organisations?

We want to hear from our readers!

Some people feel that our day-to-day choices are controlled excessively by other people or organisations. We would like our readers to submit their opinions on the following question.

How important is it to have the freedom to make our own choices in life, even if they might be harmful to ourselves or others?

Email us your opinion, in no more than 250 words, to the address below. A selection of opinions will be published in next week's edition.

B Read some comments about being allowed freedom. Do the people mention your ideas from Ex 5A? Do you agree with the comments? Why/Why not?

Andy ✎ 2 posts ⚲ GB A day ago
What I don't like is how the government tries to control what we eat, saying what is and what isn't heathy! You know, taxing sugary products and so on. I can make my own decisions on that, thank you!

Andy ✎ 2 posts ⚲ GB A day ago
Ratings on films – deciding who can or who can't watch a film! Surely that's up to me?

Andy ✎ 2 posts ⚲ GB A day ago
Parents need to control their kids – fine – up to a point. But some don't let kids have a say in what clothes they wear for years, insist that they eat foods they don't enjoy and also track their phones without telling them. That's going too far.

C Write a newspaper opinion piece. Go to the Writing Bank.

▶▶ page 110 **WRITING BANK**

SPEAKING

prioritising essential items

4 A Imagine you are going to spend three months in an isolated cabin. You will have heating, water and basic food to last you for the period. You will not have wifi and cannot take an electronic device with you. However, you can take with you ONE of each of the items below. Make your choices.

- a book
- a game
- a musical instrument or sporting equipment
- a favourite snack (one item for each day)

B Work in pairs. Tell your partner about the choices you made and explain why you chose them. Use the Key phrases to help you.

KEY PHRASES

This may sound weird, but I'd …
I'm torn between two books, but just don't know which …
Good choice! Very readable …
I hadn't thought about that … of course, …
I'd never get fed up with ….
This tops my list because …

C Take a quick survey of the class. Which items are most popular, least popular and the strangest?

GRAMMAR
omitting words

1 Identify which words have been omitted and rewrite the sentences.

1 The novel the writer considers her best has won several awards.

2 Were you aware there have been reports some people are keeping dogs in their apartment?

3 Good news, but not sure I can make the party on Friday.

4 Decisions made quickly are not always the best.

5 The sound David was listening to was a fox.

6 Companies investigated included several based in the USA.

prepositional phrases

2 A Complete the sentence starters with the prepositions in the box.

against (x2) for (x2) in (x2) of (x2)

1 According to the recent news, there's less likelihood .... …

2 People often react .... being …

3 I need to set aside some time .... …

4 It's astounding, the increase .... …

5 One way of protecting .... …

6 It's always important to be mindful .... …

7 Something that aids me .... concentrating on work is …

8 There's no justification .... people who …

B Complete the sentences with your own ideas. Work in pairs and compare your ideas.

VOCABULARY

3 A Complete the statements with the correct words.

1 If you can't decide something, I advise .... on it.

2 Everyone has second .... from time to time – it's inevitable.

3 I'd rather be .... for choice than be restricted to two options.

4 If the majority of people know what they want, I take the .... of least resistance and go with their decision.

5 There is never a good reason to sit on the .... We should know our own minds.

6 There is no point digging your .... in if the decision isn't going your way. You'll have to give in sooner or later.

B Work in pairs. How far do you agree with the statements in Ex 3A?

4 A Complete the blog post extract with the correct prepositions.

Posted 25th May by Stevie N   • • •

When deciding whether to buy something, I usually read ¹ .... on the product first and then dip ² .... a few shopping sites to see what they have to say. It's easier to look online rather than flick ³ .... print catalogues I find – unlike my mother, who spends ages poring ⁴ .... leaflets that come through the door! And when I do decide to go ahead and buy something, I never plough ⁵ .... the terms and conditions but always skip straight ⁶ .... the end to click on 'accept'. I do cast a quick eye ⁷ .... the returns policies, but that's it.

B Work in pairs. Are you similar or different to the writer of the blog post in Ex 4A in how you shop? In what ways?

5 A Complete the news report with the adverbs in the box.

actively deeply hotly patently strictly unduly

The decisions of the judges during the recent TV reality show *Whose Life?* have been ¹ .... debated on social media. It is ² .... obvious that they had been ³ .... influenced. The competition rules specify that judges should have no links with the contestants, but these rules have not been ⁴ .... enforced. What's more, the head judge is known to have been ⁵ .... involved in swaying the other judges' decisions throughout the competition. The decision to choose Grant Thompson as the series winner last Saturday has ⁶ .... divided the viewing public.

B Work in pairs. Do you usually trust the decisions made by judges on TV competitions? Why/Why not?

body and mind

8

VLOGS

Q: Which quality do you like most about yourself?

1 ▶ Watch the video. Do you have the same answers as any of the people?

2 What qualities that the people mention would you also like to have?

GSE **LEARNING OBJECTIVES**

8A READING | Read an article about endurance swimming: idioms and collocations: skills and abilities; compound adjectives

Pronunciation: linking consonants

Give a shout-out to somebody who deserves it: noun phrases

8B LISTENING | Understand a radio programme about synaesthesia: adjectives to describe sensations and reactions; verbs to describe reactions

Pronunciation: contracted *will*

Talk about sensory reactions: uses of *will* and *would*

Write a description of a fictional character

8C HOW TO ... | explain the purpose and benefit of something: well-being

Pronunciation: intonation in sentences containing contrasting ideas

8D BBC PROGRAMME | Understand a comedy panel quiz show

Talk about psychological effects: thoughts and ideas

Write a story about strange effects

8A No limits?

GRAMMAR | noun phrases
VOCABULARY | idioms and collocations: skills and abilities; compound adjectives
PRONUNCIATION | linking consonants

READING

1 Read the news headlines. Work in pairs and answer the questions (1–4).

> ### Man finishes 563-kilometre nonstop run
>
> ### AUSTRIAN FREE-DIVES 253 METRES ON ONE BREATH
>
> ### Danish woman completes 366 marathons in 365 days
>
> ### Tennis match ends after three days and 183 games
>
> ### YOSHIDA DOES 10,507 PRESS-UPS

1 How do you think the people prepared for these events?

2 Why do you think they attempted them?

3 Which event do you think would be the most difficult?

4 Would you be tempted to participate in endurance events like these? Why/Why not?

2 A Read the title of the article and look at the photo. What do you think the article is about?

B Read the article and check your ideas.

C Read the article again and answer the questions.

1 What feats of endurance are mentioned in the text?

2 How is Pugh able to complete these challenges?

3 How did he first discover his ability?

4 Why is the water available for him to swim in?

5 Why does he take on the challenges?

6 Why does he refer to these swims as both 'a tragedy and a triumph'?

Arctic swimmer shines a light on global warming

In 2007 a city lawyer, dressed only in swimming trunks, a cap and goggles, spent nearly nineteen minutes in the coldest water ever endured by someone who lived to tell the tale.

Lewis Gordon Pugh became the first person to complete a long-distance swim at the North Pole, having overcome many setbacks in order to fulfil a lifelong ambition.

The feat was not only unprecedented in physical terms, it also provided compelling evidence that global warming is breaking up the Arctic ice cap. The adventurer, the only person to carry out endurance swims in all five oceans, swam 1 km (more than half a mile) along a temporary crack in the ice in eighteen minutes and fifty seconds. Most people would die quickly in a water temperature of −1.7°C (29°F) through a rapid process of hyperventilation, shock and drowning. But Mr Pugh is made of sterner stuff. After recovering in his support boat though, he confessed that the pain was excruciating.

It should not be possible to swim at the North Pole, at ninety degrees north in the Arctic Ocean, but an increase in global air temperatures has resulted in a decrease in sea ice. As a result, patches of open sea are appearing in summer. Scientists predict that by 2040 there may be no sea ice left in the Arctic in summer and this will have far-reaching consequences. Mr Pugh wanted to draw attention to the effects of global warming and put

pressure on world leaders to cut carbon emissions and find long-term solutions. He referred to the swim as both a triumph and a tragedy, the triumph being that he could swim in such ferocious conditions, but a tragedy that it was actually possible to swim at the North Pole.

Pugh carried out the swim after years spent acclimatising his body to extreme cold. His ability to survive in such an extreme environment has been baffling scientists for years. Although not clear-cut, it appears that his cold-water endurance swims are made possible by a phenomenon he calls 'anticipatory thermogenesis', the ability to elevate his core body temperature while psyching himself up before he enters the water. 'As soon as I enter cold water, my body shunts all my warm blood to my core to protect my vital organs. It then generates incredible heat,' he said. 'Before I even enter the water, I am able to elevate my core body temperature by as much as 1.4°C.' This phenomenon has, to our knowledge, not been noted in any other human.

Mr Pugh discovered his rare gift by accident when he began to perspire and feel thirsty while staring at freezing water before an earlier Arctic dip. Prof Tim Noakes, a professor of sports science from the University of Cape Town, who has been monitoring the swimmer, said he had pushed the boundaries of what was humanly possible, and he mentioned something very interesting. While Mr Pugh was able to raise the temperature around his heart, lungs and brain before a swim, the temperature of his muscles dropped to 30°C during the event, which would prove fatal for most people. The adventurer believes he has trained himself to experience a kind of Pavlovian response to cold water, which results in his body heating up.

This ability has allowed Mr Pugh to perform other feats of endurance over the intervening years to raise awareness of how critical the threat of climate change is, and in 2020 he went to the other end of the Earth to become the first person to swim under the ice in Antarctica. The glacial thaw caused by global warming opens cracks that develop into subglacial rivers and Pugh's ten-minute swim was through one of these tunnels.

Lewis Pugh has certainly earned worldwide respect and admiration for using his body's unique ability in order to focus attention on perhaps the most difficult challenge humanity has ever faced. What could be next on his agenda?

3 Read the blog post about heroes. Compare the information given with that in the article in Ex 2A. Underline and correct any sections in the blog post that are not correct.

Posted 1st Oct by Deepak Mahto   • • •

Today's hero!

OK, so my 'hero of the day' for yesterday was a musician. Today it's someone with a very particular knack for doing exceptional things – a guy called Lewis Gordon Pugh. Most of us think we're in good shape and I've got a lot of friends who do open-water swimming, but Pugh goes a few steps beyond, and well outside most people's comfort zone. It seems he's swum in both the Arctic and the Antarctic, and without a wetsuit! It sounds impossible, but apparently, he can manage to survive colder temperatures than most human beings because of this strange ability he's got where he can raise the core body temperature around his major organs, which then only drops to 30 degrees during the swim. Sounds weird to me. Because of climate change, the glaciers and ice are melting, which opens up areas of water people can swim in. Well, where *he* can swim! In the Arctic, he actually swam under the ice – can you believe it? He says it was both exciting and really painful. Why anyone would put themselves through that I have no idea. Apparently, he does these challenges to show what the human body is capable of and to encourage others to do endurance training and get healthier. I think he also raises some money for charity. So, for showing drive and determination and getting to grips with all manner of challenges, Mr Pugh has the honour of being my hero of the day. Watch out for someone else with a natural aptitude for a particular type of activity tomorrow. You might be surprised!

VOCABULARY

idioms and collocations: skills and abilities

4 A Complete the idioms (1–8) with words from the article and blog post on pages 92–93.

1 Can you give an example of a(n) .... **you've had to overcome** this year?
2 Does anyone in your circle of friends **have a rare** .... **for** doing something?
3 Did you **have a particular** .... **for** anything when you were a child?
4 Would you say you **are in good** .... ?
5 Have you ever **stepped outside your** .... **zone**?
6 Name someone who has **shown** .... **and determination** in your workplace recently.
7 What problems have you had to **get to** .... **with** recently?
8 Do you **have a natural** .... **for** helping people to grasp new concepts?

B 🔊 **8.01** | Listen to the responses to the questions in Ex 4A. Match the questions (1–8) with the responses (a–h).

C Work in pairs. Take turns to ask and give your own answers to the questions in Ex 4A.

D Learn and practise. Go to the Vocabulary Bank.

⏩ page 141 **VOCABULARY BANK**
compound adjectives

GRAMMAR

noun phrases

5 A Complete the sentences from the article on pages 92–93 with the correct words and phrases in the box.

> dressed   endurance   of global warming
> ten-minute   very interesting

1 … a city lawyer, ... only in swimming trunks …
2 … the only person to carry out .... swims in all five oceans.
3 Mr Pugh wanted to draw attention to the effects .... …
4 … and he mentioned something ....
5 … Pugh's .... swim was through one of these tunnels.

B Look at the noun phrases you completed in Ex 5A. What would be a longer way to phrase them?

1 … a city lawyer, who was dressed only in swimming trunks …

6 A Rewrite the sentences using noun phrases to shorten them.

1 Someone that I have great admiration for is the owner of a fish and chip shop in my town. He runs a group which raises funds for charities in our area.
2 The only person who was capable of making geography lessons fun for me was Mr Turner. I vividly remember one lesson that lasted half an hour about Denmark. He played us some songs that had been recorded by a Danish pop duo. It was a lesson that was both informative and enjoyable.
3 I have a respect that is growing for a contact in business that I have recently made. He has a passion for his work that is fiery. His knack of engaging with people who are at all levels in our company, which is based on years of experience, is admirable.

B Complete the sentences with your own ideas. Use noun phrases.

1 I love to eat delicious ....-covered ....
2 I'd be nervous about committing to a long-term ....
3 I have a highly developed sense ....
4 I can't stand people who ....
5 I'd like to go somewhere ....

C Learn and practise. Go to the Grammar Bank.

⏩ page 133 **GRAMMAR BANK**

PRONUNCIATION

7 A 🔊 **8.02** | **linking consonants** | Listen to sentences 1–4. How does the speaker connect the two words in bold?

1 He gave a **ten-minute** speech which was absolutely hilarious.
2 She always keeps her **long-term** plans in mind – she's very focused.
3 She's someone who will always **take part** enthusiastically in everything she gets involved in.
4 He has an **amazing knack** for understanding other people's points of view.

B 🔊 **8.03** | Listen and repeat the phrases.

C Work with a partner. Tell your partner about anyone you know who is described in sentences 1–4 in Ex 7A.

SPEAKING

8 A 🔊 **8.04** | Listen to a recorded 'shout-out' that has been submitted for a company's recognition award. What two skills are mentioned?

B Choose someone you know or have heard about whose skills and abilities you respect. Note down points you would use to give this person a shout-out.

C Record your shout-out and play it to the class. Take a vote on which people in the shout-outs the class admires most.

8B Bridging the senses

GRAMMAR | uses of *will* and *would*
VOCABULARY | adjectives to describe sensations and reactions; verbs to describe reactions
PRONUNCIATION | contracted *will*

VOCABULARY

adjectives to describe sensations and reactions

1 A Answer the questions and compare with a partner. Share with the class and find the most common and the most unusual answers.

1 What are your favourite and least favourite tastes, smells, sounds and textures? Why?

2 What colours do you associate with the numbers one to eight?

B 🔊 **8.05 |** Listen to an extract from a podcast about unusual sensory reactions and answer the questions.

1 What does the speaker say about memories?

2 What examples of negative and positive stimuli does he give?

3 What is ASMR?

4 Why does the speaker mention online videos?

C 🔊 **8.05 |** The words in the box describe sensations. Write the adjective forms. One word does not need to change. Listen again and check.

> nostalgia   settle   distress
> shrill   soothe   comfort
> volunteer   tingle   hypnosis

D Work in pairs. Take turns to describe another sound or sensation for each adjective. Do you both have similar reactions?

E Learn and practise. Go to the Vocabulary Bank.

> ⏩ page 141 **VOCABULARY BANK**
> verbs to describe reactions

LISTENING

2 A Read the information about the BBC Radio programme and answer the questions.

1 What brain quirks are mentioned?

2 What other types of synaesthesia do you think there might be?

When senses merge

The brain holds many secrets and each one of us is individual in how we perceive the world. You'll have heard about how memory can play tricks on us. Sometimes these tricks are quite significant. A small number of people can remember absolutely everything they have experienced, others remember nothing. Some people can pick out faces they've only ever seen once, and there are others who have face blindness and have difficulty even remembering their own family's faces. Some people will call these quirks defects, which is not entirely fair. People live with all manner of brain quirks, often without realising that they are perceiving the world any differently from anyone else. This series looks at these 'differences' and tonight's episode is about the senses, and how they can overlap or link up in strange ways. You may have heard of synaesthesia – the most common type of which is probably where people can hear colours, but some of the ways senses overlap are even stranger!

B 🔊 **8.06 |** Listen to the first part of the programme and answer the questions.

1 What does James say about these names?
   • James • Doreen • Peter • Guy

2 What does James say about hearing and reading words?

3 What is Julia's opinion about the impact on a person of having synaesthesia?

4 How did James first become aware that he had synaesthesia?

5 Why does he mention Tottenham Court Road?

C 🔊 **8.07 |** Listen to the second part of the programme and answer the questions.

1 What evidence is there that synaesthesia is a real condition?

2 What physical problem does James experience?

D Work in pairs. What did you learn from the programme? What do you think is the most interesting point? Why?

GRAMMAR

uses of *will* and *would*

3 A Complete the sentences (1–6) with *will*, *won't* and *would* and the correct forms of the verbs in brackets.

1 I .... (guess) it's because our brains are all wired a little differently, though others may disagree.

2 I'm sure you .... (hear) that images, sounds and smells have a nostalgic effect …

3 There are, of course, plenty of sceptics who .... (insist) that this is all nonsense, but the evidence is clearly there.

4 It's quite commonplace that some people .... (wince) on hearing fingernails on a blackboard …

5 For some reason, this .... (trigger) a nasty shivery sensation when I touched it.

6 I know people who always squirm at the sound or feel of tinfoil, and just .... (not use) it.

B 🔊 **8.08** | Listen and check.

C Which of the sentences (1–6) in Ex 3A express the following?

a certainty

b typical behaviour in the present

c typical behaviour in the past

d typical behaviour that is irritating

e refusal in the present

f a way of softening a statement or making it less definite

D Tell your partner about a friend or family member who matches the information below. Give examples and reasons where possible.

- absolutely won't do something however much they are encouraged
- will always do something amusing
- will always do something irritating
- would regularly do something many years ago
- will be doing something at this moment

E Learn and practise. Go to the Grammar Bank.

▶▶ **page 134 GRAMMAR BANK**

PRONUNCIATION

4 A 🔊 **8.09** | contracted *will* | Listen to the sentences. Which speaker uses the contracted form of *will*, A or B?

B 🔊 **8.10** | Listen and repeat the sentences, focusing on the contracted sound of *will*.

1 They'll drum their fingers on the table when they're bored.

2 He'll allow you to ask anything you want.

3 You'll have seen what the teacher wrote on the whiteboard.

SPEAKING

5 A Read the questions from a survey about sensory reactions for scientific research below. Which of the questions (1–7) is each person answering?

A Yes, I always feel really nostalgic when I smell roasted vegetables, as my mum would do them every weekend. There's something really warm and comforting about that memory.

B I'll always have to leave the room when I hear someone eating an apple. All that crunching is revolting.

sensory reactions survey

1 What smells do you find extremely unpleasant?

2 Do any smells make you remember things from your childhood?

3 What sounds do you find relaxing?

4 What noises do you find hard to tolerate?

5 Are there any textures you particularly like?

6 How do you react if you see explicit scenes of operations in hospital films and dramas?

7 How well do you remember people's faces and names?

8 ....

B Work in pairs and discuss your own answers to the survey questions in Ex 5A. Write one more question to add to the survey and ask the rest of the class.

C Collate the survey results and find the most common answers.

WRITING

a description

6 A Read the title of the blog post, *The colour of sound*. Work in pairs and discuss what the book the blog post describes might be about.

B Read the blog post. Have you ever read a book where the narrator's perspective is unusual or a book that appeals to the senses? Describe it to your partner.

C What does the writer mean by 'more of a blessing than a curse'? How far do you agree?

D Match the words and phrases in bold in the blog post (1–5) with the categories (a–d). Why does the author use this type of language?

   a complex sentence structures using multiple clauses

   b interesting adjective–noun collocations

   c interesting adverb–adjective collocations

   d a sentence that uses the 'rule of three'

7 A Work in pairs and discuss a real person or a fictional character you would like to write about, and what you might include. Consider the following points:

- their current life
- background
- special gift or ability
- habits
- character

B Write your description. Try to include language to bring your description to life.

C Share with the class and choose your favourite description, giving reasons to justify your choice.

The colour of sound

I was recently first baffled, and then completely drawn in by a character in a book I was reading. Jasper is the narrator of *The Colour of Bee Larkham's Murder* and is an [1]**ingeniously conceived and beautifully crafted** individual whose complex perception of the world has been clearly carefully researched by the author, Sarah J. Harris. Young Jasper sees life in a completely different way to the majority of us and I use the word 'narrator' loosely as he does not so much 'tell' a story as reveal it in fragments. For readers it can be quite challenging (although ultimately very rewarding) to follow his journey.

Jasper is thirteen years old, having lived with his father since his mother died, and the boy has a strange neurological condition – or rather a combination of conditions. Jasper sees sounds as colours, [2]**some soothing, some unsettling and some distressing**. For example, he describes the sounds of the parakeets on the branches of the tree in his friend Bee's garden as 'deep, cornflower blue with yellow hiccups' and they give him joy. Some voices, however, are [3]**sharp colours** that will make him flinch. Another difficulty Jasper faces in his life is the fact that he has face blindness; he cannot recognise people's faces – not even his own father's. To identify people Jasper picks up on the colours of their voices ('toothpaste white', 'cobalt blue') and other associated sounds. He'll see the colour of a dog barking and link that to the person he associates with that dog. Jasper also likes order in his life. He records things he experiences in sets of folders and anyone touching them or putting them out of order will [4]**trigger a ferocious reaction**.

[5]**In the novel Jasper needs to step outside his comfort zone and engage more actively with strangers when his friend Bee Larkham disappears, which pushes his father's patience to the limits**. But despite the predicament Jasper finds himself in, the boy never indulges in self-pity, just an understandable irritation that others won't try to understand what he is saying. And when we leave the world of Jasper's colours, it is with an element of regret that his world is indeed strange but beautiful, and his condition is perhaps more of a blessing than a curse. Maybe we all need some more colour in our lives?

Have you read about a character with an unusual ability or gift? Or perhaps you know (or know of) someone like Jasper in real life. Post a description here. I'd love to read about them.

8C Feeling good

HOW TO ... | explain the purpose and benefit of something
VOCABULARY | well-being
PRONUNCIATION | intonation in sentences containing contrasting ideas

VOCABULARY

well-being

1 A Work in pairs and look at the photos. Discuss the questions.

1 Why might these activities be good for us?
2 Do you do any activities like these? Why/Why not?

B Read the article and check your ideas for question 1 in Ex 1A. Which idea do you find most interesting? Why?

C Replace the phrases in bold in the questions (1–8) with the correct form of the collocations in bold from the article.

1 Do you **tell people about your feelings** if you're having problems?
2 How important is it to **set aside moments to relax**?
3 What do you do to **remain happy** if you're feeling low?
4 Do you ever need to eat well to **make up for unhealthy eating**?
5 What might be good exercise for **making your neck muscles more relaxed**?
6 What do you drink or eat first thing to **start your brain working**?
7 Can **making ourselves think optimistically** help our sense of well-being?
8 What practical things can we do to **make ourselves calmer**?

D Work in pairs and ask and answer the questions in Ex 1C.

How to get healthy?
It's not what you might expect.

Maintaining a healthy body and mind is a major concern for most people today. There are numerous studies about what types of exercise we should or should not incorporate into our daily routine and what to eat in order to **offset food indulgences**. There is a vast amount of both solicited and unsolicited advice – particularly online – on how to restore our peace of mind and **alleviate symptoms of stress**. However, keeping healthy and combatting depression is not all about physical exertion or meditation, or even just **taking time to unwind**. There are some activities that we already engage in that are naturally good for us, and we probably don't even know we're doing them. Read on and you may be able to bin the self-help books!

Fidgeting Do you sometimes find yourself tapping your feet, clicking your pen, jiggling your knees or doodling while you should be focusing on the task at hand? Apparently, as long as your fidgeting is not causing a distraction for others, it can actually improve concentration. Many repetitive actions – like clicking a pen – can **kick-start our brains** and help us think. In addition to this, it is the body's natural way of regulating weight by burning calories while we're sedentary, and activities like knitting and pottery can help **loosen muscles** and joints and overcome chronic pain. So, twiddle away – that is unless you get so engrossed in the doodle that the doodle itself becomes more interesting than the task you're endeavouring to complete!

Laughing As well as oiling the wheels of social interaction, laughter has real health benefits, both physically and mentally. A good, full-on, laugh-out-loud belly laugh, or a few moments of contagious giggles can give the ribs a good workout. And just as running can increase the endorphins in the brain, laughing can do something similar. It can **foster a positive outlook** and encourage us to **keep our spirits up** if we're feeling bad. There is a potential downside. Too much laughing can put a lot of pressure on the heart and lungs, and throughout history there have been stories of people who quite literally died laughing. However, this is extremely rare, so you're quite safe if you want to simply have a laugh and get some excellent exercise.

Talking to yourself How odd does that sound? Talk to yourself? It has been shown that talking out loud to ourselves (probably when there's no one else around) is very good for us. It slows down our thoughts and helps us process them in a different way. When we feel that our thoughts are bombarding us, just speaking them aloud on purpose helps us to deliberate carefully, reducing stress levels and clarifying problems. Opening up in this way to ourselves can be almost as good as **opening up to others**.

How to …
explain the purpose and benefit of something

2 A 🔊 **8.11 | Listen to an extract from a radio programme. What do the two guests say they like about the following?**

1 hot yoga   **2** singing in a choir

B 🔊 **8.11 | Listen again and complete the phrases used in the programme.**

1 The _____ is that you …

2 Another real _____ about …

3 And _____ at all the benefits, of course …

4 I think a big _____ for me is …

5 … that's what I _____ out of …

6 You've only _____ to look at …

7 … it's just _____ in so many ways.

8 It's not that we're all great singers, it's _____ we love singing together.

C Work alone and write down at least three things you do to relieve stress in your daily life and how these benefit you.

D Work in small groups. Use phrases from Ex 2B to explain the purpose and benefits of your ideas. Try to agree on the three most convincing ideas.

E Learn and practise. Go to the Grammar Bank.

⏩ **page 135 GRAMMAR BANK**

PRONUNCIATION

3 A 🔊 **8.12 | intonation in sentences containing contrasting ideas | Listen to the sentences (1–4). How does the intonation help to reinforce the ideas in the sentences?**

1 It's not that yoga is bad for you, it's just that lots of people find it dull.

2 It's not about meeting people, it's just about being away from the office for a while.

3 The point isn't to make people work harder, the point is to help them feel more relaxed.

4 It's not about forcing people to change diets, it's about making them more aware of what they're eating.

B 🔊 **8.12 | Listen and repeat the sentences.**

SPEAKING

4 A Read the ideas about how a college can help create a healthier study environment for students. Choose three that you think would be the most effective. Add one or two more ideas of your own.

10 Steps towards a healthier study environment

1 Teach exercises students can do while studying at their desks.

2 Make sure students have access to fresh fruit during the day.

3 Allow time for compulsory walk-around breaks every hour.

4 Offer a vegetarian lunch option at the college canteen, and price it below the meat options.

5 Arrange social outings once a month.

6 Remove high-calorie food, like doughnuts, from the vending machines.

7 Give awards as incentives for achieving fitness goals.

8 Organise counselling sessions for students who have problems.

9 Provide good lighting and non-glare computer screens.

10 Install ergonomic desks and chairs to minimise back and muscle problems.

B Read the Future Skills box. Then think about the ideas you selected in Ex 4A and how you can justify your choices concisely.

FUTURE SKILLS
Goal setting: time management

In order to make decisions effectively, it is often important to make efficient use of the time available and impose a time limit for discussion. This means you should make more concise contributions and avoid prolonged input that wastes time.

C Work in groups. Discuss your ideas and agree on five ideas to action.

MEDIATION SKILLS
keeping the conversation on track tactfully

make a decision as a group

⏩ **page 158 MEDIATION BANK**

8D BBC Entertainment
Effects and illusions

VOCABULARY | thoughts and ideas
SPEAKING | describing psychological effects
WRITING | a story about strange effects

PREVIEW

1 A Work in pairs. Discuss which of the following things you've experienced. Why do you think they happen?

1 learning a new word and then suddenly hearing it everywhere
2 checking the time every day at the exact same time
3 hearing a word at exactly the same time as reading it

B Read the programme information. What illusions and psychological effects do you know about?

QI

QI is a popular comedy panel quiz show in the UK. The letters QI stand for 'Quite Interesting' and the idea is that the panellists' responses to obscure questions are interesting or amusing. In this clip Stephen Fry, the host, asks about certain psychological effects: the IKEA Effect, the Rhyme-as-reason Effect and the Frequency Illusion.

VIEW

2 A ▶ Watch the BBC video clip. In your own words, briefly describe what the psychological effects are (1–3).

1 the IKEA Effect
2 the Rhyme-as-reason Effect
3 the Frequency Illusion

B ▶ Watch the video again and answer the questions.

1 What does Sarah initially think the IKEA Effect is?
2 How does Stephen make it easier to understand the IKEA Effect?
3 Which phrase does Josh use to first illustrate the Rhyme-as-reason Effect?
4 Why, according to Stephen, does rhyme have power?
5 How does Josh exemplify the Frequency Illusion with reference to *Pointless*, another game show?
6 How does Stephen define a 'cognitive bias'?

3 A Match the saying beginnings (1–3) with the endings (a–c) to form rhymes that were mentioned on the show. What do they mean?

1 In it
2 An apple a day
3 Red sky at night

a keeps the doctor away.
b shepherd's delight.
c to win it.

B Work in pairs and discuss the questions.

1 What phrases from your own language do you know that give advice in a rhyme?
2 Would you agree that people see them as truer than a more complex phrase?

B B C

describing psychological effects

5 A Work in pairs and join another pair. Pair A: Go to page 142 and read about two effects. Pair B: Go to page 143 and read about two different effects. Think about how you can summarise the effects in your own words.

B Invent a new effect or illusion with you partner. Make notes about:

- what to call it (be imaginative!).
- what this effect or illusion is about.
- examples to support the effect or illusion.

C Present your three effects to the other pair. Take turns to summarise the two real effects from Ex 5A in your own words alongside your invented one from Ex 5B. The other pair must guess which effect has been invented. Use the Key phrases to help you.

KEY PHRASES

You know, that sounds quite credible …

I can imagine that being true …

Although it appears convincing, do you really think anyone would …

That is just too way out! But then again, …

That one has got to be the made-up one. It sounds incredible – funny, but incredible …

I think there's an element of truth in that … I've known people to …

D Share your invented effects with the rest of the class and decide which of them is the most plausible.

VOCABULARY

thoughts and ideas

4 A Read the extracts from the video. Match the phrases in bold (1–5) with their meanings (a–e).

1 … this week I shall be **messing with** your minds.
2 … to another group of people you **put** the same sentiment that doesn't rhyme …
3 … you're more likely **to pass it on to** someone else …
4 … and now it keeps **cropping up** everywhere.
5 … they **push you into a way of thinking** …

a communicate something
b encourage/force someone to think or do something
c play tricks with
d suggest
e appearing

B Work in pairs. Tell your partner about:

1 something that happened to you that pushed you into a different way of thinking.
2 an idea you love so much that you'll pass it on to anyone who will listen.
3 an idea which when you learnt about it totally messed with your mind.
4 an interesting idea someone put to you recently.
5 something that crops up in your life more often than it logically should.

WRITING

a story about strange effects

6 A You are going to write a short story based on a strange effect that someone experiences. Work in pairs. Discuss what life would be like if:

- you knew what everyone was going to say ten seconds before they said it.
- you could communicate with other people through their dreams.
- you could command any animal to follow instructions.
- you could tell how people you care for were feeling, even when you were not with them.

B Write a story about strange effects. Go to the Writing Bank.

▶▶ page 111 **WRITING BANK**

GRAMMAR

noun phrases

1 Underline the noun phrases in the anecdote. Match them with the descriptions (a–f).

> The forest was always beautiful at this time of year. If I needed a place to go and relax and feel calm, it was perfect. This morning, I saw something a little unusual. A baby deer stepped out into a clearing in front of me and stood a few metres away gazing at me in surprise. It was an amazingly beautiful moment, but it lasted only a matter of seconds before the deer took off into the forest again. Anyone who experiences this kind of moment is truly lucky.

a a noun + infinitive

b a noun used as an adjective to form a compound noun

c an adverb and adjective following a noun

d a prepositional phrase

e a relative clause functioning as a noun

f an adverb and adjective before a noun

2 A Rewrite the sentences using noun phrases to shorten them.

1 Children whose parents are not accompanying them are not allowed into this section of the museum.

2 My sister goes running for fifteen minutes every morning and evening.

3 People with tablets that they have to take before and after meals should swallow them with a glass of water.

4 I've just read an article about how we remember recent events that interested me considerably.

5 I talked to a doctor yesterday and he told me that I needed to do more exercise.

6 T'ai Chi, which is a martial art that is traditional, has a following that is worldwide.

B Work in pairs. Compare your answers to Ex 2A.

uses of *will* and *would*

3 Look at the phrases in bold and select the correct function of *will* or *would* (a or b).

1 Whenever he has time, he**'ll come** and visit me.
  a habit   **b** future action

2 I**'ll be gone** by the time you get home today.
  a habit   **b** future action

3 I asked him several times but he just **wouldn't do it** for me.
  a past habit   **b** past refusal

4 You**'ll have heard** the name Dave Whitmore before.
  a future action   **b** certainty

5 Don't call at five. I **won't have finished** by then.
  a future action   **b** certainty

6 He usually **won't answer the phone** if he's feeling lazy.
  a future action   **b** present refusal

7 He **would come** if he had time.
  a conditional behaviour   **b** present habit

8 I**'d always wait** at my window for my father to come home from work.
  a conditional behaviour   **b** past habit

4 Rewrite the sentences using *will* or *would*.

1 When she was young, my sister had the annoying habit of smelling everything before she ate it.
When she was young, my sister would smell everything before she ate it.

2 Some people refuse to accept the fact that being in physically good shape helps our mental state, too.

3 I'm sure you've read about recent policies regarding mental health issues.

4 In the past my father refused to listen to doctors' advice if he didn't like it.

5 My grandmother often cooked greasy fried eggs when we stayed with her, and this used to make me feel nauseous.

6 I know my brother well. He's undoubtedly learnt new vocab at school today, so now he's memorising it all!

7 It irritates me how many people refuse to consider their mental health important.

8 Dave always follows the same route on his morning run. He turns right at the gate and runs to the crossing. Then he crosses the road to the park, runs down to the lake and round it five times before returning the same way.

VOCABULARY

5A Choose the correct options (A, B or C) to complete the extract from a job description.

We are looking for someone to join the team with a strong ¹............ for website design and who is willing to get to ²............ with complex problems. The successful candidate will show ³............ and determination in developing a project, with a particular ⁴............ for drawing the best out of fellow team members. At times they will be required to step outside their comfort ⁵............ and find different ways to ⁶............ setbacks.

1 A ability	**B** aptitude	**C** skill
2 A grips	**B** handles	**C** problems
3 A speed	**B** drive	**C** attack
4 A knack	**B** habit	**C** capacity
5 A area	**B** zone	**C** place
6 A solve	**B** overcome	**C** answer

B Which aspects of this job description would suit you? Tell your partner.

6A Complete the statements with the correct adjectives in the box. There are two adjectives you do not need.

distressing   hypnotic   involuntary   nostalgic
shrill   soothing   tingling   unsettling

1 I just flinch whenever I hear a car horn – it's a(n) .... reaction.
2 I detest the .... sound of a dentist's drill – I would guess I'm not alone!
3 I find classical music really .... so I always put some on if I'm a bit stressed.
4 When I feel .... I put on music from my student days and remember some great times.
5 Some songs are very moving, and I often get a .... sensation at the back of my neck when I listen to them.
6 I don't enjoy scary movies that make you jump. I even find the music ....

B Work in pairs. How far do you agree with the statements in Ex 6A?

7 Complete the second sentence so that it has the same meaning as the first sentence, using the word given. Use between four and six words.

1 It's important to warm up for five minutes before vigorous exercise. DO
It's important to .... before vigorous exercise.

2 Kim can imitate the voices of famous people very well, which is unusual. RARE
Kim has .... the voices of famous people.

3 If a violin is badly played, the sound makes me shudder. SETS
The sound of a violin being badly played ....

4 When a choir of young children sing folk songs, it can be quite moving. BY
Folk songs .... young children can be quite moving.

5 Managers should encourage their staff to think positively. FOSTER
It's up to managers to .... among their staff.

6 If I have several late nights, I sleep in at the weekend to catch up. OFFSET
At the weekend I sometimes have a lie in ....

7 We would often sing in order to prevent ourselves from getting sad. SPIRITS
We would often sing in order to ....

8 I'm sure this isn't the first time you've heard this speech. WILL
I'm sure .... this speech before.

9 It took me a long time to understand the new software we were asked to use. GRIPS
It took me a long time to .... the new software we were asked to use.

10 He refused to give me the name of the successful candidate. WOULDN'T
He .... of the successful candidate.

1D a nomination for an award

1 A Read a nomination for the 'Most Appreciated Teacher' award. What is the main topic of each paragraph?

I am pleased to nominate Ms Gina Daniels for consideration for this year's 'Most Appreciated Teacher' award.

I've never had a history teacher like Ms Daniels before. I love the way she brings events from hundreds of years ago to life, and she has a real talent for making complicated aspects of the subject much more accessible. What's very clear is how much passion she has for the subject. It isn't just a job for her – it's a calling, and it shows.

Aside from her expertise in her subject area, Ms Daniels goes above and beyond in the way that she supports students with non-academic matters and helps them look at issues from different perspectives. I have had the good fortune to have Ms Daniels as my form tutor this year and have received the benefit of her advice on multiple occasions. On one occasion, she was quick to offer support when she could see that I was struggling with my workload and she was able to offer me some practical solutions to my problems. On another, she took the time to talk me through some of my options for the coming academic year.

To sum up, both her expertise in the classroom and her kindness outside of it make Ms Daniels an excellent candidate for this award.

B Think of a teacher you admire now or admired in the past. Look at the description in Ex 1A again and underline phrases that might help you write a description of that teacher.

C Write your nomination for 'Most Appreciated Teacher' using your ideas from Ex 1B.

D Work in small groups and share your nominations. Have a vote on which teacher should win the award.

2B an informative summary

1 A Read the blog post (Text A) and the advertisement (Text B) and make notes for questions 1–4 from Ex 8A on page 25.

A

Posted by Felix M | 05 July

You've probably seen me in the corner of your screen moving my hands in strange ways and exaggerating my expressions! Sometimes I'm there during the morning news, sometimes during interviews, sometimes you can turn me off – and sometimes you can't! I'm an 'In-Vision Signer' and I must tell you that it's a long way from being an easy job – it's demanding, requires thinking on your feet, and is at times physically draining and exhausting. But the rewards are abundant. I think I'm very lucky. So, to give you an idea of the variety of my day ...

Early morning

Up at the crack of dawn to sign the news. This is where I really need to be on the ball because it's live and I have to be prepared for anything to happen. I have to dress appropriately for each type of programme I'm signing for, and my overall demeanour must reflect that, too. The news requires me to look professional and business-like. My job is to convey the information – not my own attitude, so I have to be careful of that, too. However, I do need to reflect the attitude or emotion of the person speaking, so factor that in too, which is tricky!

Late morning

A break, and then I'm recording the signing for a detective series. This is different. I've had time to watch the programme and prepare. I know how the plot line will develop and I know how I'm going to approach it. For this signing I go into 'actor' mode and get ready to change character all the time.

Afternoon

After lunch now, and it's a children's programme. Yet again, I have to switch modes and project a cheerful, happy personality to match the content and jokes (which is sometimes VERY hard) and there's a lightness to my behaviour. These are fun programmes but again, exhausting.

Late afternoon

That's me done for the day – at least my paid work. I also run a free evening class, teaching sign language to hearing-impaired adults. It's great to see how their eyes light up when they communicate with their hands properly for the first time!

B

Searchlight Agency

We are an agency that provides a range of interpreting services for the hearing-impaired, and we are always looking out for new talent, as our range of services continues to expand.

We currently have opportunities for trained professionals to work in several roles. They include:

- signing live and face-to-face at interviews, in meetings, at lectures/presentations.
- signing online and on-screen for business and educational purposes.
- 'In-vision' signing for TV programmes, live or recorded.
- entertainment: live signing in theatres, or recorded for films.

Requirements:

ability to sign simultaneously at speed, be fully proficient in English and BSL (British Sign Language), have an extremely wide vocabulary covering many different areas, including technology and culture.

Contact us at:

searchlightagencyonline.com

B 🔊 **WB2.01 | Listen to the podcast and add to your notes for questions 1–4 in Ex 8A on page 25.**

C Work in pairs and compare the notes you have made. What kind of information have you left out?

2 A Read the pieces of advice (1–4) about synthesising information precisely. Which advice do you think is most important?

1 Work from your notes, without referring back to the original unless really necessary.

2 Include the salient points only, omitting specific examples.

3 Let the questions focus you and remember that you are providing objective information not personal anecdotes.

4 Use a semi-formal style, structure the information into clear paragraphs and use a variety of phrases to link the information and help the language flow.

5 Remember your audience. Check your first draft. Will the reader be well informed?

B Use your notes from Ex 1A and Ex 1B to write your informative summary.

C Work in pairs. Compare your summaries to see how similar or different they are.

2D a blog post about a food hotspot

1 A Read the blog post. Which of the topics below does the author include?

- the history of the area
- what it offers
- problems in the area
- the atmosphere
- their favourite thing about it
- how to get there

💬 6   🔁 12   ♡ 1   ✉

So, let me take you to my favourite area to eat. We're walking down this uneven cobbled street, and it's all just an assault on the senses – shouts from people **on all sides** demanding that we eat at their place, the intriguing smell of exotic herbs and spices and the steam from kitchens **emanating from** every other window. It's **chaotic**, but it's such a **buzzing** atmosphere that you can't help but feel that extra bit alive. Where are we? We're in Brick Lane, East London.

Brick Lane offers an **array** of treats for exhausted Londoners, from the bagel spots selling their trademark **melt-in-your-mouth** bread topped with cream cheese or salt-beef to its **renowned** curry restaurants.

The rise of Brick Lane is very much a product of immigration from South Asia, and especially Bangladesh. The area has **surged** in popularity over the years and is now a deserved spot on a London tourist's to-do list. Visiting Brick Lane is not just visiting a **foodie hotspot**, however, but also stepping into a **vibrant** East London community.

What do I love about it the most? Well, probably a post-work curry after a **gruelling** day in the office, with Garlic Chilli Chicken **a must**. The cosy tables and the **punchy** flavours combine to work their magic, and you can lose yourself for a marvellous hour, watching the local community going about its business.

So, what are you waiting for? Give it a shot.

B Match the descriptive words and phrases in bold in Ex 1A with the words and phrases (1–12).

1 strong		**7** coming from	
2 difficult and long		**8** famous	
3 lively (x2)		**9** grown quickly	
4 range		**10** taste delicious/soften in your mouth	
5 disorganised		**11** a place food lovers like	
6 everywhere		**12** something essential	

C Think of an area you have enjoyed visiting to eat out. Make notes about:

- the atmosphere.
- what food it offers.
- the history of the area.
- your favourite thing about it.
- any interesting words/phrases you could use to describe the area.

D Write a short blog post about the area. Use your notes and the vocabulary from Ex 1B to help you.

3A a cover email/letter

1A Read the job advert. What do you think a cover email for this job should include?

Graphic Designer

SBI International
Midhampton MH51 2XP
remote

- degree in graphic design
- experience (at least three years preferred)
- interest in campaign projects
- flexibility and ability to meet deadlines
- good interpersonal skills to deal with clients
- job type: full-time, permanent
- Send examples of work with CV and covering email to …

B Read the cover email and check your ideas. Would you be impressed by the cover email? Why/Why not?

Dear Mr Turner,

I am writing to apply for the position of graphic designer advertised on the SBI company website. I was excited to discover this opening as SBI International has an excellent reputation in the industry, and I have been particularly impressed by your recent online anti-hacking campaign.

Aspects of my background which I consider relevant include the following:

- In my three years as a freelance designer I have been involved in projects very similar to the anti-hacking campaign.
- I have extensive experience working with key design programs.
- My freelance experience has taught me to adapt to the demands of different project types essential for a graphic designer in a corporate context.

I have a flexible working style and am accustomed to working under pressure and to tight deadlines. I am a good team player, with excellent communication skills and the majority of my freelance projects have involved working with a group of designers. I am passionate about my career and see myself working long-term with a company. I consider SBI to be an ideal context for me to showcase my best work and to develop further as a professional in the field. I feel my expertise, initiative and enthusiasm would be a real asset to your company.

As requested, I am attaching my CV, which includes further details and contact information for three references.

I would be grateful for the opportunity to discuss my application with you and to explore my suitability for the position you have advertised. Please contact me at your convenience. Thank you for your consideration.

Kind regards,

C Read the checklist. Find examples in the cover email of the points mentioned.

Style
The writer has:
1 avoided contractions and colloquial language.
2 used formal verbs and expressions.
3 used standard, polite opening and closing phrases.

Content and organisation
The writer has:
4 clearly outlined why they are writing.
5 referred to their suitability for the position.
6 given an outline of their hard and soft skills.
7 included and referred to attachments and given contact information.

D Read these sentences from other cover emails. Rewrite the sentences using more appropriate language.
1 I loved your ad campaign last year.
2 Here are some things I've done that you might like.
3 I've got lots of experience working in marketing.
4 I love what I do.
5 I think your company could really use me.
6 Please let me know if you'd like me to come for interview.

2 Work in pairs. Tell your partner about a job you would really like to do. Write a job advert for your partner's choice of job. Exchange adverts and write a cover email.

OR

Work alone. Write an advert for a job you would really like to do. Then write the cover email to apply for the job.

Think about:
- the job.
- the role.
- skills and experience.

3D a report on work experience

1A Read a report on a student's experience of holiday employment for the website. Has the writer covered the points requested in Ex 6A on page 41? If so, where?

The job and my expectations

The work experience I'd like to write about sounds incredibly exciting, but in fact it was far from it. During the summer break between the first and second years of my university degree, I had a job on a cruise liner sailing around the Mediterranean Sea. I was studying languages, loved travelling and thought it was way more exotic than the hotel or shop assistant jobs that my friends had **opted for**. I thought I'd **get a lot out of it** – a holiday job that was a real holiday. How wrong was I?

The reality of the experience

I realised my mistake after the first full day on the job. I was a waiter in the ship's restaurant and was expected to **be on my feet for hours on end**. By the end of the day, I was exhausted, my feet ached and I hadn't managed to **squeeze in** any time to eat. I had **no real grounding** in the skills of serving large numbers of people simultaneously and I was on the receiving end of more complaints than compliments. My disappointment and distress were **compounded by the fact** that I didn't have any freedom to enjoy the sun, visit the ports we called at or do any shopping, and **to top it all off**, I suffered from constant seasickness.

My advice

There are many good work experiences out there for students, but I would most definitely advise against taking on something without properly **thinking it through**. I **paid the price** for not doing that. Yes, my waiting skills did improve, but I still wish – how I wish! – that I had stayed on dry land.

B Match the phrases in bold in the report with their synonyms (1–9).

1 considering something carefully
2 no basic experience or knowledge
3 chosen
4 not take a break for a long time
5 do something in a short time
6 intensified or made worse by something
7 suffered
8 in addition to all the other things
9 receive something useful from the experience

2A Work in pairs. Choose a job to write a report on and discuss what you might include. Consider:
- your expectations before starting the work.
- the working conditions (income, hours, etc.).
- the skills required.
- the work culture/teamwork.
- the overall value of the experience.

B Write your report. Share your report with the class and agree on the best three to be posted on the website.

4D an opinion essay

1 Look at the sentences (1–8) and decide which section of an essay they might belong to (a–c).

a Introduction
b Discussing opposing points of view
c Conclusion: your stance on the issue

1 The loss of plant life is **an issue which has been hotly debated in recent years**.
2 **While some people see** extinction **as** a natural thing, **others argue** that it is happening at an unprecedented rate.
3 **Recently, we've been experiencing a growing number of** negative effects of climate change.
4 **In the end, there will simply be** no need to decide what to do because the decision will have already been taken for us.
5 **In contrast to this view,** others may believe that we need to prioritise the success of our species over all others.
6 **To what extent should we** allow this damage to our flora and fauna to continue?
7 **Some might say that** there is absolutely nothing we can do to prevent the situation from occurring, **while others take the view** that there is plenty which can still be done.
8 **Whatever we do, we need to ensure that** we don't leave our children in a worse position than they already are.

2 Think about the essay question on page 53. Make some notes using the language from Ex 1 to help you.

1 General facts you could give on the topic
- .... is an issue which has been hotly debated in recent years.
- Recently, we've been experiencing a growing number of ....
- ....

2 Questions you could ask your reader
- To what extent should we .... ?
- .... ?

3 Contrasting opinions that people might have
- While some people see .... as ...., others argue ....
- In contrast to this view, ...
- Some might say that .... while others take the view ....
- ....

4 Conclusions and calls to action you might make
- Whatever we do, we need to ....
- In the end, there will simply be ....
- ....

3 Write your essay in response to the question on page 53. Use your notes from Ex 2 to help you.

5D a contribution for a website

1 Read a contribution for a website about footballer Marcus Rashford. In what ways has he contributed to society outside of his profession?

Marcus Rashford is a superb football player, and he plays for one of the most successful teams in the world, Manchester United, but this is not the limit of his achievements. Alongside his busy sporting career, he has also found the time to do a lot of work for charity, which I find incredibly impressive. The list of the different organisations Marcus has helped is long. It includes support for a charity providing services for young people experiencing homelessness, which encouraged people to prepare boxes full of essential items that homeless people might require. Marcus personally delivered 300 of these boxes, which is an extraordinary act for a man with so much on his plate.

Among the other good causes Marcus has supported have been campaigns for the British National Health Service. He also ran a campaign to protest against the removal of free school dinners from students from low-income households, which was effective in preventing the government from trying to take away this vital service not once but twice. Marcus Rashford is still young, but he has achieved so much and is a great role model not just for young people who want to play sports, but those who want to change the world for the better, too.

2 A Look at the sentences from the contribution (1–4). Decide what 'which' is referring to in each case (a or b). Use the contribution in Ex 1 to help you.

1 … which I find incredibly impressive.
  a the charity
  b the fact that Marcus has found time to do it

2 … which encouraged people to prepare boxes full of essential items that homeless people might require.
  a the charity
  b the fact that Marcus supported it

3 … which is an extraordinary act for a man with so much on his plate.
  a the boxes
  b the fact that he delivered so many

4 … which was effective in preventing the government from trying to take away this vital service not once but twice.
  a the campaign
  b the fact that he was involved

B Look at the clauses in Ex 2A again. Which of them:
  a provides a comment about the whole of the first part of the sentence?
  b refers to something specific in the first part of the sentence?

C Match the sentence beginnings (1–4) with the endings (a–d).

1 She ran a full marathon,
2 They gave the money away,
3 Most people had ignored her,
4 He failed repeatedly,

a which, rather than making him give up, made him stronger.
b which is sadly all too easy to believe.
c which is impressive for someone who only started exercising six months ago.
d which was an extraordinary act of generosity.

3 A Write your contribution to the website about the person you chose in Ex 5C on page 65. Try to include clauses with 'which' to add comments about what this person has achieved.

B Share your contribution with the class. Vote on which celebrity is most admired.

6A a review

1 A Read a review of a recent film. Why might people want to watch it?

29 Jan | Movies

>

Hidden Figures ★★★★

Did it slip under your radar?

So, you think you know all about the Apollo space missions in the 1960s? There have certainly been enough photos, footage and interviews about them over the decades. But the truth is, you probably don't know the full story about the people who made it happen. An excellent film released in 2016 puts matters right, and, inexplicably, it appears to have passed a lot of people by. I aim to correct that!

Aptly named *Hidden Figures*, the film puts the spotlight on three highly intelligent women, Katherine Johnson, Dorothy Vaughan and Mary Jackson, who worked for NASA on the U.S. space programme in the 1960s. Katherine was a real genius, with an amazing talent for maths, evident at a very early age, who went on to perform the calculations that made the manned space missions of the time possible (notably the moon landing). Dorothy Vaughan, also a mathematician, was an expert in NASA's programming code, heading up the computing department and working with Katherine on vital calculations. Mary Jackson, another fiercely intelligent woman, became NASA's first black female engineer in 1958, assisting in the development of the space programme. Three gifted women, who succeeded in spite of a total lack of encouragement from the space industry because of their gender and colour, and who had to wait decades for their contributions to space exploration to be recognised.

The film follows the struggles of the women with warmth, humour, disbelief and admiration, and we are shown just how difficult it was for talented black women at that time to succeed and be recognised for their achievements. However, it is not only the story that is fascinating. As well as being informative and thought-provoking, *Hidden Figures* showcases some brilliant acting talent and with an excellent script and clever directing, it engages our attention throughout. If, like the women themselves, this film slipped under your radar, it is well worth tracking down and watching. It is an education.

B Look at a list of points to consider when writing a film or book review. Find examples of each in the review.

A good review should …
1 have an engaging introduction that interests the reader from the start.
2 include some interesting information about the story.
3 involve the reader through direct and rhetorical questions.
4 use semi-formal language to keep the review light and maintain interest.
5 use clear paragraphing to structure the review and guide the reader.
6 use a variety of adjectives and modifiers.
7 finish with a summary and a reason for watching.

C You are going to write a review of a film or book you have recently seen/ read. Either choose one that you discussed in Ex 4B on page 70 or choose another. Make notes, plan and write your review.

D Share your review with the class. Which reviews were the most persuasive?

6D an account of an exhibition

1 A Read the account of an exhibition for the website. Would you have liked to go to this exhibition? Why/Why not?

I missed Alice

It's my biggest regret of last year. I didn't make it to the **awesome** *Alice in Wonderland* exhibition in the Victoria and Albert Museum. And by all accounts, it was an experience like no other, inspiring rave reviews with comments and photos shared across all social media platforms. I saw them. I read them and I wept in frustration (well, not literally, but you know what I mean). For someone who has had a lifetime fascination with the *Alice* books it is almost **incomprehensible** that I should have missed the opportunity. I blame it on my workload, my lack of planning and on my tendency to procrastinate. 'I'll go next month,' I said. And next month came and went. And so did Alice.

The exhibition was aptly named 'Curiouser and curiouser', a line of Alice's in the first book. Alice's adventures took her down a rabbit hole into a **surreal** world, and the designers of this exhibition appear to have done the same for the visitors. Photographs show **dazzling** sets linked by psychedelic corridors and halls of mirrors. The reviews speak of **impressive** video projections, sound effects, even a **mind-blowing** VR experience where visitors can play the **absurd** croquet game in *Alice*.

To put it plainly, I am really put out that I missed an experience described as **stupendous**, **enthralling**, **mesmerising** and a complete 'visual joy'. No matter how often I browse the image galleries of the exhibition, it cannot make up for the feeling that I missed out on something very special indeed. If you get wind of a pop-up exhibition of interest to you coming to your locality, be advised – don't put it off.

B Work in pairs. Use the adjectives in bold in the account in Ex 1A to describe something you have experienced recently.

2 A Think about an exhibition (real or imaginary) that you either missed, went to or would like to see. Plan what you would include in a written account of it, including:
- what encouraged you to go/what prevented you from going.
- a description of the exhibition.
- why it was special.
- how you felt about experiencing the exhibition/ missing out on the exhibition.

B Write your account of the exhibition. Share your account with the class. Which of the exhibitions would most people like to see?

7D a newspaper opinion piece

1 A Read an opinion on a different topic for the same newspaper. How does the writer:
1 consider both sides of the question?
2 give their own view with justifications?
3 expand on their opinion?

Should the age for learning to drive remain at 17 in the UK?

1 A tricky question to answer, and I know there are strong opinions on both sides. Broadly speaking, older people back the age remaining as it is. However, there are many younger people who feel that they would be perfectly good drivers at sixteen. Although I'm older, I think lowering the age to sixteen might not be a bad idea.

2 The reasons given for keeping the age at seventeen, or even raising it to eighteen, are usually that younger people are more reckless on the roads, that they do not concentrate enough and are easily distracted. To counter that, I'd like to point out that the statistics do not support this view. In fact, younger drivers are among the most disciplined and considerate drivers on the roads. We should also bear in mind there are drivers of all ages who are overconfident and drive dangerously.

3 Much depends on the quality of the teaching and the type of testing used, as well as the limitations on new drivers who have just passed their tests. I would advocate limiting the number of passengers allowed in a new driver's car – and that is for ALL age groups – for a defined period. I would also advocate the introduction of regular driving assessments for all drivers, to correct bad habits and promote continued awareness of rules of the road. In addition to this, I would like to see repeat driving tests brought in for older drivers, who often become complacent.

4 Let's allow younger drivers on the road, but also ensure driving is a skill that is continually assessed, so that our roads are safe for all.

B Match phrases in the text with the definitions (1–7).
1 firm views for and against (para 1)
2 in general (para 1)
3 support (a point of view) (para 1)
4 give an opposing point of view (para 2)
5 there is no evidence for this opinion (para 2)
6 consider (para 2)
7 I recommend (para 3)

C Write your opinion piece in response to the request in Ex 5A on page 89. Use phrases from Ex 1B.

8D a story about strange effects

1 A Quickly read the short story. What unusual effect did the writer experience?

B Work in pairs. Discuss how you think the story might end, and what lessons the writer might learn about the strange power he possesses.

C Look at the story again. What words and phrases does the author use to communicate:

1 that they are surprised?

2 that something is strange?

2 A Choose one of the effects from Ex 6A on page 101. Make notes about the following:

1 how you might discover that you suddenly have this ability.

2 how you would check that you truly have the ability.

3 what you might use the ability for.

4 what life lessons having the ability might teach you.

B Write a short story about discovering the strange effect and what you would do next.

On the first day it happened, I was really taken aback. I'd fallen asleep as usual and was dreaming I was at work. Which was nothing out of the ordinary for me, I often had work dreams, but the bizarre thing was how much control I had over what was happening. To my surprise, I was able to direct myself around the office, and having hunted down Billy, who always annoys me with his loud voice, I was able to explain to him very lucidly that he should try and keep his voice down. I woke up feeling refreshed and invigorated. If that wasn't odd enough, what followed was even odder. I got to work the next day and while wandering around the office I came across Billy, who was barking into the phone as usual. Upon noticing me, however, he shot me a very disturbed look and instantly lowered his voice. As I made my way back to my desk, I scratched my head and tried to work out whether what I'd just experienced was real or not. Had he really just lowered his voice in response to seeing me? Had what I dreamt actually had an effect on the real world? I shook my head in disbelief and went back to my office duties, thinking to myself 'just a trick of the mind'.

As I climbed into bed, I'd completely forgotten about the weird affair with Billy, so imagine my surprise when I started to dream that I was once again back in my office, and once again able to move round it under my own control. I passed Billy, who was now doing everything at a reasonable volume, and after passing him I caught the eye of Claire. Claire, ah lovely Claire! If I weren't such a coward, I'd have told her long ago that I liked her, and maybe here in the safety of my dream I could finally tell her my true feelings. I approached her and she turned to look at me. All of a sudden, I blurted out how I felt about her, how long I'd liked her, and she responded with, well ... silence. Seconds passed, which felt like decades, and then she finally looked at me and to my horror said the words nobody wants to hear: 'That's nice, Bernard, but I think we're better as friends.'

I woke up in a cold sweat and immediately my mind started racing. Two nights in a row of controlling my dreams; it was far less likely to be a coincidence. Was I really able to control my dreams and communicate with people? And if so, what awaited me when I reached the office in the morning and saw Claire?

GRAMMAR BANK

1A conditional forms

REFERENCE ◀◀ page 10

Mixed conditionals

We use mixed conditionals to speculate about possible results in the present, past or future of hypothetical situations or actions in a different time.

To speculate about the possible result in the present of a hypothetical action or situation in the past, we use *if* + past perfect + *would* + infinitive without *to*.

If I**'d known** about the road closure, I **wouldn't be** in this traffic jam.

To speculate about the past result of a hypothetical action or situation that is still true in the present, we use *if* + past + *would have* + past participle.

If I **earned** more money, I **would have bought** that car yesterday.

To speculate about the future result of a hypothetical action or situation in the past, we use *if* + past perfect + *would* + infinitive without *to*.

If I **hadn't agreed** to work this weekend, I**'d go** swimming with you.

Alternatives to *if*

Should + subject + infinitive without *to* can replace *if* in first conditionals, when something is unlikely or not particularly probable.

Should we **manage** to get a ticket, we**'ll give** you a call.

We use *provided/providing (that), on condition (that)* and, less formally, *as long as* to mean *if and only if*, especially where we have reservations.

We'll sign the contract **providing that** we can sign today.

Unless in conditional sentences means *if not*.

Unless you have a boarding card, you can't get on the plane.

Unless can be used formally with a past participle, or to express an afterthought.

Let's go to see a movie – **unless**, of course, you want to stay at home.

Without + noun or *-ing* form can replace *unless* + verb.

Without a boarding card, you won't be allowed on the plane.

Without having a boarding card, you won't be allowed on the plane.

We use *whether or not* or *even if* to emphasise that something will still be true if another thing happens.

I exercise every day, **whether I feel like it or not.**

But for (+ noun or *-ing*) in written and more formal situations means *if something hadn't happened*.

But for her mother's unstinting support, Lena would have given up.

Alternative forms

We can use *if it* + *not be* + *for* in second and third conditionals when someone/something affected or has affected the outcome of a situation.

If it weren't for my poor French, I'd apply for the job in Paris.

We can use *if I were to* + infinitive without *to* when we want to make a second conditional less likely.

If I were to buy that bike, I know I'd regret spending the money later.

Inversion

We can use inversion in third conditionals to replace *if*.

Had you **been** at the meeting last week, you'd have heard the news.

We can also use inversion in second conditionals with *were to*.

Were I to retake the test, I'd definitely pass it.

Note: inversion also adds formality to the sentence.

PRACTICE

1 Write mixed conditional sentences about these situations. Start each sentence with *if*.

1 I have to go to a conference later. I didn't stay up late last night.

2 I didn't learn Spanish at school. I can't communicate with the locals here.

3 Lara doesn't enjoy superhero films. She didn't go to see the latest *Avengers* film last night.

4 The tap was leaking all night and today the whole floor is wet.

5 Oliver has a really good singing voice. He entered the TV talent show.

6 We went swimming in cold water yesterday and I'm sneezing a lot this morning.

2 Rewrite the second sentence so that it means the same as the first.

1 If the doctor hadn't intervened quickly, the patient would be seriously ill.
But for ....

2 He can't go to the dance if he doesn't have a partner.
Without ....

3 Let him sleep late unless there's an emergency.
Let him sleep late as long ....

4 I'll attend the meeting unless I'm obliged to speak.
I'll attend the meeting provided ....

5 You can't use a TV without a licence.
Unless ....

6 The meeting will go ahead tomorrow if no one contacts you later today.
Should ....

3 Complete the sentences with the correct words.

1 If it .... for the essay I have to write, I'd come with you to the theatre.

2 .... we listened to the weather forecast before setting out, we wouldn't be soaking wet now.

3 If it hadn't .... for the power cut, we'd have had a much longer video call.

4 .... they to build on the nearby park, many residents would complain.

5 If you .... offer me the position, I would inform my employer today.

1B nominal relative clauses

REFERENCE ◀◀ page 12

A nominal relative clause is a type of noun clause that is used to express ideas more concisely.

In a nominal relative clause, a noun/pronoun and another pronoun are 'fused' together into one relative pronoun. Typical relative pronouns are: *what, who, when, where, how, why, whatever, whoever, whichever*.

I know ~~the things which~~ **what** I like.

~~The person who~~ **Whoever** is elected will serve five years.

Some nominal relative pronouns can be followed by *to* infinitive.

I considered **what to say**.

The manual illustrates **how to troubleshoot** problems.

Nominal relative clauses can be in subject or object position.

What other people think is irrelevant.

Did you tell them **where we're meeting**?

Notice that in subject position, the clause can function as a cleft structure and add emphasis.

We use nominal relative clauses after the phrases *This/That/It + be + just, exactly, precisely*.

This is **what I feared would happen**.

That's exactly **when we're away**.

It's just **what I wanted**!

We don't use *what* in a normal relative clause.

It's a video ~~what~~ I made ages ago.

We use *that/which* or nothing (if the relative pronoun is the object of the verb).

whoever, whenever, whatever, whichever

We use *whoever, whenever, whatever, whichever* in nominal relative clauses to replace *anyone who/any person who, any time that* or *anything which/that, the one that*.

I'll do **whatever** you want.

Coffee? Yes please, **whenever** you're making one.

Whoever wins goes forward to the next stage.

Notice the difference with *who*:

Who we're looking for is a genuine entrepreneur. (the specific person who)

PRACTICE

1 In each sentence (1–8) find a noun + pronoun or a pronoun + pronoun combination and replace it with a single pronoun. Make any other necessary changes.

1 I remember the time that we actually enjoyed weekends.
2 Anyone who thinks writing a book is easy should try it for themselves.
3 If you don't like the way that she treats you, tell her.
4 I'll have my eggs any way that you want to make them.
5 Don't forget the things that are important to you and you can't go wrong.
6 There are two routes to the airport, so you can choose the one that you prefer.
7 The person who I like the most is best kept a secret.
8 You can have anything that you want, just name it.

2 Complete the replies with a pronoun.

1 I meant your cousin Susan, not your classmate Susan.
   a That's exactly _____ I was talking about.
   b _____ you meant, I haven't spoken to either of them this week.
2 We've got them some new kitchenware as a wedding gift.
   a That's just _____ we wanted to get them!
   b We're giving cash, then they can get _____ they want.
3 The first week of October works for me.
   a That's exactly _____ we were planning to be away.
   b OK, _____'s good for you.
4 Pizza for dinner?
   a That's precisely _____ I was thinking!
   b _____ you want is fine by me.

1C How to ... manage interaction during a discussion

REFERENCE ◀◀ page 15

The key to a successful discussion is being able to manage the interaction. We may wish to interrupt politely, return to a point previously mentioned or direct the interaction by initiating discussion of certain points and encouraging contributions from others.

Interrupting

If I can come in here, ...

Sorry, I didn't mean to cut you off ...

Could I just make a point here?

If I could just add that ...

Returning to a previous point

And going back to what I was saying earlier, ...

Sorry, you were saying ...

To go back to my earlier point, ...

What I started to say was ...

As we were saying before, ...

If I could just finish, ...

Earlier, you raised an important point ...

Directing the interaction

To get the ball rolling, let's start with ...

I'd like to hear ...'s thoughts on this.

Let me pick up on that.

If I can just bring ... back in, ...

Let's see what ... makes of this ...

Would you like to comment on ... ?

Can we just hear what ... has to say on this?

I think we might be getting off the topic.

We're running out of time, so let's move on.

PRACTICE

1 Use the prompts to write phrases for managing interaction.

1 I / make / point? ....

2 go / back / earlier point ....

3 Earlier / raise / important ....

4 me / pick up / that ....

5 run / time ....

6 If / finish ....

2 Complete the first part of a discussion with the correct words.

Becks: So, today's topic for debate is 'Taking a gap year before university is good for students.' Let's see where we stand on the issue. To [1]............ the ball rolling, let's [2]............ with Kenny.

Kenny: Well for me, taking a break before going to university seems a great idea. Students can get a real taste of ...

Ashley: If I can [3]............ in here, surely that breaks the flow of education, doesn't it? They might get used to earning money and not want to return.

Kenny: What I started to say was that they will appreciate learning more if they've had some work or travel experience.

Ashley: Sorry, I didn't mean to [4]............ you off.

Kenny: No problem. [5]............ I was saying, a taste of working is really important and, who knows, some might change their mind about the course they were planning to study.

3 Put the comments (a–d) into the correct places (1–4) to complete the second part of the discussion. Then complete the comments with the correct words.

1 ....
Becks: I'd like to hear Sara's [1]............ on this.

2 ....
Becks: Ashley, would you like to [2]............ on that?

3 ....
Sara: But that's not to say that older people can't still study, is it?

4 ....

a Sara: Yes, let me [3]............ up on that last point. If they make that decision, then surely that's better than getting onto a university course and dropping out after a few weeks.

b Becks: I think we might be [4]............ off the topic somewhat. Earlier, Kenny, you [5]............ an important point about travel experience. How do you think students can benefit from ... ?

c Ashley: But [6]............ back to what I was saying earlier, they might decide not to go to university at all!

d Ashley: I see your point. I just think it's a shame to break the flow, as I said before. If your brain is in that learning zone, then you should profit from it.

2A advanced ways of comparing

REFERENCE ◀◀ page 22

like

We use *like*, sometimes modified by *a bit, a little, somewhat, rather, a lot, nothing*, etc. to compare two nouns.

Waiting for an interview is **a bit like** going to the dentist: pretty scary.

Our new museum is **nothing like** the ones I've seen in other cities.

The play we went to see last night was **a lot like** watching paint dry. It was so boring.

as

We use *(not) as … as* with an adverb or adjective to make equal or unequal comparisons.

The painting was **not as** old **as** he'd maintained.

For emphasis we can modify a comparative with words such as *easily, nothing like, nowhere like, nowhere near, equally*, etc.

The laptop was **nowhere near as** expensive **as** we'd been led to believe.

The exam was **nothing like as** difficult **as** I'd been expecting.

The man was **easily as** eccentric **as** I had imagined.

His talk about the history of the town was **equally as** interesting **as** his previous talk on its architecture.

We use *so … as to* to replace a result clause.

His handwriting was **so** bad **as to** be almost indecipherable.

We use *not so much … as* to stress the second element.

It was**n't so much** an interview **as** an interrogation.

Other structures and phrases

We use *can't/couldn't* + verb + *any* (*more*) + adverb/adjective + (*than*) to add emphasis.

The story line **couldn't have got any more complicated**.

I **can't work any faster than** I am, so please wait.

The flat is great for getting to work. You **couldn't live any more centrally**.

We use *more* + adjective + *than* + adjective to emphasise one thing.

To be honest, I'm **more nervous than worried** about the test.

Some phrases and verbs reflect similarity and contrast.

The meal cooked by the new chef **wasn't a patch on** the delicacies the previous chef produced.

The twins **differ considerably** in appearance and personality.

What he's saying now about planning is **at complete variance** with what he was saying six months ago.

PRACTICE

1 Complete the sentences with *as* or *like*.

  1 The new series is nowhere near _____ good as the first was.

  2 Visiting my childhood home was a lot _____ going back into the past; the owners hadn't changed a thing.

  3 The autobiography of the author was equally as interesting _____ the plot of his novel.

  4 My passport picture looks nothing _____ I do now – it's nearly eight years old.

  5 The road was so heavily covered in snow _____ to be almost impassable.

  6 It wasn't so much an invitation to attend the meeting _____ an order.

2 Match the sentence beginnings (1–6) with the endings (a–f).

  1 You couldn't find a location any

  2 This holiday cottage isn't

  3 To tell the truth, I'm more

  4 The cottage and its location are at complete

  5 Take whichever room you like. They differ

  6 The journey here took nothing

  a a patch on the one we had last year.

  b more peaceful than this one.

  c like as long as I'd thought it would.

  d relieved that we got here safely than disappointed with the place.

  e variance with how it was described online.

  f in size a little, but the views are the same.

3 Rewrite the second sentence using the word given so that it has the same meaning as the first sentence. Use between four and six words.

  1 This painting is the most lifelike I have seen.
    GET
    You couldn't _____ than this one.

  2 My original job description was very different to what I'm having to do now.
    VARIANCE
    What I'm having to do at work now is _____ my original job description.

  3 His manner irritated me more than his words.
    SO
    It wasn't _____ his manner that irritated me.

  4 He made some claims that were ridiculous and we almost laughed at them.
    AS
    His _____ be almost laughable.

  5 We'd been warned that climbing to the top of the tower would be exhausting and it was very true.
    EASILY
    Climbing to the top of the tower _____ we'd been warned.

  6 You could compare the dry steak we ate last night to cardboard.
    BIT
    That steak last night was so dry _____ eating cardboard.

GRAMMAR BANK

2B reporting

REFERENCE ◀◀ page 24

When reporting people's speech, questions, thoughts or beliefs at a later stage, change the pronouns, tenses, auxiliary verbs, time or place references as appropriate.

'I think the new system will have a profound impact here.'

Paola thought the new system **would have** a profound impact **there**.

Where a situation has not changed, or the present or future situation is still present or future, there is no need to make any changes.

'There will be storms tonight.'

The forecast said there **will be** storms **tonight**.

Past modal verbs don't change.

'You shouldn't have overstated the case.'

I told them they **shouldn't have overstated** the case.

We use *whether* (instead of *if*) in more formal reported questions and also after prepositions.

We talked about **whether** to strike or not.

Notice that in spoken English we often just change the words rather than use complicated grammatical rules. The most important thing is to make sure the message is clear.

'Isn't he amazing?'

Julia thinks he's amazing.

Adding variety to reporting

We use a range of reporting verbs to summarise the main meaning of an utterance, e.g. *accept, acknowledge, cite, claim, counter, echo, implore, maintain, profess, point out, question, reiterate, stipulate.*

The exam rules **stipulate** that no dictionaries can be used.

He **professed** never to have seen the letter before.

The footballer **echoed** his manager's comment that he would be match fit by Saturday.

We can also use verb + noun collocations.

He **raised the issue** of traffic congestion.

We **voiced our concerns** about the short deadlines.

We can use adjectives instead of reporting verbs, e.g. *assertive, concerned, confident, fearful, hesitant, hopeful, insistent, regretful, satisfied.*

The politician was **confident** that the law would be passed without delay.

The manager was **satisfied** that the contract was as comprehensive as it could possibly be.

We can use nouns rather than clauses to follow reporting verbs.

She accepted **the difficulty** involved in planning a concert on such a large scale.

He questioned **the manager's ability** to deal with the problems they were facing.

We can also use phrases to introduce reported speech.

According to my doctor, I should be eating far more fruit and vegetables than I currently am.

As mentioned in the article, it was not the first time that residents had experienced heavy flooding.

PRACTICE

1 Use the prompts to write sentences. Make changes in tenses only where it is absolutely necessary.

1. Valerie / just / tell / she / be / in / hospital / last week / that / why / not / come / my party
2. In 1543, Copernicus / publish / his theory / state / the Earth / go / round / Sun
3. application form / state / recent photo / must / attach
4. When / we / be / young / our father / assure / we / will / never regret / go / college
5. Last night / Sue / explain / me / she / travel / a lot / her / current job
6. When / he / see / broken / window / Mr Harris / ask / I or my brother / do / it

2 Report the direct statements using appropriate verbs in the box.

> accept   echo   implore   maintain
> question   reiterate

1. 'That's fine. I realise that I'm never going to be a teacher.'
   She ....
2. 'I agree with Marty's point. We've been too lenient with students missing deadlines.'
   He ....
3. 'I'm not sure that these records are completely accurate. Can we check?'
   She ....
4. 'As I said before, my view is that we haven't invested enough in maintaining the buildings.'
   He ....
5. 'The steps I have taken have been in the best interests of the company.'
   She ....
6. 'I would ask you all to please think very carefully about donating more money to the charity.'
   He ....

3 Write what the people being reported might have actually said. Use direct speech and do not use the reporting verbs in the sentences.

1. The committee member called for action to improve road safety.
2. Kelly raised the issue of students bringing unhealthy snacks into school.
3. The chair was hesitant about taking a vote at that time.
4. The police were satisfied that my brother had nothing whatsoever to do with stealing the car.
5. The politicians pondered the difficulty of introducing new legislation too quickly.
6. According to the restaurant owner, a significant number of customers had left without paying their bills in the previous month.

2C How to ... maintain and develop interaction

REFERENCE ◀◀ page 27

In order to maintain and develop a discussion, rather than simply stating our opinions in a turn-taking style, we can use phrases to say how far we agree or disagree with someone, and also to show our interest.

Expressing agreement

I'm not arguing there.
OK, I take your point.
Fair enough.
I get where you're coming from.
I'm with you there.
I couldn't agree more.

Expressing disagreement

But surely ...
I think there's a flaw in your argument.
You're looking at things the wrong way round.
Maybe we're talking at cross purposes here?
I'm afraid I beg to differ.
I think we have to agree to disagree.

Expressing interest

You make a good point.
That's a relevant point.
You've put that really well.
Really? I'd never considered that.
That's an excellent way of putting it.
It's clear you both have strong views here.

PRACTICE

1 Choose the correct words to complete the sentences.

1 That's interesting, but I think there's a **flaw / fault** in your argument.
2 You **put / make** a good point, but I'm still not convinced.
3 I've heard that argument before and I couldn't agree **better / more**, but **certainly / surely** we've moved beyond that.
4 Thanks. That's a really **relevant / reliable** point, and one I'd never **considered / thought** before.
5 Free train travel for students? I'm definitely with you **there / everywhere**!
6 I've a feeling we're talking at **opposite / cross** purposes here. I wasn't thinking about asking everyone – just our close circle of friends.
7 You express yourself so well – that's an excellent way of **putting / making** it.

2 Match the sentence beginnings (1–5) with the endings (a–e).

1 You're looking at things   a beg to differ.
2 I'm afraid I   b we have to agree to disagree.
3 OK, I'm not
4 We're getting nowhere! I think   c fair enough.
5 You have your opinion and that's   d arguing there.
     e the wrong way round.

3 Complete the discussion with the phrases in the box.

> a flaw in your argument   agree to disagree
> fair enough   make a good point   surely
> take your point   where you're coming from

Alex: So, what are your feelings about the new leisure centre that the council's putting so much money into? It's costing a fortune.

Ben: About time. People need to have access to sports facilities, get healthier and put less strain on the health service.

Alex: ¹_____ . I ²_____ that the health service is stretched, but what I can't come to terms with is why people can't just exercise more. There are plenty of parks and gardens! This leisure centre is being built with my – a taxpayer's – money, and I'll probably never use it.

Ben: I think there's ³_____ . You're talking about taxpayers' money, but new hospitals will cost the taxpayer a lot more if we don't become healthier as a nation.

Alex: OK, I get ⁴_____ , but ⁵_____ just renovating or revamping existing centres would be sufficient? There's no call for all this latest state-of-the-art sports equipment that the new centre is advertising.

Ben: But that's what will attract people to the centre, and we all need some encouragement to get exercising or doing sports.

Alex: You ⁶_____ , but I think we'll have to ⁷_____ ! Getting fit doesn't need to cost the earth.

3A modal verbs and phrases

REFERENCE ◀◀ page 33

Modal verbs

We use modal verbs to express the probability or likelihood of a situation.

That **must be** Dave at the door.

We **might be seeing** Rosa at the weekend.

I'm sorry, it **can't be done** in the time you want.

Other phrases

We can use other phrases to show:

- certainty.

  She**'s bound to** have prepared carefully.

  It**'s guaranteed to** save you money.

  The economy **is undoubtedly** in trouble.

  The decision **will inevitably** lead to tensions.

  It's **a given that** they will get the contract.

- probability/possibility.

  You **may well** be right.

  I **would guess that** she earns about a million.

  In all probability, the car will be ready by midday.

  There's a strong likelihood that it will rain before the weekend.

  It is **expected/highly likely that** she'll study law at university.

  There's a chance that we'll miss the meeting.

  The odds are that our teacher will be leaving in a few months.

- improbability.

  It seems totally unimaginable that they'll lose.

  It's highly unlikely that we'll get any news before tomorrow.

- necessity.

  It's (absolutely) crucial/vital/essential/imperative that no one speaks to the media.

  This **needs to** be discussed further.

- obligation.

  We**'re expected to** do two hours' homework.

  It**'s obviously (my) responsibility to** welcome new trainees.

  Students **are supposed to** leave their mobiles at home.

  A requirement is that new staff have a university degree.

- ability.

  Do you think he**'s capable of** managing a team?

  He **has an aptitude for** painting and drawing.

PRACTICE

1 Read the sentences from a tourist brochure. Find the mistakes and correct them. Two sentences are correct.

1 In probability you will see wildlife that you've never seen before.

2 It's a chance that some parts of the park will be closed during the rainy season.

3 We should guess that most of our customers come through recommendations from former clients.

4 It seems totally unimaginable that a visitor wouldn't find this exhilarating.

5 This will undoubtedly be the most memorable experience of your lifetime.

6 Visitors are not suppose to tip their guides, but the practice is not overtly discouraged.

7 It's essentially absolute that you keep your car windows closed.

8 Even the fastest human is not able of outrunning an elephant.

9 You guarantee of having a great time!

2 Complete the sentences with the words in the box.

> a requirement   able   aptitude
> crucial   expected   likelihood
> undoubtedly   well

1 It's .... that the cabin staff explain emergency procedures before take-off.

2 There is .... that all candidates have a minimum set of qualifications.

3 There's a strong .... that someone will lose their job over this.

4 If a child shows a(n) .... for a particular craft, they should be encouraged.

5 It's .... that everyone involved in the project will be in attendance.

6 Being .... to work in high places without feeling a sense of vertigo is important.

7 The staff may .... know more about the subject than the painters themselves.

8 Most passengers will .... enjoy the services offered on the new trains.

3B passives

REFERENCE ◀◀ page 37

We use passive structures:

- to keep the focus on a particular subject.
  Robert left at 6 a.m. He **was picked up** by a taxi at 6.10.
- when the agent is unimportant, obvious or unknown.
  The meeting's **been cancelled**.
  Your room **is being cleaned**.
- in formal writing and speaking.
  Taking photographs **is prohibited**.

We use *get* in informal spoken English or in situations where things happen outside our control.

I **got paid** yesterday.

Emma's hat **got knocked off** by a branch.

We use passive infinitives and *-ing* forms in subject or object position in a sentence. Note the position of the negatives.

Being 'liked' on social media is addictive.

Not to have been consulted is unforgivable.

I hate **not being believed**.

He expects **to be promoted** soon.

We use passive with *it* to front a sentence with reporting/thinking verbs.

It is thought that the opening of the new hospital will be delayed by up to two months.

It was decided not to continue with the new rail links because of the costs involved.

We can also use an alternative impersonal passive structure.

The novelist **is said to** have been born in Portsmouth.

The employee **was thought to** have been suffering from stress for several months before seeking help.

We use modal passives to express necessity, possibility, etc.

Something **must be done**.

It **could have been painted** earlier than we thought.

We use *There is everything/a great deal/a lot/much/not much/very little/nothing* + *to be* + past participle to talk about amount, often in a slightly formal way.

There's a great deal to be gained by talking.

There's nothing to be said.

We can use *have* + object + past participle for a (usually paid) service.

I**'m having my car checked** today.

Have you **had your hair straightened**?

We can use *get* + object + past participle to sound less formal.

I **got my teeth fixed** last year.

Have + object + past participle can also be used for a negative experience.

She **had** her **bike stolen**. = Her bike was stolen.

Notice that in the causative there is an emphasis on the situation rather than the person.

PRACTICE

1 Choose the best option (a or b) for continuing the situations and sentences.

1 Did you see the story about world famine on TV?
   a Something has to be done.
   b Somebody has to be something.

2 Having just discovered that the company is relocating, I wanted to flag how distraught I was
   a that someone didn't tell me how I feel about it.
   b not to have been asked how I feel about it.

3 I was at the hairdresser's and
   a I had my hair completely messed up.
   b she completely messed up my hair.

4 Excuse me, Madam. Would you please turn off your recording device?
   a Recording this concert is not permitted.
   b You're supposed to record this concert.

5 Oh no, my laptop's crashed again.
   a Maybe I should get it repaired by someone different this time.
   b Maybe it should be repaired by someone different this time.

6 I'm glad I brought my raincoat.
   a There's a lot that I might say about being prepared!
   b There's a lot to be said for being prepared!

2 Complete the text with the correct form of the verbs in brackets. Use the active or passive voice as appropriate.

Thank you, and goodbye

It's not just employees who [1]_____ (catch out) on social media and find their jobs in peril. Company managers need to be wary of who sees their posts and how they [2]_____ (might interpret). Managers [3]_____ (expose) boasting about getting workers to do overtime without getting paid and competing with other managers for who [4]_____ (spend) the fewest hours in the office. In one remarkable example, a department store manager [5]_____ (video) himself posing as a shoplifter in the very store he worked in, and [6]_____ (make) it into a 'how-to' video uploaded for public viewing. The security department of the store [7]_____ (inform) and used the content of the video to [8]_____ (improve) their anti-theft measures. The store's owner was appreciative – a thank-you note to the manager [9]_____ (include) along with the notice informing him that his employment [10]_____ (terminate), effective immediately. There's a great deal [11]_____ (gain) by thinking twice before pressing the 'upload' button. [12]_____ (sack) for something so obviously irresponsible is perhaps not too high a price to pay.

3C How to ... check understanding by paraphrasing and summarising

REFERENCE ◀◀ page 39

We use the following phrases to check understanding and respond during a discussion.

Checking understanding

So, in other words, you're ...

So, am I right in thinking that ... ?

Please correct me if I'm wrong, but it sounds like you're talking about ...

So, what you're basically saying is ...

If I've got this right, you think ...

Are you suggesting that ... ?

Just to clarify, are you saying that ... ?

Responding

Let me rephrase that.

OK, I'll put it another way.

Not at all, what I said was ...

You're twisting my words.

No, let me put it another way.

No, you've got it all wrong.

Absolutely, that's exactly what I mean.

PRACTICE

1 Complete the phrases.

1 No, let me put _____ . I don't think we should offer to do it for free.

2 You're twisting _____ . I never said we should give him all the bad jobs.

3 Absolutely, that's _____ . The more we invest, the more we get back.

4 Am I right in _____ she did this without asking anyone else first?

5 Please correct _____ , but it sounds like you're asking everyone to give their time up for free.

6 Not at all, what I _____ that he's not always the most reliable, that's all.

2 Add the missing word to each sentence.

1 Not all – what I said was I needed more thinking time.

2 So, you're basically saying is that we've run out of time to rectify the situation.

3 If I've got this, you'd rather go with the third candidate.

4 You're twisting words – I shall definitely vote for getting an extension.

5 Let rephrase that – I would like to see more people working remotely.

6 No, you've got all wrong. I don't want to work from home myself.

7 OK, I'll put another way – I would love to find employment with this company.

8 It sounds you're talking about making a large number of people redundant.

3 Match Speaker A's comments (1–4) with Speaker B's reactions (a–d).

1 A: I feel that Tanya has put forward some relevant points and I think there's a lot to be said for the proposal.

2 A: I wouldn't go so far as to say we should commit to this course of action, but take time to consider other factors.

3 A: So, what you're basically saying is that we ought to abandon the project altogether.

4 A: So, am I right in thinking that you'll vote against us?

a B: Please correct me if I'm wrong, but it sounds like you're talking about another delay.

b B: No, let me put it another way. I'm not 100 percent in favour, but I won't actually oppose the plans.

c B: So, in other words, you're in favour?

d B: Not at all. You're twisting my words. What I said was that I think we need to ask for additional consultations.

4A verb patterns

REFERENCE ◀◀ page 46

Verb + -ing

We use an -ing form after prepositions.
It's **for making** bread.

This includes prepositions after certain:

- adjectives: *committed to, justified in, meticulous about, renowned for.*
- nouns/noun phrases: *thanks for, in addition to, with a view to, the idea of, the purpose of, devotion to.*
- verbs/verb and object combinations: *specialise in, feel like, admire someone for, compliment someone on.*

-ing forms also follow:

- many verbs: *involve, imagine, can't help, suggest, bother.*
- phrasal verbs: *end up, put off, give up, take up, burst out.*
- some adjectives: *(not) worth, hopeless*, pointless*.*
- time linkers: *when, before, since, on, upon, until, while, whilst.*

* These adjectives can also be followed by the *to* infinitive.
Kit broke his arm **while skiing**.

-ing forms when functioning as nouns (gerunds) are often the subject of a sentence. **Overfishing is depleting the cod species.**

-ing forms can also function as adjectives (participles).
satisfying results, a **mystifying** problem, **participating** countries

Notice the use of the -ing form in the passive:
He doesn't enjoy **being corrected** when he speaks English.

Infinitive with *to*

We use infinitive with *to* after:

- certain verbs/verb and object combinations/verb phrases: *arrange, manage, fail, prepare, bother, persuade someone, allow someone, want someone, occur to someone.* It **didn't occur to me to resign**.
- adjectives: *bound, inclined, interesting, liable, ready, reluctant, willing.*
  The road is **liable to flood**.
- nouns/noun phrases: *a (long) way, (it's her) ambition, (go to) great lengths, (there's) no need, (the) aim/motive is.*
  Kate has **gone to great lengths to set** improvements in motion.

We use infinitive with *to*:

- after *too* + adjective/quantifier. It's **too heavy to lift**.
  There's **too much to see**.
- to express purpose. He's saving **to buy a house**.

-ing form or infinitive with *to*

Some verbs can take either the -ing form or infinitive with *to* depending on the meaning: *go on, remember, forget, start, regret, try, stop.*
I **remember locking** the door but I can't find the key.
Remember to lock the door before going out.

With other verbs there is little or no difference: *start, begin, like.*

We use the perfect infinitive or -ing form to emphasise the order of activities. I would love **to have met** Salvador Dalí.

Notice the use of the perfect infinitive in the passive. **The report is still to be completed.**

PRACTICE

1 Find and correct one or two mistakes in each sentence.

1 Sonya's renowned for not answering her emails in addition to never check her voice mails.

2 Since see the film, Ron bursts out cry every time he sees a cat.

3 I'm not looking forward to turn forty, so there's no need to organise a party.

4 The judge decided they were justified in having leave the restaurant without paying while running from the fire.

5 It's worth remembering packing your case the night before so you don't forget taking everything.

6 It was great to have visit so many countries but pointless trying picking which was the best.

7 When Dan was complimented on having prepared such a good meal, he admitted to have ordered it from a caterer.

2 Complete the text with the correct form of the verbs in brackets.

Trailblazers?

A team of volunteers committed [1] .... (extinguish) forest fires have taken their organisation's name too literally and will end up [2] .... (spend) some time behind bars. All nine members of the volunteer firefighting unit The Trailblazers initially denied [3] .... (start) the fires they were putting out, but after police went to great lengths [4] .... (collect) the evidence, they admitted their crime. 'I've always admired firefighters for their devotion [5] .... (protect) the community,' commented the mayor, 'and I will go on [6] .... (do) so – I think this is a situation where one or two bad apples persuaded an impressionable group [7] .... (carry) out an activity that they will later regret [8] .... (have) got involved in.' A police spokesperson said their motive seemed to be [9] .... (make) heroes out of themselves. 'We noticed that The Trailblazers were remarkable at [10] .... (put) out fires quickly, as if they knew where one was liable [11] .... (start). They enjoyed the admiration and it was simply too rewarding [12] .... (give) up what they were doing.'

4B continuous and perfect aspects

REFERENCE ◀◀ page 48

The continuous aspect

The continuous aspect focuses on an action/ activity and its duration rather than its result. It is used:

- to show that an activity is temporary and its duration is limited.

  The train **was nearing** Paris.

  I**'m trying** to sleep.

  Ben **will be waiting** to pick you up outside.

  The team **is** currently **taking** a week's holiday.

- to describe a repeated action.

  At that time, I **was getting up** at 6 a.m. Monday to Friday.

We can use the continuous aspect in stories or anecdotes to describe a past situation for drama or emphasis.

Right, he**'s stamping** up the stairs, obviously angry, and I**'m wondering** what on earth I've done!

The perfect aspect

The perfect aspect links two timeframes. It is used:

- to emphasise that an action is completed before a point in time.

  I realised I**'d sent** the wrong email.

  By 2040, electric cars **will have replaced** petrol models.

- when the exact time is unimportant or unknown.

  Has anyone **seen** my glasses?

  She**'s been** to Morocco a couple of times.

- to emphasise the result rather than the process.

  I**'ve** already **eaten**, thanks.

  The company **has made** a huge investment in the country.

- to describe a period leading to a point of time.

  I**'d lived** there for six years before I met him.

Continuous and perfect together

Both aspects can occur, showing the linking of two times and the duration or temporariness of an activity.

The CEO **had been planning** the merger for months before the announcement.

By next June I**'ll have been working** here for a year.

PRACTICE

1 Choose the correct words to complete the sentences.

1 I was queueing for the checkout when I realised my wallet **had been / was** stolen.

2 Once you**'d / 've** finished, text me and I**'m / 'll be** waiting for you in the car park.

3 **Didn't you find / Haven't you found** the book you **were / 'd been** looking for yet?

4 The letter said **he'd missed / he missed** the payment, but he was sure he **hadn't / didn't**.

5 Spending on the new infrastructure **will have doubled / will have been doubling** by 2040.

6 By midnight they**'d been / were** on the road too long and **were needing / needed** nothing more than a warm shower and a comfortable bed.

7 I wouldn't **be / have been** telling you this if you**'d / 've** been up front with me when we first met.

8 I **was / 've been** having problems with my phone since I **downloaded / 've downloaded** that new app.

9 I**'ve been meaning / 've meant** to change my electricity provider for months now, but I **haven't had / didn't have** the time yet.

10 You can't park on my street because they **do / 're doing** some roadworks. Hopefully **they finish / 'll have finished** by tomorrow.

2 Complete the story with the correct perfect or continuous form of the verb in brackets. In some cases, more than one form may be possible.

The Voice

This happened last year. I ¹_____ (take) part in lots of ventriloquist competitions before but I ²_____ (never, feel) so nervous, and while I ³_____ (wait) to be called in I had this sensation that I ⁴_____ (lose) my voice and along with it Giovanni's – he's my dummy. But I ⁵_____ (work) far too hard to mess this one up, so I told myself, 'If you don't win, then a year from now you ⁶_____ (look) for a new job again with only yourself to blame.' Finally, my name was called and while I ⁷_____ (walk) on stage, the oddest thing happened. Giovanni, who of course never speaks without my help, turned to me and said, 'Hey, Rennie, you're the best. See, even now your lips ⁸_____ (not move).' Of course they ⁹_____ (not move). I was petrified! Giovanni carried on and as he ¹⁰_____ (give) me his pep talk, I realised the performance ¹¹_____ (start) and I ¹²_____ (stand) there on stage with this previously inanimate dummy talking to me. Then he stopped, lifeless, as if he ¹³_____ (not say) a word, and there was this hanging silence, followed by massive applause. I ¹⁴_____ (never hear) an audience clap so loud before or since.

4C How to ... present survey results

REFERENCE ◀◀ page 51

When presenting survey results, we use certain phrases to summarise and reference the results.

Generalising

On the whole, ...
Generally speaking though, ...
The consensus seems to be ...
The overall picture was one of ...

Exemplifying

To cite one example, ...
Another illustration of this ...
People expressed a ...
There was limited interest in ...
Most respondents tended to ...
An interesting fluctuation was ...

Speculating

Our impression was simply that ...
One might speculate ...
Their interest presumably reflected ...
This might lead us to assume ...

Contrasting

Having said that, ...
Other results appear to contradict this.
When putting these results against ...

PRACTICE

1 Match the sentence beginnings (1–6) with the endings (a–f).

1 I'd like to begin by citing
2 On collating the results, it seemed that the overall
3 In spite of the campaign there was limited
4 A later survey revealed an interesting
5 Our first survey showed general agreement with the policy, but
6 Younger people's interest in the selected series

a interest in buying the products advertised.
b further results appear to contradict this.
c one example of how results can be biased.
d presumably reflected their film tastes in general.
e fluctuation in the number of positive comments.
f picture was one of total satisfaction.

2 Correct the mistakes in the phrases in bold.

¹**In the whole**, most of the people surveyed ²**tendency** to feel that there weren't enough places for young adults to meet in public. ³**The census seems to be** that public spaces were primarily designed for children, families and the elderly. ⁴**To slight one example**, a group of university students were kicked out of a playground for being too old, then sent away from the park benches, ⁵**presumptuously** for being too young. ⁶**Another illustrator of this** is that nearly everyone we surveyed said they meet their friends in cafés but hated spending so much on coffee. ⁷**One might specialise that** young people would opt for cafés anyway, as they are so used to frequenting such places. ⁸**Generically speaking though**, ⁹**our impressive was that** young people desperately want to spend their time healthily, without the cost. To that end, we have a few suggestions to make regarding public spaces ...

3 Read part of a presentation. Identify the places where words are missing. Then complete the presentation with the words in the box.

> cite consensus illustration impression
> reflects ~~speaking~~ speculate tended whole

Generally **speaking**, a majority of respondents to feel that while a shortened (four-day) work week is an appealing idea, it would be too problematic in practice. The seems to be that the resulting paperwork for human resources and management and the decline in productivity wouldn't be worth the benefits. To one example, a factory manager indicated that reducing the working week to four days would require increasing his workforce by 20 percent. Another of this is that many people said they would have to work at home to make sure their tasks got done anyway. This view presumably the degree of inflexibility of many companies. On the our was simply that people in fact like their routine, and one might that they identify so much with their work that they can't imagine life with less of it.

GRAMMAR BANK

5A giving emphasis: inversion, clefting, tailing, fronting

REFERENCE ◀◀ page 58

Inversion

We can use inversion after adverbs/adverbial phrases with a negative meaning: *no sooner, never before, little, in no way, only when, scarcely, hardly, barely, under no circumstances, at no time, so, such.*

Only when I checked through the assignment **did I realise** I had misinterpreted the question.

Notice that usually *so/such* + inversion is used in more formal English.

So strong was the competition that he failed to reach the finals.

Cleft sentences

We use *It* and *wh-* clefts to change normal sentence structure for emphasis and to focus on particular information.

It was in 2021 **when** the new course was added to the curriculum.

It was deciding who would lead the presentation **that** was the most difficult problem.

What I love about living here **is** the peace and quiet and a great community spirit.

What surprised me **was** how much traffic there was on the motorway that early.

We can also use other starters for a cleft sentence.

All I needed **was** to talk to someone about the issue.

The reason why Laura did not get the position **was** her lack of qualifications.

Tailing

In informal spoken English, the topic can be put after the main clause for emphasis. A pronoun is included in the main clause to refer to the final phrase. Notice the position of the comma.

It was the best we'd ever stayed in, **that hotel**.

The students like **her** a lot, **their new teacher**.

Fronting

In informal spoken English, a phrase or adverb can be moved to the beginning of the sentence for emphasis.

Some TV programmes I think are too violent.

Why did she resign? **The reason for that** I really can't say.

Question-word clauses are often fronted.

When I'm going to do my homework I have no idea.

Headers are a type of fronting where a pronoun or possessive adjective is added later to refer to the initial phrase. Notice the need for a comma.

That man you were talking to, who was **he**?

My sister, her husband's a lawyer and **she** …

PRACTICE

1 Rewrite the sentences using inversion for emphasis.

1 No one questioned him at any time during his talk.
At ....

2 I had just logged off the site when an email came through from them.
No ....

3 I won't go home until I've finished writing up the review.
Only ....

4 His handwriting was so bad that I couldn't read a word.
So ....

5 You must never click on an unknown link.
On ....

6 I had never been so furious with my brother before.
Never ....

2 Write one or more cleft sentences for each of the statements, emphasising the information in bold.

1 The amount of work we have still to do on the project **is depressing**.

2 **Having to get up so early in the morning** is a particular problem for me.

3 I was saying that **I think Leo is the best person for the job**.

4 **The way we reach a solution** is sometimes more important than the solution itself.

5 **Tommy** came top in the exam, not Martin.

6 **The origin of words** really fascinates me.

7 I chose this research topic **because it has always interested me**.

8 We were motivated by **the teacher's enthusiasm for the subject**.

3 Complete the conversation using the words and phrases in the box. There are two that you do not need.

> challenge   enjoyment   having a goal
> having fun   other sports   that (x2)
> that's   the lessons   those

A: Having a goal, ¹............ what keeps me motivated long-term.

B: Me too. Well, for gym training anyway, but not for other things.

A: ²............ , you mean?

B: No, things like learning English.

A: Really? That's what keeps me going, ³............ .

B: Not me. ⁴............ themselves, I need to enjoy them.

A: So ⁵............ , is that what you're talking about?

B: Not necessarily. Really tough grammar tasks though, I like ⁶............ .

A: Really? ⁷............ I don't get. Grammar's hard.

B: The harder the better! I like the, erm …

A: ⁸............ I think is the word you're after.

B: Yeah, that's exactly the word!

5B participle clauses

REFERENCE ◀◀ page 60

We usually use participle clauses in more formal language to make texts more succinct and sophisticated.

Past participle clauses are passive, while present participle clauses are active.

Derided by all, she nevertheless went on to become a renowned scientist.

Having a fertile imagination, he approached the building cautiously.

The perfect form can be active or passive.

Having considered the problem at length, we propose the following solution.

Jenny still had a slight accent, **having been brought up in the USA**.

We use participle clauses:

- to describe simultaneous actions.

   Tom ran towards his father, **laughing and with arms open wide**.

   Caught in the headlights, the deer stood frozen.

- to describe something happening before the main action. Where necessary, the perfect form can emphasise this.

   Created by IBM, the first smartphone from Apple wasn't produced until fifteen years later.

   Having been warned about health risks, he still didn't change his diet.

- to show the cause or reason for the main action, replacing *as* or *because*.

   Motivated by a desire to help others, Sonia became a doctor.

   Having lost his wallet and phone, Stefan had to walk home.

- to give essential information or extra descriptive detail, often replacing relative clauses.

   The police **sent by the investigating officer** proved to be too few too late.

   The train **approaching platform five** is the 2.15 from Paris.

- to express a condition, replacing *if* (usually with the past participle).

   Barbecued slowly over a low heat, the vegetable skewer tastes wonderful.

It is important that the subject of the participle clause and the main clause are the same.

After driving for 60 km, ~~the road becomes a motorway.~~ (It sounds as if the road has been driving!)

After driving for 60 km, **you**'ll find the road becomes a motorway.

PRACTICE

1 Choose the correct words to complete the text. In three cases both alternatives are correct.

[1]**Blessed / Having blessed** with a family of amazing individuals, I had many people to look to for guidance, and my mum stands out as the most inspiring. [2]**Affected / Having been affected** by polio as a young adult, she literally couldn't stand up on her own, but [3]**confronted / confronting** with any injustice, she stood up for her principles like no one else I know. Once, when a poor family knocked on our door, [4]**having had / having** their electricity cut off because of a mix-up with their bill, it was my mum who got on the phone, [5]**having persuaded / persuading** the electric company to restore the family's electricity – that very night.

She was a dreamer and a doer who disregarded conventions and rules, [6]**determined / having determined** to achieve whatever she set out to do. [7]**Advising originally / Having originally been advised** by doctors that she could never have a family due to her illness, she went on to have two children: me and my sister. And [8]**having seen / seeing** many of her own dreams destroyed by her illness, she taught me to believe in my own. I remember when at the age of four I ran into her room, [9]**buzzed / buzzing** with excitement about my big idea of organising a nursery school party, she didn't laugh but sat down, [10]**planned / planning** out the event with me down to the last detail. At seventeen, [11]**having learnt / learning** English and [12]**obsessed / obsessing** with the idea of going to England but [13]**having not / not having** the resources to do so, I turned to her for help. [14]**Handing / Having handed** me a pen and paper she said, 'Well then, write a letter to the Queen.' So I did.

2 Replace the phrases in bold with a participle clause. Where possible, start the sentence with the clause and make any other necessary changes to punctuation and wording.

1 It can survive for hundreds of years **if you keep it away from direct sunlight**.

   Kept away from direct sunlight, it can survive for hundreds of years.

2 They decided to leave the shelter after **they had eaten all their food**.

3 **Resources which are allocated to the health service** have been reduced each year.

4 We had to phone for directions as **we didn't have any idea how to get there**.

5 Eamonn decided to quit because **he had jeopardised his chances of a promotion**.

6 Julia saw no point in denying accepting the bribes once **she was caught red-handed**.

7 The kids **emulated their favourite pop star** and all wore torn T-shirts and black jewellery.

5C How to ... use persuasive techniques in presentations

REFERENCE ◀◀ page 63

We can use certain phrases when attempting to persuade someone to take a course of action.

Persuading

To be perfectly honest, you couldn't do better than ...

If it were up to me, I would definitely ...

You might want to consider ...

There are no two ways about it, the answer is ...

I would recommend ... without a moment's hesitation.

If what you want is ... , then the way forward is ...

It's a win-win situation.

Come on – what have you got to lose?

Just consider for a moment the benefits of ...

Techniques for persuasion

The following persuasive techniques can be used in presentations:

- direct speech:

  And they'll say things like, '**You look fantastic**' and '**You're totally different!**' – you'll be amazed at what a change people will see in you.

- simile and metaphor:

  Your friends will **follow you like sheep** and show the **loyalty of a spaniel**.

  Your social life will become **a river of opportunity**.

- negative inversion:

  At no time in your life **will you** feel so well positioned for your own personal great leap forward.

- repetition:

  It can be seen as a **huge** opportunity and a **huge** breakthrough.

- rhetorical question:

  What have you been waiting for?

- the rule of three:

  You'll feel **confident**, **composed** and **courageous**.

PRACTICE

1 Match the sentences beginnings (1–6) with the endings (a–f).

1 If it were up to me,
2 I would recommend the series
3 If what you want is a new start,
4 This is definitely the right answer –
5 To be perfectly honest, you
6 Just for a moment consider

a then this is the way forward.
b the benefits of using this new software.
c couldn't do better than giving this a try.
d without a moment's hesitation.
e there are no two ways about it.
f I would definitely think about giving this at least a trial.

2 Imagine you are giving a presentation to persuade people to learn another language. Complete the sentences with your own ideas.

1 If it were up to me, ...
2 Just for a moment consider the benefits of ....
3 You couldn't do better than ....
4 There are no two ways about it: ....
5 Without a moment's hesitation I would recommend ....
6 This is a win-win situation: ....

3 A Complete the extract from a presentation with the phrases (a–f).

Are you fed up with your job? ¹............... Have you heard about the three-step programme? ²............... you need to turn your life around. You'll be as ³............... with your new life, ⁴............... . ⁵............... find yourself sitting at a desk, despairing about your lot in life. Your friends will marvel at the new you and ask, 'How did you do it?' ⁶............... It's no secret, it's no mystery, it's the three-step programme. And here's how it works ...

a 'What's your secret?'
b happy as a dog with a bone
c It's easy, it's exciting and it's everything
d Do you want the career of your dreams?
e on cloud nine
f Never again will you

B Decide the name of each persuasive technique (a–f) in Ex 3A.

GRAMMAR BANK

6A narrative tenses review

REFERENCE ◀◀ page 70

We use a range of different tenses to talk about events in the past. Traditionally, these include the past simple and continuous, and the past perfect simple and continuous.

Past simple

We use the past simple for finished events, sequences of events at specific times, finished time periods and past habits.

The prime minister **informed** the public of the new regulations late yesterday afternoon.

After the long walk he **showered**, **had** something to eat and **fell** into bed, exhausted.

Amira **swam** every day of the year and sure enough, we saw her in the water as we drove to the village.

Past continuous

We use the past continuous to describe action in progress at a point of time in the past, to describe a setting or scene, and for temporary past situations and planned events that did not happen.

Paul phoned me earlier, but I **was trying** to start the car and I missed the call.

My aunt **was getting** breakfast and the smell of buttered toast **was making** me hungry.

In the summer of 2019, I **was working** at a local restaurant to save up some money for university.

Past perfect

We use the past perfect for an action preceding a point of time in the past.

The meeting **had been arranged** for 9.15, but it didn't start until 10.00.

By the time I got to the office someone **had parked** in my designated space and the car park was full.

Past perfect continuous

We use the past perfect continuous for an action in progress over a period before and up to a past event or time.

It rained earlier than we **had been expecting**.

I**'d been thinking** about going to Canada for a long time, so the invitation from my cousins who lived there was very welcome.

Present tenses when narrating past events

We use present tenses when narrating past events:

- to talk about the plots of films or books.

  Charlie **grows** up in Texas and then **moves** with her parents to London. There she **attends** a private school, **run** by a very strict head teacher. One morning after **she's had** a particularly nasty exchange with the head, she is befriended by a group of girls. Over the course of a few weeks they **get** up to all kinds of mischief, and **end** up being chased by students from a neighbouring school. While **she's trying** to escape from her pursuers, Charlie **falls** down an open hole into a cellar …

- to add a sense of drama or immediacy to the account.

  So, it's Sunday morning and my **dad's sitting** there in the kitchen **eating** his Sunday fry-up as always, and suddenly my brother **hurtles** down the stairs and out of the front door without a word. Dad **gets** up quickly, fried egg and toast **hit** the floor and he **runs** after him. Ben **is legging** it down the road, my dad's **shouting** after him and the neighbours **are** all **watching** from behind their curtains!

PRACTICE

1 Complete the text with the correct form of the verbs in brackets.

Cian had ¹_____ (promise) me a lift to my interview and that he ²_____ (pick) me up at 2 p.m., so I ³_____ (wait) for him outside the house on the dot. I ⁴_____ (wait) and ⁵_____ (wait). My neighbour ⁶_____ (go) past with his dog and we ⁷_____ (chat) for a few minutes. Two buses ⁸_____ (go) past, ten cyclists and fifteen pedestrians. I ⁹_____ (count) them all. And still there was no sign of Cian. By this time I ¹⁰_____ (get) a bit panicky. I ¹¹_____ (go) to be late for my interview. I ¹²_____ (tell) in the letter to be punctual. I ¹³_____ (check) the time on my phone. I ¹⁴_____ (wait) for over twenty minutes. I was just about to call him when I ¹⁵_____ (hear) the unmistakable sound of his van turning the corner. At last. Perhaps I ¹⁶_____ (go) to make it on time after all.

2 Complete the story with the correct form of the verbs in the box.

call	do	forget	hear	look	say
not see	sit	smile (x2)	start		

OK, so we get to the airport at 3.30, leaving plenty of time to get checked in and everything else. So, we ¹_____ in the departure lounge when I suddenly ²_____ my name ³_____ loudly. I ⁴_____ up and there's this guy I ⁵_____ since university. Talk about a surprise! He ⁶_____, I ⁷_____ and then when I ⁸_____ to introduce him to my wife I realise I ⁹_____ his name – nightmare. I just ¹⁰_____ 'This is …' and nothing. ¹¹_____ that? So embarrassing!

3 Complete the sentences with your own ideas, and add one more sentence.

1 So, I arrange to meet up with Sophia for a coffee. We're sitting there, happily chatting, when _____ .

2 The gig finished at 11.30 and we were walking out of the theatre when _____ .

3 The film begins with _____ .

4 It was the first of January and my brother had _____ .

5 Declan was absolutely furious when he _____ .

6 Although the meeting was scheduled to begin at 9.30, _____ .

6B adverbials

REFERENCE ◀◀ page 73

Sentence adverbials

We use single adverbs or adverbial phrases at the beginning of a sentence to show the speaker's attitude. These can show:

* surprise or disbelief.

  Unbelievably, Difficult as it is to credit, Strange as it sounds, To my astonishment …

* other emotions.

  Confusingly, To my horror, Sad to say, With some embarrassment …

Intensifying (strengthening) adverbs

We use *very* and *really* with gradable adjectives: **very deceptive, really congested**

We use *really* or strong intensifiers with ungradable adjectives: **totally inappropriate, absolutely hectic, completely atypical, remarkably healthy**

We can use *quite* with ungradable adjectives to add the idea of 'completely': **quite perfect, quite fascinating, quite extraordinary**

The main stress is on the adjective.

The concert was amazing – quite brilliant!

Notice that in informal spoken English, *totally*, *absolutely* and *very* are often used interchangeably:

very hectic = absolutely hectic

Modifying (weakening) adverbs

We use *fairly, relatively, slightly, somewhat, pretty, rather* with gradable adjectives:

relatively easy, somewhat irritated, fairly shy, slightly amused, pretty stupid

Rather is often used with negative adjectives or ones expressing difference:

rather difficult/slow/different/strange

We can use *quite* with gradable adjectives to give the meaning of 'a little/a bit':

quite pushy, quite conventional

The main stress is on *quite*.

The lecture was OK – quite interesting.

Collocations

Many adverbs collocate strongly with:

* adjectives.

  roughly/remarkably similar, closely associated, inextricably connected/linked, perfectly clear, utterly exhausted, heavily dependent, widely/readily available

* verbs.

  vaguely/distinctly remember, instantly invoke, thoroughly recommend, fully appreciate/understand

1 Complete the adverbials in the art review.

Art through a child's eyes

Strange as it might sound for a serious art critic like myself, for years it has disturbed me that children's drawings are [1]en_____ absent from art criticism. I took advantage of an invitation to a nursery school art show to put things right. I should point out that I arrived [2]to_____ exhausted, and found myself instantly uplifted by this [3]ut_____ delightful event. The young artists were present, some [4]fa_____ shy, some [5]re_____ poised and outgoing, and I was [6]sl_____ amused by one – I shall only call her 'E' – who took me by the hand and led me directly to her 'works'.

As any parent with an eye will [7]fu_____ appreciate, children's art can be very deceptive, as the simplest of lines represents an honesty that is [8]qu_____ fascinating and sometimes [9]de_____ moving. E's first painting, a market scene where the figures of sellers and customers conveyed the [10]ab_____ hectic atmosphere, was also [11]co_____ atypical compared to other children's depictions, most of which had the veggies and fruit but no people present at all. Given that a child's approach is [12]in_____ linked to their world view, I felt [13]hu_____ privileged to peer through the eyes of these budding artists.

2 Put the words in bold in order and remove the extra word.

1 **horror to very his,** Brendan realised the brakes had failed.

2 **credit as to its difficult is it,** Stella was once a keen runner.

3 **it sounds just as strange,** I actually like winter more than summer.

4 **my be to much astonishment,** I won first prize.

5 **say sad to you,** Roger left the company last year.

6 **embarrassment with your some,** I have to admit that I haven't even started yet.

6C How to ... tell an anecdote

REFERENCE ◀◀ page 75

We can use the following features when telling informal anecdotes.

Reported speech

We can use *be like* instead of *says/said* to report exactly what was said.

She **was like**, 'Who are you?'

Vague language

We use phrases such as: *stuff/things like that/I think it was/some random/sort of*, *kind of* + adjective.

A year ago, **I think it was**.

Bring food and drink and **stuff like that**.

Determiners

We can use *this* instead of *a/an* in a neutral way.

There was **this** guy standing there.

We can use *some* instead of *a/an* indicating this person/thing is of no importance. It doesn't matter who or what they are. It can also indicate annoyance.

Some guy tried to skip the queue.

Phrases to involve the listener

We can use adjectives such as *strange* or *funny* to start a sentence.

Strange, but I had the feeling we had met before.

We use phrases such as *You know what I mean*, *It was one of those things* to show shared experience.

We clicked straightaway. **It was just one of those things.**

Start the anecdote by setting the scene colloquially.

We can use *so/well/you see/OK/right*.

So, I was at the bus stop and ...

OK, Dave had called to say ...

We can use present tenses for immediacy and dramatic effect (see Grammar Bank 6A on page 127).

PRACTICE

1 Complete the story with the words and phrases in the box. There are two words or phrases you do not need.

> funny   I think it was   some   sort of
> stuff like that   things   this   was like
> were like   you know what I mean

Lost and found

This happened quite a few years ago when Robbie, our little one, was about three ¹_____ . We were living in this little village and I drove with our three kids to the supermarket fifteen minutes away. It's ²_____ tricky to shop with three kids, ³_____? Anyway, I did the shopping, got the usual five litres of milk, boxes of cereal, tons of pasta, ⁴_____ . Packed it all in the car, kids climbed in and we got home. As I parked, I turned around and I ⁵_____ , 'Uh, where's Robbie?' and the two kids ⁶_____ 'How should we know?', and I realised of course that I'd left him in the supermarket! ⁷_____ , driving back to get him I felt completely calm. Robbie was fine of course – still by himself in the cereal aisle, trying to open ⁸_____ box of chocolate cereal.

---

2 Cross out seven of the words in bold which are not needed.

Friday, ¹**when I think it was**, and I was at the checkout and I ²**was like**, 'Where's my wallet?' Panic stations! And ³**some of** woman in the queue behind me started ⁴**sort of** sighing. So rude, ⁵**you know what do I mean**? And ⁶**there it was one of those moments** when you really don't need ⁷**the stuff like that**. Then ⁸**this the** guy comes over waving my wallet! ⁹**Funny experience**, how finding something you've lost is the best kind of feeling.

3 Rewrite the story as an anecdote using phrases and substitutions from Ex 1 and Ex 2.

> I'd just got home from work – it must have been about 6 p.m. – and my phone rang. And there was a man on the line whose voice I didn't recognise. And he said, 'Susie Draper, is that you?' I get loads of cold calls. I was going out at 6.30, and I didn't want to get caught up in a long discussion about accident claims or similar. It's strange, but I don't like just ending the call abruptly. The caller has a job to do, hasn't he? So, I said, 'Thanks, but no thanks,' and then the man made a noise that sounded like a giggle. I realised that it wasn't a random seller, but my cousin Liam.

7A omitting words

REFERENCE ◀◀ page 82

Omission

- relative clauses

  When the relative pronoun is omitted, two nouns/pronouns can occur next to each other.

  The wallet a boy found on the steps has been left in my office. (which)

  This can be particularly problematic if a relative clause ends with a preposition.

  The role model Jane most looked up to was her mother. (who)

- past participle clauses

  The relative pronoun and the auxiliary can sometimes be omitted, making the past participle easily mistaken for the main verb.

  People caught hunting will be prosecuted. (who are)

  Phones hacked into included those of celebrities and ordinary people. (which were)

- *that* clauses

  That can be omitted, making the sentence tricky to disentangle.

  Did you know [ ] people are saying [ ] Jill believes [ ] she's going to be sacked?

Subject

We often omit a subject pronoun in spoken language.

Don't really know.

Haven't read it, I'm afraid.

Didn't get to the end of the film.

Must be difficult, getting such an early train every morning.

Auxiliary

We can omit the auxiliary in informal questions.

You going to the party later?

They finished the roadworks outside your house yet?

Notice that we don't omit *am*.

Am I bringing the sandwiches? NOT ~~I bringing the sandwiches?~~

Pronoun + auxiliary

We sometimes omit both the pronoun and the auxiliary in spoken language.

Interesting news this morning.

Not seen him today.

Articles

If we are sure who or what we are talking about, we can sometimes omit an article.

Teacher said we've got an assignment coming up.

Essay I did last week got full marks.

Book's really good. You must read it.

Lecture went on for ages!

PRACTICE

1 Make the text below easier to understand by adding words that have been omitted.

Four people [1]_____ charged with vandalising a sign [2]_____ first erected in 1908 to welcome visitors to their town have turned themselves in to the authorities. One of the many outraged residents speaking out about the group [3]_____ placed in custody just hours earlier was Mayor Bainbridge, who said [4]_____ anyone [5]_____ prepared to act in such a manner was nothing short of a 'menace to society'. The people [6]_____ arrested have not been named, but it's expected [7]_____ they will appear in court on Monday.

2 Underline the words that can be omitted in the conversation.

A: We have got to get a move on. It's nearly 8.30. The train leaves at 8.40!

B: Have you fed the dog?

A: I fed him half an hour ago. I've also unloaded the dishwasher and I've left some notes for the dog sitter.

B: That's brilliant. Is she coming over soon?

A: She'll be here in about half an hour. I gave her a new key yesterday. The key that she had didn't work very well.

B: It sounds like we're all sorted. Are the cases by the door?

A: They are ready and waiting. The taxi's been outside for ten minutes.

B: Have you seen my …

A: Come on, hurry up! Do you want to go on this holiday or not?

7B prepositional phrases

REFERENCE ◀◀ page 84

Prepositional phrases can follow adjectives, nouns and verbs and consist of a preposition + noun/-*ing* verb/a clause.

Dependent prepositions with adjectives, nouns and verbs

We can use prepositions after:

- adjectives: *accustomed to, angry about/with, annoyed about/with, aware of, amazed at/about, ashamed of, based on, certain of/about, committed to, concerned about, conducive to, confident of/about, conscious of, convinced of/about, eligible for, guilty of, horrified at/by, indicative of, justified in, keen on, mindful of, terrified of/about, proud of, typical of, upset about/at.*

- nouns: *necessity of, talent for, motivation for, hope of, a consequence of, the risk of, hesitation in, implications for, anger about, a/no/little chance of, a course in, a hint of, an increase in, no justification in, the likelihood of, a possibility of, a reason for, a regret about, the thought of, a focus on.*

  There's **no hint of** the strike being called off.

  The figure is **based on** recent research.

  He is **guilty of** not giving detectives the full story.

When an adjective, noun or verb has a dependent preposition, the same preposition is usually used with all word classes, e.g. *rely on, a reliance on, be reliant on.*

- adjectives + *for* + object: *essential, vital, crucial, important, (im)possible, normal, common.*

  It's common for people who can't sleep to use relaxation techniques.

- verbs: *believe in, benefit from, compliment on, decide on/against, depend on, dream of/about, insist on, plan on, pride yourself on, result from, struggle with, specialise in, succeed in.*

  I think the soup would **benefit from** more salt.

  Mum **prided herself on** how she brought up us kids to have good manners.

Fixed prepositional phrases

We also use fixed prepositional phrases which can act as adjectives and adverbs, e.g. *out of work, at an advantage, at the beginning of, at the scene of, by mistake, within limits, in the face of.*

Is your brother **out of work**?

Give me a ring when you're **at a loose end**.

At present, there are twenty students **in the group**.

Fixed prepositional phrases cannot be changed, but some verbs with objects will split the verb and preposition.

He complimented me on my talk.

PRACTICE

1 Add nine missing dependent prepositions to the text below.

How our heroes have changed

In ancient mythologies, such as Indian or Greek, heroes tended to be men who benefited the support of gods and goddesses and succeeded destroying their enemies on an epic scale. To some extent, cinema and literature still follow this model, although these days we are becoming more accustomed women wielding weapons as well as men. The rise in cinema of the female hero may be indicative women's changed role in society. However, nowadays, our heroes tend to be people who show courage the face of adversity and are committed acting for society's greater good: a charity worker in the field or a first responder at the scene of an accident. Our modern-day notion of a hero is based the saving of lives as opposed to a focus how many enemies or monsters a hero can slay. One thing we can be certain, however, is that humans will always have an innate desire for a hero to look up to.

2 Rewrite the sentences using the words in brackets and dependent prepositions.

1 I know all about the issues surrounding climate change. (AWARE)

2 Nadia feels very bad that she spread rumours about Warren. (ASHAMED)

3 It's impossible for you to get an interview with her today. (CHANCE)

4 Pictures in magazines are very often manipulated. (COMMON)

5 Anyone caught up in the mis-selling scandal can get compensation. (ELIGIBLE)

6 The landlord is within his rights to raise rents annually. (JUSTIFIED)

7 What do you hope to focus on during your third year? (SPECIALISE)

8 You'll win the contract as long as you don't gloss over the problems. (DEPENDS)

GRAMMAR BANK

7C How to ... hedge an opinion and express reservations

REFERENCE ◀◀ page 87

During a discussion, we need to develop the interaction by asking for and giving opinions with justifications, often prioritising facts. Sometimes we may be hesitant or unsure, or want to soften our opinions by using phrases to hedge.

Asking for an opinion

What's your take on this?

What's your reaction to ... ?

What are your thoughts on ... ?

How do you see this?

Giving/justifying an opinion

You've only got to look at ...

I have to say I'm totally against ...

To me that makes a whole lot of sense.

In that respect I'm with you.

No one would disagree with that.

Looking at all the information out there, I'd have to say ...

Why should it be any different with this?

That doesn't surprise me in the least.

Hedging and giving reservations

Maybe it's just me, but ...

Obviously, it's important to ... , but ...

I'm no expert, but ...

I just think that ...

There are some things I agree with, but ...

The idea has a lot going for it, but ...

I agree up to a point, but ...

This would suggest that ...

Well, this might be true to some extent.

I think that is somewhat exaggerated.

Well, I wouldn't go so far as to say ...

I wouldn't be surprised if that were the case.

Prioritising facts over supposition

On the face of it, it seems ... , but actually ...

Well, supposedly so, but look at the facts.

The facts speak for themselves.

Don't be blinded by all the hype around the topic.

It's a very emotive issue, when it comes down to the facts.

PRACTICE

1 Complete the comments with the words in the box. There are two words you do not need.

agreeing	down	extent	far
going	only	somewhat	take

1 I would say that is .... oversimplistic.

2 When it comes .... to the evidence, there is nothing to support that idea.

3 This is to some .... a matter for individuals to decide.

4 Your suggestion has a lot .... for it, but I think we need to be realistic.

5 Regarding a ban on hunting, you've .... got to look at the number of people who ...

6 We've heard the latest reports. What's your .... on the issue?

2 Read the two conversations. Correct one word in the sentences (1–10).

1 A: [1]What's your mistake on this?

  B: [2]On the fate of it, it seems a good idea to go vegetarian, but actually I couldn't give up meat completely.

  A: [3]In that prospect I'm with you.

  B: [4]And, I'm really opposite any form of coercion, like someone telling us what to eat.

  A: [5]No one might disagree with that.

2 A: This thing about banning wifi in public spaces – [6]How can you see this?

  B: Well, they bluffed about banning mobiles. [7]Why should it be all different with this?

  A: Bluffing again? [8]I'd be surprised if that's the base. They've actually created wifi-free zones in some areas, and it worked, technically I mean.

  B: [9]Well supposedly so, but look at the factors. Everyone has mobile internet ...

  A: But they can block that. Or they say they can block it.

  B: [10]That doesn't surprise me in the last. They'll say anything that's convenient for them.

  A: I still think it's a good idea ...

3 Complete the extracts from a discussion about climate change with your own ideas.

1 What's your reaction .... ?

2 Well, you've only got ....

3 I have to say I'm totally .... because ....

4 What's your take .... ?

5 Looking at all the ....

6 Maybe it's just ....

7 The facts speak ....

8 On the face of ....

8A noun phrases

REFERENCE ◄◄ page 94

A noun or pronoun can be pre-modified (have words before it) or post-modified (have words after it) to make a noun phrase. Noun phrases make writing and speaking more succinct and sophisticated.

Pre-modification

Before a noun we can use:

- simple or compound adjectives.

  a **vulnerable** person, **mutual** respect, a **persuasive** argument

  a **high-rise** building, a **waterproof** phone

- nouns used as adjectives to form compound nouns.

  a **business model**, a **pilot study**, an **echo chamber**

- past and present participles as adjectives.

  an **educated** guess, a **growing** problem

- adverb and adjective combinations.

  a **frustratingly ambiguous** ending, **slowly moving** traffic

  Tech companies are **highly beneficial** to the economy.

Post-modification

After a noun or pronoun we can use:

- prepositional phrases; relative clauses; infinitives with *to*; participle clauses (replacing relative clauses).

  The implications **for society** are …

  a course **in infant psychology**

  Someone **who influenced me greatly** was my uncle.

  The image **you convey** will make all the difference.

  Emma needs somewhere **to stay**.

  It'll take a long time **to dry**.

  Evidence **suggesting a cover-up by the council** is emerging.

  A tree **twisted out of shape by the wind** stood on the cliff face.

- adjectives, which are actually relative clauses without *who/which/that + be*. These are often used with pronouns such as *someone*, *anything*, *no one*.

  The only tickets **available** are in the stalls. (which are available)

  Wear something **warm**.

  We need someone **capable** of taking the initiative.

  Did you notice anything **interesting**?

PRACTICE

1 Complete the noun phrases using the appropriate form of the words in brackets and adding words where necessary.

1 A (nurture) environment (characterise / a focus / individuality) is what makes the course so special.

A nurturing environment characterising a focus on individuality is what makes the course so special.

2 After a (large / dry) start (day) we've got rain (move in / the north) and winds (gust / 100 km / hour).

3 (cut / edge / pilot) studies (conduct / researchers / three countries) support the initial hypothesis.

4 I need more time (relax / let / ideas flow) if I'm going to create something (original / worth / write).

5 We believe there is a (rapid / expand) market (app / can monitor / blood / sugar / levels).

6 The ideas (we / come up with / yesterday) could help bridge the gap (folk / jazz / audiences).

2 Shorten each sentence in the text using noun phrases.

[1]People, and I mean the ones who are overwhelmed by pressures from work, they no longer have an excuse for not exercising. [2]Our seven-minute workout, which was inspired by high-intensity interval training (HIIT), is the go-to option for people who are busy with packed schedules that leave them with no time for extensive exercise. [3]The workout consists of bursts of exercise that last for thirty seconds separated by rest periods that last for ten seconds. [4]There is scientific support, and it's very persuasive, for the benefits for health of HIIT when it is compared to longer activity which is also less intensive. [5]Some people dislike exercise and for those people, there is the attraction which they can't resist, that no matter how bad it feels, it's over before you notice.

People overwhelmed by work pressures no longer have an excuse for not exercising.

GRAMMAR BANK

8B uses of *will* and *would*

REFERENCE ◀◀ page 96

will

We use *will* when talking about the future for: predictions, facts, decisions made while speaking, activities in progress, an activity that is part of a normal sequence of events, an activity completed or in progress before a future point of time.

The government **won't honour** that promise – wait and see!

The concert **will finish** late, so don't expect us home before 11.30.

The trains are running late so **I'll get** a cab. See you soon.

I'll be working in Edinburgh next week. Might you be free to catch up?

Dan **will be going** to the supermarket this afternoon – is there anything you'd like him to pick up for you?

5.30? I **won't even have left** college by then.

We can also use *will* in other ways not related to the future. We use *will* to talk about typical (and irritating) behaviour.

Every evening after dinner, he**'ll shut** himself into his room and listen to really loud rock music.

She **will leave** half empty coffee cups all over the house.

We use *won't* or *will not* to express refusal to do something.

We've tried to persuade him that it's not a good idea, but he **won't listen**.

The website **won't allow me access** no matter which password I use.

We use *will* to express certainty.

They**'ll have finished** the debate by now, so we should know the results soon.

She**'ll probably be boarding** the plane, so don't expect a call from her just yet.

It's 9.30. He**'ll be** at the office now.

would

We use *would* to report speech, talk about hypotheses, be polite and soften statements.

He insisted he**'d be** fine.

Would you **be concerned** if the voting age were lowered?

Would you **give** us a hand, please?

I **would guess** that it will be decided later.

I **would imagine** that it's not our responsibility.

We use *would* to express typical (and irritating) behaviour in the past.

She **would change** her computer password every two weeks in order to protect her files.

He **would come** in from a walk and leave muddy footprints all over the floor.

We use *wouldn't* to express refusal to do something in the past.

My parents wanted to build an extension on our house, but the planning officers **wouldn't let** them.

As a child he **wouldn't eat** any green vegetables. Now he loves them.

PRACTICE

1 Complete the message with *will* and the correct form of the verbs in brackets.

Sorry, but I ¹_____ (not / be able) to come round tomorrow evening as planned because I've just been told by the manager that I ²_____ (work) in London for the rest of the week. I ³_____ (leave) first thing in the morning. The 7.30 train will get me into Waterloo station at 9.30 and I ⁴_____ (get) a cab to our London branch from there. According to the forecast, it ⁵_____ (be) cold and rainy in London tomorrow, so I ⁶_____ (not / walk)! I ⁷_____ (finish) work by 5.30, so will give you a call then. With luck, you ⁸_____ (manage) to get your laptop fixed by then, so could we have a virtual meeting? I ⁹_____ (see) Fran tomorrow at one of the meetings and I ¹⁰_____ (find out) how her holiday went and let you know when we chat. Have a great day and speak soon.

2 Rewrite the sentences using *would* to make them sound more polite or to soften the statement.

1 I need some help.
2 I imagine he'll fail.
3 I think this will take a lot of time.
4 I guess he's busy.
5 Don't speak so loudly.
6 Move your car.

3 Rewrite the sentences using *will* or *would*.

1 He's definitely going to be ill if he continues to eat next to nothing.
   If he _____ .
2 He refuses to ask for directions or check his phone, so of course he gets lost!
   He _____ !
3 Darren always used to leave things to the last minute and then risk being late.
   Darren _____ .
4 His electricity bill is bound to go up if he leaves all the lights on overnight.
   If he _____ .
5 Sarah put the dog outside because it refused to stop barking.
   The dog _____ .
6 I'm sure they've got caught in the traffic, but they'll be here soon.
   They _____ .
7 She's most likely doing her assignment at the moment, so let's go round later.
   She _____ .
8 Mark is undoubtedly sitting with his phone out, waiting for your call.
   Mark _____ .

8C How to ... explain the purpose and benefit of something

REFERENCE ◀◀ page 99

A key part of any good discussion is explaining the purpose and benefit of your ideas. How you do so depends largely on the formality of the situation.

Informal

What I've found works is .../What I think would really work is ...

The point is that ...

Another real positive about ... is ...

And looking at all the benefits, of course ...

I think a big plus for me would be ...

And I'm speaking from experience here ...

You've only got to look at ...

That's what I get out of ...

I feel confident to say that ...

It's not that ... it's just that ...

Let me correct you there. The reason I say this is ...

Let's be realistic here. You have to consider ...

I take your point, but the advantage of something like this is ...

It's just beneficial in so many ways.

Without a doubt, it's ...

Let me give a couple of examples here ...

I'm not the only one to think this .../There's a general consensus that ...

Formal

The reasoning behind my stance on this topic is ...

With the benefit of hindsight, it becomes apparent that the purpose of this was to ...

One pertinent example to support my stance on this topic would be ...

I appreciate what you're saying, but there is no evidence to back that up, whereas ...

PRACTICE

1 Find and correct the mistakes in the sentences.

1 And glancing at all the benefits, I would say that we have to go with this idea.

2 One relative example to support my stance on this topic would be the number of resignations last year.

3 I think a large plus for me would be the speed at which we could put the plan into action.

4 The cause behind my stance on this issue is the excessive costs involved.

5 There is a wide consensus that this is not the best path to follow.

6 It's not why it's stupid, it's just that it's not quite as useful as you think it is.

2 Match the sentence beginnings (1–6) with the endings (a–f).

1 To be clear, I'm speaking from experience

2 I totally understand where you're coming from,

3 Let's be realistic here,

4 With the benefit of hindsight it becomes

5 I'm not the only one to

6 I take your point, but the advantage of

a we have to consider the impact of this on several groups of people.

b my suggestion is that it will help a broader spectrum of people.

c apparent that the purpose of these measures was to save money, not to help people.

d but the point is that it's been tried before – unsuccessfully.

e here when I say this course of action simply won't work.

f see no benefit in what you're proposing.

3 Complete the conversations with phrases from Ex 1 and Ex 2. Use the words in the box.

> coming   consensus   only
> plus   realistic   stance

A: Why do you have such strong feelings on this issue?

B: The reasoning [1]............... is the detrimental effect it will have on the economy.

A: So, you fully support the idea?

B: I'm not [2]............... think this. There's [3]............... that it's the best way forward.

A: A [4]............... would be the ability to take on more staff quickly.

B: I understand where [5]..............., but let's [6].............. . Where will the money come from?

TRANSITION TO 100% RENEWABLE ENERGY

Target **2040**

WIND	47%	HYDROGEN	6%
SOLAR	40%	BIOMASS	4%
GEOTHERMAL	0.5%	OCEAN	2%

1A idioms

◀◀ page 8

1 A Complete the sentences (1–10) with the words in the box. Then match them with the follow-up sentences (a–j).

> along changed cut knocked fly
> good hung share strides threw

1 I don't usually get .... up about minor setbacks.

2 I would go .... with anyone who believes that you need to make mistakes in order to learn.

3 I had my fair .... of problems when I first started learning to drive.

4 I'm not saying that learning Russian will be easy for me, but I'll give it a .... go.

5 In the middle of the art course I realised I really wasn't .... out for it.

6 The authorities are making .... in helping eliminate illiteracy.

7 I know a few teachers whose methods .... in the face of educational advice.

8 My mother used to teach in a secondary school but .... tack to become a writer.

9 The runner realised he was injured and couldn't win so .... in the towel.

10 Failing my maths exam completely .... my confidence.

a For example, a new community learning project is offering free adult classes for those who need it.

b I tend to think 'get over yourself' and then I look at the problem from a different angle.

c However, the results they are getting are simply amazing.

d Some things we learn from our errors stay with us for life.

e This proved a good decision and has brought in a lot of money.

f So I transferred to photography.

g Most of these were because I was too scared to go any faster than 30 km per hour!

h It will be a challenge, but you have to try new things, don't you?

i Particularly after I'd put so many hours into revising for it.

j It was the right thing to do because he had more races later in the season.

B Choose five idioms from Ex 1A and write one sentence for each that is true for you.

As a photographer, it's important not to get hung up about equipment and technical specifications – just get out there and take photos!

1B compound nouns

◀◀ page 11

1 A Match items from box A with items fro[m] box B to make compound nouns.

A
> blended continuous critical
> external peer rote student
> tuition virtual learning vocation[al]

B
> accreditation assessment (x2)
> environment fees learning (x2)
> loan thinking training

B Match the compound nouns from Ex 1[A] with the definitions (1–10).

1 money paid to a university or colleg[e] for its courses

2 money borrowed from the governm[ent] or a bank to finance studies

3 judging ability by a person's coursework rather than by an exam

4 a web-based study platform for the digital aspects of a course

5 learning based on the skills needed [to] do a particular job

6 a combination of online and face-to-face studying

7 the memorisation of information ba[sed] on repetition

8 objective confirmation of someone'[s] standard by an independent person [or] organisation

9 comparison and checking of work b[y] classmates of a similar age and leve[l]

10 skills developed in addition to mainstream topics to help with problem solving

C Work in pairs. Which of the things in Ex [1B] do you have experience of? Explain you[r] answers.

2A binomials

◀◀ page 20

1 A Complete the binomials in bold with the correct words from paragraphs 5 and 8 in the article on page 21.

1 .... **and foremost** is the idea that this will facilitate cultural development.

2 Storytelling and everything else that is .... **and parcel** of the creative culture ... can disappear.

B Complete the binomials in bold with the words in the box.

> by   cut   give   hustle   live   make   out
> peace   pick   short   slowly   sooner

1 Parks and open spaces need to be developed to ensure .... **and quiet** for those who want it.

2 Pollution levels in city centres are coming down, ... **but surely**.

3 I love the .... **and bustle** of market days in the city centre, and this will appeal to visitors.

4 For many cities, becoming a City of Culture and getting income from tourists is .... **or break** for them.

5 Unfortunately, the solution to inner-city problems is not .... **and dried**.

6 We'll need two or three months, ... **or take**, to get an application together to be City of Culture.

7 The meeting about the application was .... **and sweet**, just a quick transfer of information.

8 For tourists who are .... **and about** in the city all day, the transport system needs to be cheap and easy to use.

9 .... **and large**, a City of Culture is one of the lesser-known cities in the country.

10 .... **or later** we will have to look at plans to restore the old Central Theatre.

11 We can't .... **and choose** our neighbours, but luckily mine are very kind.

12 I had no idea about the culture awards for cities until recently, but you .... **and learn**, don't you?

C Look at the binomials in Ex 1A and Ex 1B. What do they mean?

2B multi-word verbs for reporting

◀◀ page 23

1 A Underline the multi-word verb and circle its object in the sentences (1–6). Which verbs are separable?

1 Many viewers are calling for more signers, particularly on news programmes, to help the hearing impaired.

2 Do fill me in on what happened at the conference. I'm sorry I missed it.

3 My friend talked me into watching the dubbed series with him, but I really prefer subtitles.

4 They say I didn't interpret his conclusion well, but you heard the original. Please back me up.

5 Someone tipped me off that the delegate spoke very quickly, so I asked for a copy of his speech before the meeting.

6 Jack reeled off the names of all the politicians he'd worked with, and I was impressed.

B Match the multi-word verbs from Ex 1A with their definitions (a–f).

a to say or show what someone is saying is true

b to persuade someone to do something

c to ask publicly for something to be done

d to warn someone secretly, often about illegal activities

e to tell someone about recent events, especially if they have been away

f to say a lot of information quickly and easily, often from memory

C Work in pairs. Student A: Say a sentence in direct speech. Student B: Report Student A's sentence using one of the multi-word verbs from Ex 1A.

A: You need eggs, butter, rice, chicken, onions, garlic ... .

B: She reeled off the ingredients for a recipe.

3B metaphors

◀◀ page 36

1 A Read the dictionary entry. Choose the correct words to complete the metaphors relating to water (1–8).

> **met•a•phor** /ˈmetəfə, -fɔː -fɔːr/ ●●○ noun
> [countable, uncountable]
> **1** a way of describing something by referring to it as something different and suggesting that it has similar qualities to that thing.
> Longman Dictionary of Contemporary English online

1 Your screen **ices / freezes**. There is a weird echo.
2 Honestly, I'm so busy I can barely keep my head **above / over** water.
3 Information from management takes a long time to **surge / trickle** down to us employees.
4 I sometimes have to **water down / freeze** my language to avoid making people angry.
5 I can't stand people around me who are **wet blankets / dripping taps**.
6 Sometimes ideas and creativity just **flow / stream**.
7 I'm lucky to have a friend who I can **gush / pour out** my frustrations to.
8 My inbox is **flooded / drowned out** with spam.

B Work in pairs. Which sentences in Ex 1A can you relate to?

3C politics

◀◀ page 38

1 A Complete the sentences with the words in the box.

> ballot   constitution   far   left   liberal   manifesto
> monarch   polls   right   spin   state   vote

1 Politicians make promises in their _____ which are designed to persuade people to vote for them.
2 A socialist party is one which is **on the** _____ of political beliefs, and a conservative party is _____-**wing** in its beliefs.
3 Even though **exit** _____ aren't official, they're often a good indication of the final result of a vote.
4 A member of the _____ **right** or **left** holds more extreme views.
5 Most nations have a **written** _____ of the basic laws and principles by which they are governed.
6 The **head of** _____ can be an elected president or a **hereditary** _____ .
7 The party leader is elected **by secret** _____ where every party member can **cast a** _____ .
8 Those with _____ **political views** share a belief in liberty and equality for all.
9 In politics, party leaders usually try **to** _____ any defeat to make it sound positive.

B Work in pairs. Use five phrases from Ex 1A to describe the political system in your country.

4A adverb–adjective collocations

◀◀ page 46

1 A Which other adverb(s) could be used to replace the adverbs in the collocations in bold?

1 Costs involved in the exploration of space and the sea should become **significantly cheaper**.
2 Being able to spend a short time in space has become a **startlingly realistic** prospect.

B Complete the summary of a news programme about pioneers with the adverbs in the box.

> blindingly   gravely   immediately   infinitely
> ludicrously   vehemently   wildly

The interview earlier today with experts in the space industry and ocean research has elicited some interesting comments from viewers. Many appear to be ¹_____ opposed to investment in space programmes, with many stating that investing in ocean research would be ²_____ preferable, as results could help deal with more ³_____ important issues such as climate change. One viewer even went so far as to say that it was ⁴'_____ obvious' that we shall not be establishing tourist facilities on the Moon any time soon. A former space engineer commented that in his opinion, the statistics quoted in relation to the proposed space mission are ⁵_____ inaccurate and added that those people who thought that space tourism would become affordable in their lifetimes were ⁶_____ mistaken as the prices will remain ⁷_____ high for a very long time.

C In pairs, write a comment of your own about pioneers, using one or more adverb–adjective collocations. Share your comments with the class.

4B adjectives to describe people

◀◀ page 48

1 A Match the words in the box with their meanings (1–8).

> aloof   appreciative   compassionate   conscientious
> enterprising   intuitive   resourceful   selfless

1 feeling sympathetic towards people who are suffering
2 grateful for everything
3 caring about others and not yourself
4 able to think of new and clever solutions to problems
5 always doing your work with a lot of care
6 keeping your distance and appearing not to want to interact with others
7 knowing what people think or need without being told
8 using what is at hand to solve a problem

B Do you know or know of someone who could be described in these ways? Give an example of how they show this quality.

5A adjectives and adjectival endings

◀◀ page 57

1 A Complete the sentences with the adjectives in the box.

> bereft   industrious   pompous   reassuring
> successive   unperturbed

1 I feel _____ if I'm somewhere abroad without my dictionary or translation app.

2 If a news presenter sounds _____ , I refuse to listen to him or her.

3 I'm _____ if people can't understand my accent. I simply speak more slowly.

4 I'm _____ when it comes to learning the grammar and vocabulary of a new language, but I'm not that concerned about acquiring perfect pronunciation.

5 I find it _____ to have the same accent as the person or people I'm talking to.

6 _____ generations of my family have spoken the same local dialect.

B Work in pairs. How far do you agree with each statement in Ex 1A?

2 A Complete the sentences with the adjectives in the box.

> disconcerting   dishevelled   distinctive   gullible
> implausible   susceptible   self-deprecating
> unapproachable   unfavourable   unintelligible

1 His accent created a(n) _____ impression which only changed when people got to know him better.

2 She has a(n) _____ way of implying that she knows just what you're thinking.

3 His excuses became more and more _____ and after a while we stopped believing anything he said.

4 Scammers rely on people being _____ and accepting what they are told as complete truth.

5 She has a(n) _____ manner, and this modesty belies her true nature.

6 Older people are said to be more _____ to falling for cold callers, but young people get caught out, too.

7 His height and severe expression often make him appear _____ , but he is actually very good-natured.

8 My accent used to be so thick that many people said I could be _____ on the phone!

9 The singer usually looks _____ , as if he flung his clothes on in five seconds.

10 She has a very _____ voice, and I can pick her out in a crowd immediately.

B Work in pairs. Think of one more adjective for each of the following endings to describe the first impression you have of a person.

-ive _____

-able _____

-ible _____

-ing _____

-ed _____

5C adjectives to describe presentations

◀◀ page 62

1 A Choose the correct words to complete the description of a good presenter.

A [1]**mediocre / captivating** speaker keeps everyone's attention and will convey their ideas in a(n) [2]**assured / self-effacing** manner with [3]**expressive / stiff** body language, using their face and hands to illustrate their point. They will put forward a [4]**muddled / cogent** argument which is well thought through and easy to follow. They will support points with [5]**pertinent / long-winded** examples and may include a number of anecdotes or [6]**subtle / inappropriate** jokes: ones which are clever, not obvious, and certainly not offensive or rude.

B Complete the conversations with adjectives from Ex 1A.

1 A: How was the lecture?
 B: Hmm. I found it rather _____ . It went on for ages.

2 A: How was the comedy club?
 B: Mixed. Mostly fine but the last guy made really _____ remarks and offended a few people.

3 A: How was the webinar?
 B: Nothing special, quite _____ in fact. Most of the information is pretty common knowledge.

4 A: How is the court case going?
 B: Well, I think. The evidence against my client is very _____ and unconvincing.

5 A: How was the play?
 B: Not bad. The only problem was the main actor. He was too _____ and formal for the role.

6 A: How is your new boss?
 B: I like him. He has a deceptively _____ manner which masks his obvious expertise.

C Work in pairs. Choose three adjectives from Ex 1A and use them in true sentences to describe a recent experience.

6A describing books and films

◀◀ page 68

1 A Complete the extracts from book blurbs (1–6) with the words in the box.

> debut   fiendishly   grips   plotted
> riveting   sheer   style

1 This is another _____ page-turner and a must-read for her fans.

2 DON'T MISS THIS STUNNING _____ NOVEL BY THIS TALENTED NEWLY DISCOVERED AUTHOR.

3 Ingeniously _____ and a _____ delight to read! Full of twists and turns.

4 IT'S _____ CLEVER AND UNPUTDOWNABLE.

5 A captivating 'whodunnit' in the _____ of Agatha Christie.

6 It _____ the reader from the first page and is a definite crowd pleaser.

B Match the words or phrases from Ex 1A (1–5) with the meanings (a–e).

1 full of twists and turns	a can't stop reading
2 crowd pleaser	b keeps surprising
3 page-turner	c detective mystery
4 debut	d popular with a lot of people
5 whodunnit	e a writer's first book

C Work in pairs. Rewrite the sentences in Ex 1A so they are true for films or TV series you have seen.

6C adjective–noun collocations: travel

◀◀ page 74

1 A Match the adjectives in bold in the collocations (a–f) with the definitions (1–6).

a a **pristine** beach
b a **dense** forest
c a **rambling** farmhouse
d a **well-appointed** hotel room
e a **rugged** coastline
f a **barren** desert

1 _____ : large and spreading out in many directions
2 _____ : land or soil that has few or no plants growing in it
3 _____ : in an unspoilt condition; extremely clean and new
4 _____ : rough and uneven
5 _____ : made of or containing a lot of things or people that are very close together
6 _____ : having a good standard of furniture and/or equipment and all necessary amenities

B Which noun does NOT usually collocate with the adjectives (1–6)?

1 rugged – mountains, hills, buildings, good looks
2 dense – undergrowth, beach, smoke, population
3 rambling – museum, trail, discussion, furniture
4 well-appointed – apartment, exhibition, quarters, conference centre
5 barren – landscape, town, wilderness, hillside
6 pristine – coffee, rainforest, condition, white shirt

C Work in pairs. Write two adjectives that collocate with each noun you chose in Ex 1B.

D Work in pairs. Tell each other about three places you know using three of the collocations in Ex 1A and Ex 1B.

7A connotation

◀◀ page 80

1 A Choose the option (a–c) which is NOT possible in each sentence.

1 Our brains are constantly _____ with choices.
  a faced   **b** confronted   **c** opposed

2 The house is quite _____, with no neighbours nearby.
  a lone   **b** isolated   **c** secluded

3 Go round the field _____ .
  a anti-clockwise   **b** counter-clockwise   **c** the wrong way round

4 The company is _____ a period of restructuring.
  a taking up   **b** going ahead with   **c** embarking upon

5 My client _____ the view that climate change is still a question of debate.
  a subscribes to   **b** concurs with   **c** sees eye to eye with

6 _____ deliveries – all city zones!
  a Take-over   **b** Take-out   **c** Take-away

7 Need to sort something with the mayor? Ask Petros to help, he's got a lot of _____ .
  a influence   **b** persuasion   **c** clout

8 The shortage of nursing staff is a _____ problem.
  a worrying   **b** vexing   **c** concerned

B What differences, if any, are there between the two correct answers in the sentences in Ex 1A? Think about shades of meaning, formality or British or American English.

7B idioms: books and reading

◀◀ page 83

1 A Choose the correct words to complete the sentences.

1 I tried to coax my brother out for a walk, but he's got his **eyes** / **nose** in a book, as always.

2 I didn't get very far with the book – a bit **heavy-going** / **hard-going** for me.

3 Can't come over, sorry. Exam tomorrow, so it's dinner now, then I **strike** / **hit** the books!

4 In my opinion, there's nothing better than getting **lost** / **away** in a book.

5 Lucy's been a **bookmark** / **bookworm** ever since she got her first Roald Dahl book.

6 You don't have to be a **live-hard** / **die-hard** book lover to appreciate the value of reading.

7 There are some books I read **cover-to-cover** / **end-to-end**, staying up into the early hours.

8 When you get a well-earned break it's good to **fold** / **curl** up with a book for a while and chill.

B Use three of the idioms in Ex 1A to write sentences that are true for you or someone you know. Work in pairs and compare sentences.

8A compound adjectives

◀◀ page 94

1 A Match words from A and B to form compound adjectives.

A

| ~~clear~~ | far (x2) | hard | life |
| long | time | up | widely |

B

| coming | ~~cut~~ | held | honoured | fetched |
| long | reaching | term | wired |

clear-cut

B Complete the documentary preview with the correct compound adjectives from Ex 1A.

Take a deep breath

You may have heard of the Ama of Japan. These are women whose [1] _____ profession is diving for pearls and food. The [2] _____ documentary about these amazing people makes for compelling viewing. They dive about 100–150 times a day, holding their breath for up to two minutes on each dive. It may sound [3] _____, but it is a fact. For scientists it has been baffling – how do they maintain such repetitive, extreme dives without suffering [4] _____ health problems? Most people would experience excruciating pain if they attempted anything similar, so it has been a [5] _____ belief that these divers have superior lung capacities. However, tests have shown that there is no real [6] _____ physiological reason for this ability; it is just [7] _____, instinctive. Sadly, today many divers are choosing to take up careers in other fields, and this will have [8] _____ consequences for the survival of this [9] _____ profession.

C Work in pairs. Think of a different noun or phrase that could be described by each of the compound adjectives in Ex 1A.

8B verbs to describe reactions

◀◀ page 95

1 A Choose the correct option.

1 Some people will **clutch** / **wince** on hearing fingernails on a blackboard.

2 The sound of the drill **set** / **started** his teeth on edge.

3 The thought of eating insects makes me **squirm** / **start**.

4 The audience **gasped** / **grimaced** when the trapeze artist nearly fell.

5 I **grimaced** / **clutched** at the bitter flavour of the medicine.

6 The actress didn't even **set** / **flinch** when the murderer brandished his knife close to her face.

7 The horror film was so scary I found myself **clutching** / **squirming** the arms of the chair.

8 She **clutched** / **started** at the sound of the phone and dropped her cup.

B Work in pairs. Tell your partner about a time you experienced a similar reaction using the verbs in Ex 1A.

COMMUNICATION BANK

2A Ex 8B

If selected, we will be co-funding the City of Arts with the government.

Benefits

- The construction of a new theatre.
- The construction of a new art gallery.
- An extensive advertising campaign that will attract tourists from around the world.
- Features in international articles and on TV programmes about our town.
- Investment in transport for visitors.
- A one-off public holiday for the city.
- ....
- ....

However, as we will have to contribute some of our local government money, there will be knock-on effects on our budget.

Possible negative effects

- No spending on improvements to school facilities for the next three years.
- No increase in spending on waste collection and other public services for the next five years.
- An increase of ten percent in taxes for local businesses.
- ....
- ....

3B Ex 8B Student A

You believe remote working is the future.
- Money needs to be invested in better tech.
- More training should be given on working remotely.
- Counselling should be made available for workers suffering from burnout.
- Workers should be encouraged to develop their own social networks.

4A Ex 7B Student A

Investment into further space research should be limited until problems on Earth have been solved.

For

- Planet Earth could be destroyed by climate change.
- Issues of poverty, imbalanced economies and equality need to be addressed.
- Space exploration risks polluting space as well as our planet.
- It opens up the opportunity for weaponising space.
- .... (your own idea)
- .... (your own idea)

4C Ex 1A

Sharing economy

An economic system built around the sharing of resources. Private individuals share assets or services for free or for a fee.

Circular economy

An industrial system that is restorative or regenerative, which involves reusing, remanufacturing, repairing and recycling to eliminate waste.

5B Ex 10A Student B

A report is needed about students' access to current news. In particular we would like information about how informed they are about both national and global issues, and recommendations on how they can ascertain that the stories are true and without bias.

8D Ex 5A Pair A

1 The Halo Effect

This occurs when one impression or perception of a person influences how we view their other characteristics. For example, we may find a celebrity attractive or talented and because of this we assume that they are perhaps kind, smart or have other positive qualities. Perceptions of one quality can lead to judgements of other qualities, which are biased.

2 The Bystander Effect

This is the belief that people are less likely to offer help to someone if there are other people present. If an emergency happens and we are the only one there, we would probably help. However, if there are two or more other people present, the likelihood of our taking the responsibility diminishes according to the number of people. A study in 1969 found that seventy percent of people would help someone in distress if they were the only person present, but this shrank to forty percent when there were others there.

3B Ex 8B Student B

You believe more face-to-face contact is important.
- Social events should be arranged to bring people together.
- Insist on one day a week for teams to physically come into the office to collaborate.
- Workers should visit each other to discuss matters before or after video meetings.

3B Ex 8B Student C

You believe morale needs to be raised.
- There should be more feedback on productivity.
- There should be individual, one-to-one online sessions with line managers to assess progress and achievements.
- Workers should be involved in decisions on how morale can be improved.
- Individual arrangements regarding contact availability must be agreed.

4A Ex 7B Student B

Investment into further space research should be limited until problems on Earth have been solved.

Against
- Reaching other planets could help solve problems on Earth.
- Space research involves countries working together which can help develop cultural understanding.
- Earth can be protected through identifying possible asteroid strikes.
- Views from space can give more knowledge of the extent of climate change and its effects.
- .... (your own idea)
- .... (your own idea)

8D Ex 5A Pair B

1 The Pratfall Effect

The Pratfall Effect maintains that we find clever, attractive and talented people more likeable if they make mistakes or are clumsy, for example spill coffee or trip over. It can even give these people advantages in life as it proves that they are not superhuman at all, however superior they may be in their intellect or abilities. Unfortunately, making a blunder does not have the same effect if it is made by someone who is seemingly average – in fact, it can make them appear less likeable.

2 The Barnum Effect

This occurs when people believe that personality descriptions apply specifically to them, even though the description is rather vague and full of information that can apply to a wide range of people. An example of this includes believing that a description in a personality test is specifically tailored to accurately describe your personality, while it has actually been written in a general enough way to be true for many people.

1C Something different

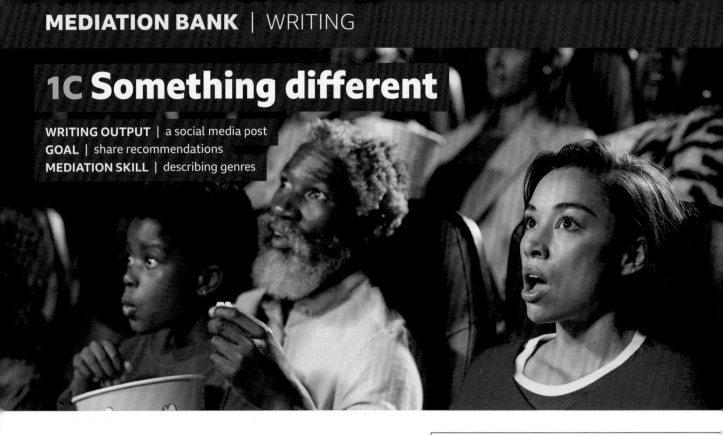

WRITING OUTPUT | a social media post
GOAL | share recommendations
MEDIATION SKILL | describing genres

WARM-UP

1 Work in pairs. Read the quote and discuss the questions.

> 'Creativity is the victory of originality over habit.'

1 What does this mean? Do you agree? Why/Why not?

2 If this is true, does the concept of fixed genres of film, music and literature stop people being creative?

3 What film genres do you enjoy most? Do the things you watch need to be creative/different in order to be enjoyable?

PREPARE

2 A Read the Scenario and answer the questions.

1 What problem does Pietro have?

2 How does he want you to help?

B Match the words (1–8) with the definitions (a–h).

1 formulaic
2 ground-breaking
3 twist
4 derivative
5 trope
6 prequel
7 mind-blowing
8 spin-off

a words, phrases or themes that are used for an unusual or interesting effect
b following a storyline that has been used many times before
c revolutionary, using ideas or methods that haven't been thought of before
d a surprising, unexpected change or difference
e a film or TV programme with characters that were previously in another programme or film
f based on previous films, books or works
g a book, film or play that tells you what happened before the original story
h overwhelming, affecting you strongly

C Look at the words (1–8) in Ex 2B. Which words convey the idea of originality?

D Find three more words in the Scenario to describe originality, or a lack of it, in films.

SCENARIO

A friend sends the following message to you and a group of friends.

Pietro
16:36 | 4 June

Hi everyone,

So you know how much I love watching TV and films. Whatever kind of movie it is, I almost always enjoy it – actually that should be 'enjoyED'. The last few times I've sat down to watch a film or tried to get into a series, I've just got bored. I even walked out of the cinema halfway through a film the other day!

When you look at cinema listings and streaming channels, they're just full of spin-offs, sequels and prequels. Even when it's a new idea, everything seems so formulaic, with predictable storylines, clichéd characters and the same old tired tropes. There doesn't seem to be anything ground-breaking out there, or even slightly innovative.

Well, here's your challenge … can you come up with some suggestions for things that will help me fall back in love with film and TV? I really hope so!

  ♥ 14 💬 3 ↪

Three of your friends have already posted replies.

3 A Work in groups of three. Student A: Read Leo's post. Student B: Read Mina's post. Student C: Read Berta's post. Answer the questions.

    1 What does the post suggest?

    2 What do you think about the suggestion?

B Tell the other students in your group about your post.

Leo
17:18 | 4 June

Do you ever watch old black and white movies? Unlike a lot of modern movies, they often take things quite slowly, and because there are none of the special effects or CGI that we can over-rely on, they really focus on the story and the characters. One film you should definitely try watching is *12 Angry Men*. It's kind of a crime drama but with a bit of a twist – you never actually find out whether the suspect committed the crime. The film is really about how we judge people. Admittedly, the cast are all men – just typical of the times, I suppose – but I really recommend it. It really gets you thinking.

♥ 34 💬 12 ↪

Mina
09:07 | 5 June

Hi Pietro, I feel your pain. I went through a similar thing with books last year. Anyway, one film I watched recently was *WALL-E* – have you ever seen it? If you look up the movie poster, it looks pretty much like any other animated movie you'd expect to see. In fact though, it's really quite unique. For a start, there's hardly any dialogue for the first half an hour – which is kind of shocking, particularly when you consider it's meant to be for kids. I don't want to give away any spoilers about it so I won't say too much but the storyline is very innovative, too.

♥ 9 💬 4 ↪

Berta
13:11 | 5 June

Maybe you should try watching *Spaced* – it's a TV show rather than a film. In some ways it's very derivative because it has a lot of references to those clichés and conventions we've got so used to seeing at the cinema. At the same time though, they take some of those predictable ideas and turn them on their heads. They make them really funny and bring them back to life. It makes it all feel quite fresh and original in that it sets these big Hollywood set-pieces and conventions in a very ordinary real-world place!

♥ 14 💬 8 ↪

4 Read the Mediation Skill box. Then read the posts in Ex 3A again. Find examples of phrases to describe genres in the post you read.

> ## MEDIATION SKILL
> ### describing genres
>
> When you are discussing films, TV, books or music, it's helpful to describe where they fit in the genre and to compare them with other works in that genre. This means other people can get an idea of whether they might be interested and helps to set expectations about any recommendations you give. Here are some ways to do that:
>
> **Give an overall impression**
> X is so/very/fairly predictable/derivative/formulaic.
> It's surprising/shocking/very different!
> It's not what you usually expect.
>
> **Give specific examples of what's different**
> Unlike a lot of action films, the hero is …
> Whereas most of the time, James Bond is basically a superhero, in this film he shows he's human!
> It's a real twist on the normal conventions/things we've all got used to.
>
> **Describe ways in which it's more generic**
> Admittedly, it has a lot of the usual tropes … but the characters are really believable. It's much easier to empathise with them.
> It's typical of (action movies) in some ways.
>
> **Say why you recommend it**
> It really gets you thinking.
> It definitely challenges the normal way of doing things.
> It might change how you think/feel about old movies.

MEDIATE

5 Think of something you watched recently and write a short post about it, recommending it to Pietro. Remember to say how it compares to other films or programmes he might have seen before.

6 Work in groups. Take turns to present your recommendations. Decide which suggestion you would most like to watch.

2C A difficult character

SPEAKING OUTPUT | an informal group discussion
GOAL | talk about a character and speculate on their motivation
MEDIATION SKILL | analysing a fictional character

WARM-UP

1 **Work in pairs and discuss the questions.**

1 Have you ever been part of a book club? Would you want to be?

2 Do you have a favourite book?

3 Think of a character you remember from a book/film/programme. What makes them memorable?

PREPARE

2 **Read the Scenario and answer the questions.**

1 Who is the message from?

2 Why are they writing?

SCENARIO

You are part of a book group in your class. The organiser sends you this message.

I just read this short story and thought that it would be an interesting one for us to talk about in the book group as it relates to what we were talking about in the class last week. I'm not sure what to make of the characters, and whether I like them or not. And I'm not even sure if I am meant to like them. Perhaps we could focus on that in our discussion.

---

3 **Read the short story and answer the questions.**

1 Who are the characters? How are they related?

2 Why are they there?

3 How would you describe their relationship with the older woman?

The visit

'Two hours, Paul. Two max OK?'

'OK Wendy, and please just try to be nice.'

'I'm **always** nice. It's her that's not.'

'You know what I mean. She's old now. Just indulge her a little.'

Paul took a deep breath and shouted hello through the open door, to be greeted by the slow determined shuffle of slippers across a stone floor. He arranged his face in what he hoped was a pleasant smile and not a rictus. Wendy tried less hard. Then Grandma was upon them.

'It's Festival Week again, Gran! How are you enjoying it so far?'

'Paul! You've been eating well, I can see, my dear boy. All that restaurant food. You should eat at home more,' chirped Gran, her eyes on Wendy.

Paul knew he couldn't leave any space in the conversation. 'Wendy and I just wanted to wish you the best of the season, Gran.'

'Come in, come in. It's been so long since your last visit. I can't even remember when it was.'

Paul could. It was last Festival Week.

A darkened parlour full of the ornaments accrued over a lifetime, more like a museum than a living room. The atmosphere set to work on Paul and Wendy's spirits.

'We got you some festival buns, Gran.'

'That's very kind! Oh. You bought them?'

'Yes, sorry Gran, I didn't have time to bake them this year.'

'Nor Wendy, it seems … '

'Paul doesn't let me near the kitch … '

'I'd always make them for my mum and dad, you know, Paul. One year I was so sick with fever that I could barely get out of bed, but I made sure they got their buns, just how they liked them. They so appreciated those buns, you know. And your mother, she would always do her best. But she can't now … '

Paul tried to ignore that spectre at the feast. Wendy couldn't stop herself now. 'Not many people have time to make them these days.'

Gran smiled and armed her response. 'No, I'm sure you're right, Wendy, they have better things to do with their time.'

4 Work in groups of three. Focus on one character from the short story and make notes about the questions (1–4).

Student A: Make notes about Grandma.

Student B: Make notes about Wendy.

Student C: Make notes about Paul.

1 How do they feel?

2 How do they respond to the other characters?

3 Why are they there, or what do they want?

4 What three words would you use to describe them? Use the words in the box or your own ideas.

> cruel   defensive   diplomatic   dutiful
> generous   honest   hostile   manipulative
> narrow-minded   patient   sensitive
> sympathetic   thoughtful   unkind

Gran bade them sit down and went to make tea to go with their shop-bought buns. Paul's brave attempt at a smile this time was directed at Wendy, whose face was a gathering thunder cloud.

'An hour max, Wendy … '

'During which, Paul, we'll be reminded of what bad people we are because we don't follow the old ways. This is the last time, Paul.'

The tea arrived in an ornate teapot and was decanted into equally ornate cups, which hadn't been used for a year. The clinks of cups only accentuated the uncomfortable silence.

Paul smiled warmly, casting around for safe conversation. Nothing is safe. 'Any plans for Festival Week, Gran?'

'I'll be doing what I've done every year on Festival Week since I was a young girl, Paul, doing the big clean. Wendy, will you be doing the big clean?'

An ambush. A trap. 'We have a cleaner, **he** comes every week, so we don't need … '

'My mother and I would do the big clean together.' Gran becomes distant, she's inhabiting the past now. 'We'd scrub, clean and polish, and laugh and laugh till the tears came. Of course, I doubt you can do that with your mother. Your mother is all the way over on the other side of the country, isn't she, Wendy? I'm guessing you don't see her very often.'

Paul laid what he hoped was a reassuring hand on Wendy's shoulder and blundered to her rescue.

'We go as often as we can, Gran.'

'Yes, she's very understanding, isn't she Paul? **And** supportive … '

'Hmm. We're both doing such long hours at work, you know how it is … '

Gran didn't know how it was.

A further hour of conversational cat and mouse followed, full of civilised accusations and desperate deflections, and then suddenly Paul and Wendy found themselves deposited outside on the street.

'How much did she give us, Paul?'

'Two thousand.'

'Wow, where does she get all the money from?'

'She doesn't spend much these days, not since Grandpa died. They used to travel, but she won't go anywhere now.'

'Well, that's the car paid for the next two months. Now, who are we seeing tomorrow?'

5 Read the Mediation Skill box. Write three sentences about the characters in the short story.

MEDIATION SKILL
analysing a fictional character

When you're analysing a character in a book, play, programme or film, there are a number of different questions you should think about.

What do they say?
He insists that …
She objects to the suggestion …

What do they do? How do they behave?
She comes across as quite cruel.
It's as though he's bitter about something.

How do they relate to the other characters?
There is (conflict/common ground) between them.
They're clearly approaching it from opposite angles.
They don't see eye-to-eye.
They're brought together by a shared goal.
She's very supportive of him.
They're trying to manipulate her.

Why? What do they want?
I'm left with the impression that it's not about the money.
It strikes me that she's quite lonely.
It's important to understand that she is from a different generation.

How do they impact the story/the other characters?
They antagonise the other characters.

A well-written character will have several different sides, depending on who they are with, and whose point of view we see them from. For a character analysis, make notes and consider the context or the situation that the character is in. Also, try to read between the lines to understand their motivation. What are the reasons for their actions?

MEDIATE

6 Work in your same group from Ex 4. Prepare a short character analysis of the character you focused on in Ex 4. Take turns to explain the character, their actions and motivation.

7 Work in pairs. Discuss the questions.

1 What traditions in your country might older people follow more than younger people?

2 Do you feel that the disconnect between generations shown in the story exists in your country? In what ways?

3C Bring in the robots

SPEAKING OUTPUT | a meeting to agree a course of action
GOAL | share and listen to viewpoints
MEDIATION SKILL | showing sensitivity to other opinions and empathising

WARM-UP

1 Work in pairs. Look at the photos and discuss the questions.

1 What can you see in the photos?

2 What are the advantages and disadvantages of using robots in the workplace?

PREPARE

2 Read the Scenario and answer the questions.

1 What change is happening at the store?

2 Who is the author of each text? Who do they represent?

SCENARIO

You work for a supermarket chain. The company has just issued a press release about a major innovation: the use of robots to stack shelves. Many of the people who work in your store are worried about the impact of the change. A staff representative has written an email to their manager to outline their concerns.

You arrange a meeting to discuss the issues.

3 Work in pairs. Predict what the attitude to the change is likely to be in the press release and the email. Why do you think that?

4A Work in pairs.

Student A: Read the press release and make notes on the most important points.

CostSave introducing robot shelf-stackers. They've been successfully trialled already …

Student B: Read the email and make notes on the most important points.

Key concern is job security and redundancies …

B Compare your notes. Are the points similar to your predictions in Ex 3?

Press release | CostSave | 16.02 | Page 1 of 1

Here at CostSave we're excited to announce that we will soon be introducing a fleet of automated shelf-stacking robots across our larger stores nationwide, following successful trials in a number of locations.

'The robots are incredibly sophisticated and can grasp, or pick and place, objects of several different shapes and sizes into different locations,' explains Amanda Gomez, our head of technology and operations. In truth, the stackers are still controlled by a human wearing a VR headset and special gloves. The human 'controllers' are also equipped with a microphone and headphones to allow them to communicate with nearby shoppers if necessary.

The advantage is that it will allow a single person to oversee and control the work of the robot shelf-stackers at multiple stores simultaneously – ensuring that shelves are consistently stocked and stores are able to rapidly report supply and replenishment issues to a central database, keeping our customers satisfied and reducing one of the main causes of stress for the rest of our in-store employees.

Over recent years, it has become increasingly difficult to recruit people to work as shelf-stackers – it's a laborious, repetitive task with various physical and mental health implications, such as repetitive strain injury, industrial accidents, mental fatigue and stress. This innovation helps us reduce risk factors for our existing workforce, who will be able to focus more on the service-dominant areas of the business: for example, dealing with customer queries and public relations – the more human side of retail.

Surveys prove that our customers are ready for such a change. The majority responded that they expect to see fewer and fewer human staff in shops over the next ten years. In fact, 13 percent of people believe there will be no human staff in stores at all by 2030.

Memo from: CostSave rep • 09.38 • 12 Recipients ⟲ Reply

I'm writing on behalf of our staff in response to the company's announcement that it will be introducing shelf-stacking robots. We've been in contact with employee representatives in other stores, and it's clear that we are far from alone in having concerns about this supposed 'innovation'.

As I'm sure you'll understand, our primary concern is about jobs, our livelihoods. You mention the importance of staff in other roles, but realistically how many positions will be required? What assurances can you offer us about redundancies?

Apart from that, we also remain unconvinced about the workability and practicality of the technology. From my understanding, the trials took place in our least busy stores during off-peak times. I can't be the only person who is concerned about what will happen in crowded stores. There are health and safety issues to consider, not to mention the impact this could have on our customers. The board say that customers expect this to be part of their shopping experience of the future – but do they really want it? It seems a real possibility that it's going to lead to reduced customer satisfaction and loyalty. We have already witnessed this with self-checkouts, for example.

We also object to the notion that this will 'lower stress levels' for staff. The truth is that there are bound to be frequent technical problems which, inevitably, will need to be rectified by the human workforce. This has the potential to increase workload, customer dissatisfaction and stress.

As with self-checkouts, which aren't necessarily faster than staffed checkouts, there will be indirect costs of maintenance and increased breakages on top of the initial set-up costs. We are led to believe that set-up costs for each store will be in excess of US$100,000. Could this not be better invested in other areas – not least the staff, who have for a number of years put up with below-inflation salary increases and cut company benefits?

We hope that there is still time to change the course of this decision and look forward to discussing this further.

Sincerely,
Andres Jimenez
Staff Representative

5 Read the Mediation Skill box. Write a sentence for each of the three headings in the box about the text you read in Ex 4A.

MEDIATION SKILL
showing sensitivity to other opinions and empathising

When you are discussing an issue which people have strong feelings about, it's important to show empathy and sensitivity. Doing so makes it more likely to resolve the problem in a positive way. Here are some ways to do that.

1 Empathise
Show you are thinking about how the other person is feeling.
I can see why you think that/you feel that …
It's understandable that you would feel disappointed by this.
Of course, you feel irritated, angry, sad, etc.
You're stuck in a tricky situation here and I see why you feel …

2 Paraphrase
Show that you have heard and understood what the other person has said.
… uh huh, so in a way you think that …
So, you feel aggrieved that you were treated in this way.

3 Understand people's requirements in order to reach agreement
Think about areas for compromise and negotiation.
So, you feel that unless we … , there won't be …
So without … , you think there'd be no point …

MEDIATE

6 Work in pairs. You are now in the meeting to discuss CostSave's announcement. Refer back to your notes in Ex 4A and your sentences in Ex 5.

Student A: You are the store manager. You represent the company. Make your points and respond to what the staff representative says.

Student B: You are the staff representative. Make your points and respond to what the manager says.

7 Discuss what you think should happen next. What would be a good way to resolve the conflict?

4C Model economy

WRITING OUTPUT | a summary of a process
GOAL | explain a complex diagram
MEDIATION SKILL | describing a process diagram

WARM-UP

1 Work in pairs. Look at the photos and discuss the questions.

1 What does each photo show?

2 What is your opinion and/or experience with these things?

PREPARE

2 A Read the Scenario and look at the diagrams. How does Hwan want you to help him?

SCENARIO

Your friend Hwan has just started a business course. He has to write an essay about recent economic trends and models: microloans, the circular economy and the sharing economy. He has found some diagrams for all three models, as well as a description for the sharing economy, but isn't sure he completely understands them all. He asks for your help.

B Label diagrams A–C with the headings (1–3).

1 circular economy

2 microlending

3 sharing economy

A

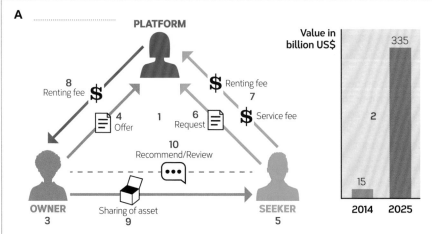

PLATFORM

8 Renting fee $

$ Renting fee 7

4 Offer

1

6 Request

$ Service fee

10 Recommend/Review

OWNER 3

Sharing of asset 9

SEEKER 5

Value in billion US$

335

2

15

2014   2025

B

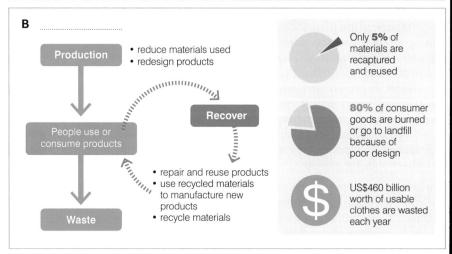

Production
• reduce materials used
• redesign products

People use or consume products

Recover

• repair and reuse products
• use recycled materials to manufacture new products
• recycle materials

Waste

Only **5%** of materials are recaptured and reused

80% of consumer goods are burned or go to landfill because of poor design

US$460 billion worth of usable clothes are wasted each year

C

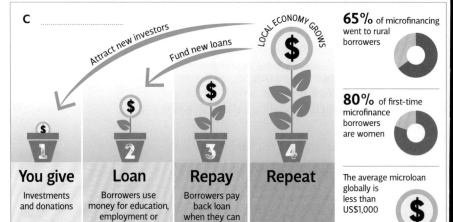

Attract new investors

Fund new loans

LOCAL ECONOMY GROWS

You give 1
Investments and donations

Loan 2
Borrowers use money for education, employment or business opportunity

Repay 3
Borrowers pay back loan when they can + interest

Repeat 4

65% of microfinancing went to rural borrowers

80% of first-time microfinance borrowers are women

The average microloan globally is less than US$1,000

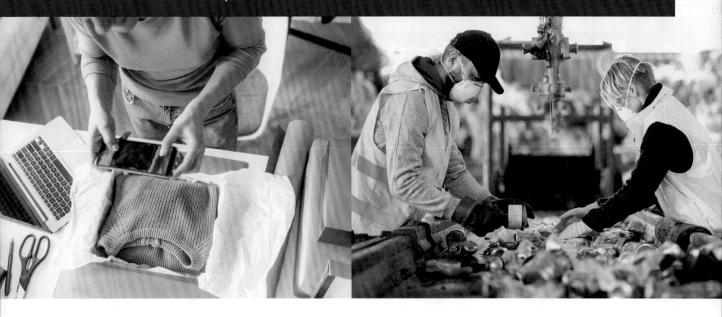

MEDIATION SKILL
describing a process diagram

To describe a process diagram, try to give an overview to summarise the process before describing the steps in more detail. Identify the beginning and end of the process, then break it down into simple steps.

Overview
Give a summary of the diagram and/or description of the overall goal of the process.
What this diagram shows is the way people can lend and borrow assets through the sharing economy.
The ultimate goal is to improve local economies.

Specifics
Describe what certain parts of the diagram represent.
This line/icon represents the flow of money from the platform to the borrower.

Supporting information
Back up the claims with relevant data.
This indicates the rate at which spending has increased in this area.

Sequencing
Explain the steps of the process.
The money is then deposited in the borrower's account.
Before/After that, the owner must accept the request.
Following that/Subsequently, people can search for assets through the platform.
In turn, the owner can review the borrower.

Cause and effect
Describe how different parts of the process are linked.
As a consequence, people have more trust in the platform.
If they are successful, they can repay the loan and more people will invest in the future.
Later on, we see that the local economy has become stronger as a result.

3 Work in pairs. Read the Mediation Skill box. Then match sentences a–j to the headings in the box.
   a The platform then pays the renting fee to the asset owner.
   b Here you can see the sharing economy will be worth $335 billion in 2025.
   c Instead of offering it directly to anyone, their offer goes through a digital platform.
   d Finally, this line represents the review or recommendation – the borrower and owner rate and review one another.
   e From this, they can make a request to borrow the asset to the platform. If the request is accepted, …
   f This allows the borrower or seeker to search for the asset through an app or website.
   g The diagram gives an overview of the interactions between owner, seeker and digital platform that make up the booming sharing economy.
   h Let's start with the owner. They have an asset – something they're prepared to offer to others for a fee – a spare bedroom, for example. But how do they find a reliable 'borrower'?
   i They pay the renting fee plus a service fee to the platform.
   j From there, the owner shares the asset with the borrower.

4 Match the sentences (a–j) in Ex 3 with the numbers (1–10) in diagram A in Ex 2A.

MEDIATE

5 Write a short description of one of the processes in order to help Hwan with his course.

   Student A: Describe the circular economy diagram.
   Student B: Describe the microlending economy.

6 Work in groups. Discuss the three models. Which do you think has the biggest impact for you, and for the world?

5C Playing with words

WRITING OUTPUT | an email for a colleague
GOAL | give opinions about a course of action
MEDIATION SKILL | describing the techniques used in advertising

WARM-UP

1 Work in pairs and discuss the questions.

1 Do you think advertising on social media, on TV or in print is effective? Why/Why not?

2 Can you think of any examples of clever advertising?

PREPARE

2 Read the Scenario and answer the questions.

1 What is your role?

2 What does your client want you to create?

SCENARIO

You work for a marketing company. You and your team are working on a social media advertising campaign for a new brand of healthy snacks and soft drinks called Nature's Candy. The client has sent this brief.

> We would like to create a slogan or tag line with interesting, clever use of language so that people will stop scrolling through their social media feeds and actually take notice. It's important that people understand what we're all about – natural, light but delicious drinks, snacks and treats which are good for the body, as well as the environment, and free from additives and preservatives.

One of your colleagues has researched some successful advertising campaigns using word-play. They send you a short article about what makes a good tag line and an ideas board with some examples for inspiration. You agree to look at their suggestions and email them with your opinions.

3 Read the article. What examples of tag lines can you think of?

What's a tag line and how do you write one?

A tag line is a short phrase or sentence – preferably no longer than five or six words so people can remember it – which sums up what a brand or product is all about. So that's where you need to start: thinking about the purpose of the product, the values of the company, and the identity of the brand. Once you have thought about that, it's time to get creative. This works best as a team. Brainstorm as many ideas as you can and write them on sticky notes. You can use the internet, dictionaries and a thesaurus to come up with words and idioms related to your product, values and identity. Play with the words and the sounds and think about different meanings.

When you have run out of ideas, look at your list and choose the ones that say most about the product and will be easy to remember. A great tag line will set you apart from the competition.

4 Read the examples your colleague has sent you. Match the products (1–8) with the tag lines (a–h).

1 sportswear brand
2 car
3 design software
4 mobile banking app
5 cosmetics brand
6 video-conferencing and call platform
7 an airline
8 a gift company

a **Think inside the box**
b **Running the world**
c **Your driving force**
d **Be. Hear. Now.**
e **In safe hands**
f **Love is in the hair**
g **Make. Believe.**
h **Cos nothing else will fly**

5 A Read the Mediation Skill box. Read the emails (1–4) and find more examples of phrases to discuss techniques used in advertising.

MEDIATION SKILL
describing the techniques used in advertising

Advertising uses language in unusual or creative ways to attract attention, to make people think and remember the brand or product. It often uses devices like similes and metaphors as well as word-play – particularly with idioms (common non-literal phrases), puns (words which sound similar but create ambiguity in meaning) and double meanings. Here are some ways to describe those techniques.

Meaning
I like the way it uses ... instead of ...
It works on different levels; on one level, it's a twist of a common idiom, but it also ...
The double meaning of ... is very clever.

Impact
I think the metaphor of ... is very effective.
It makes you stop and think.
It really grabs your attention.
It speaks to the idea of (security).

1

09.38, 3 Recipients, ↩ Reply

It's a take on a common phrase, playing with the double meaning. It helps bring your attention to the brand's key messaging – the sense of power and ambition. It's quite a clever message.

2

14.02, 1 Recipient, ↩ Reply

I like how it's very short and simple but still achieves quite a lot – and it works well as a written slogan because it gets you thinking. It makes an impact because, with just a couple of words, it effectively communicates the concept of 'creativity'.

3

12.55, 2 Recipients, ↩ Reply

This one is interesting because it's a short idiom without any word-play or pun, but it still lands its message about how using their service is convenient because you can access it on your phone while also promising security, which is very important.

4

11.32, 1 Recipient, ↩ Reply

I don't really like this one. It's a pretty simple pun based on an obvious rhyme. I'm not really sure how the original idiom connects to the product either. To be honest, it doesn't strike me as being very memorable.

B Which of the tag lines in Ex 4 do you think the emails in Ex 5A are referring to?

6 Work in groups. Discuss which of the tag lines in Ex 4 are most effective and why.

MEDIATE

7 Work in groups of three. Discuss the suggested tag lines for Nature's Candy (1–8) and say which you think are most effective and why.

 Notes   • • •

1 All sweetness and light
2 Bite off what you can chew
3 Required taste
4 Cherrypicked
5 Waist not, want not
6 Food for thought
7 When there's too much on your plate
8 A free lunch

---

8 Write an email to your colleague about the tag lines in Ex 7. Give your opinion about which are the most effective and why.

6C Arguing the point

SPEAKING OUTPUT | a class debate on tourism
GOAL | process and report a range of opinions
MEDIATION SKILL | referring to multiple sources

WARM-UP

1 Work in pairs. Look at the photos and discuss the questions.

1 What do you think is happening in each photo?

2 What is the common theme that connects the photos?

PREPARE

2 Read the Scenario and answer the questions.

1 What is happening next week?

2 What is the topic?

> ### SCENARIO
>
> You belong to a debate club. You are going to have a debate next week and the organisers have asked for suggestions on what the topic should be. Later, you are listening to the radio and hear people discussing the advantages and disadvantages of mass tourism. Different people are interviewed, representing a range of viewpoints.
>
> You suggest this should be the topic and send your teacher and classmates a link to the programme. You agree that you will debate the following motion:
>
> **We believe that people should be restricted to one return flight per year for the purposes of tourism.**

3 Work in pairs and discuss how you think you should prepare for a debate.

4 🔊 **MB6.01** | Listen to the interviews from the radio programme. Match the speakers (1–5) with the descriptions (a–e).

a resident affected by air travel

b climate change activist

c a commuter

d travel writer

e CEO of an online travel agency

5 **MB6.01** | Match the statements (a–e) with the speakers (1–5) in Ex 4. Listen again and check.

a The cost of mass tourism is simply too great.

b It's difficult for individuals to do much to tackle the problem.

c The benefits of travel and tourism are underestimated.

d Powerful decision-makers are only interested in money.

e Travel is too important a part of our culture and the economy to abandon completely.

6 Read the Mediation Skill box. Complete the sentences (1–6) about the speakers in the radio programme using phrases from the box and your own ideas.

MEDIATION SKILL
referring to multiple sources

During debates and discussions, it's common to make references to arguments made by other people or sources.

Citing specific points
The points that X and Y make are very valid.
The example that (the journalist) gives is interesting: we can't ignore the fact that …
It's like the (travel agency CEO) says, …
I see it very much like (the activist); …

Comparing opinions
While X does make a valid point, I think what Y says is more (convincing).
Both sides make fair points, but I find the arguments against are far more (compelling).
I think there must be a middle ground between the two sides.
Though I agree we have to consider (the economy), X is a more urgent issue.
It's hard to argue with the idea that (it's important). However, we also need to consider …

---

1 The example that the travel agency CEO gives is ....: we can't ignore the fact that …

2 It's like the last speaker ....; …

3 I see it very much .... the travel writer; …

4 It's hard to argue with the .... that … However, we also need to consider the role that companies should play.

5 While the travel writer does make a .... point, I think …

6 Though I .... we have to consider … , … is a more urgent issue.

MEDIATE

7 Work in groups of four and divide into two pairs. Prepare your arguments and plan which points from the programme you will mention. Read the Debate club rules before you start.

Pair A: Argue in favour of the motion. Plan what each of you will say, thinking about the interviews you heard in Ex 4. Predict what the other side will say and think about how you can argue against their points.

Pair B: Argue against the motion. Plan what each of you will say, thinking about the interviews you heard in Ex 4. Predict what the other side will say and think how you can argue against their points.

Debate club rules

- Debates are held with two teams, with two speakers in each team.

- **Team 1** argues in favour of the motion. **Team 2** argues against it.

- Both teams must prepare their arguments before they begin the debate.

- **Team 1** speaks first – each speaker can talk for up to ninety seconds. Both speakers in the team must speak.

- **Team 2** can take notes, but at this stage they mustn't interrupt.

- Then **Team 2** can give their counter-argument for the same amount of time. **Team 1** mustn't interrupt.

- When both sides have spoken, there is 'open debate'. Anyone may now speak to challenge the arguments made by the other side, make further points or add extra supporting information.

Remember, the debate is meant to be enjoyable for everyone, so don't make it personal!

---

8 Debate the motion. Refer to at least some of the ideas from the radio programme using language from the Mediation Skill box.

9 Discuss what went well in the debate. What could you, or the opposing side, have done differently? What's your personal opinion on the topic?

7C On the trail

WRITING OUTPUT | a short summary of a talk
GOAL | identify what is relevant in a talk
MEDIATION SKILL | taking notes

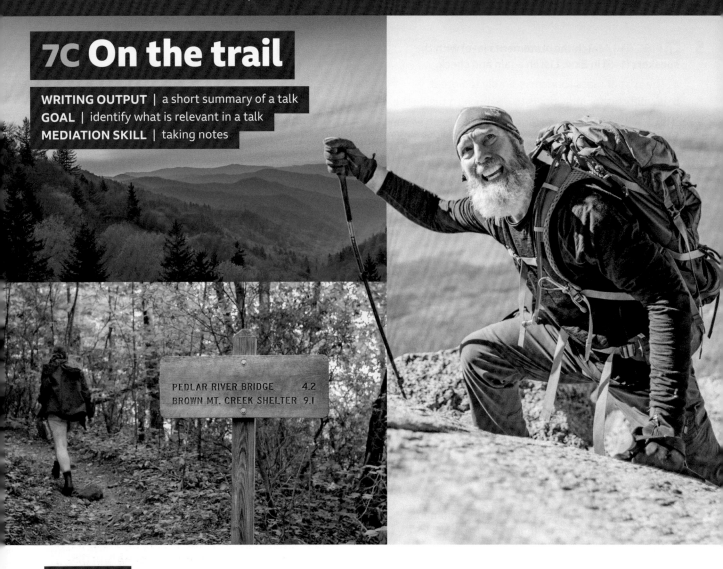

PEDLAR RIVER BRIDGE   4.2
BROWN MT. CREEK SHELTER 9.1

WARM-UP

1 Work in pairs. Look at the photos and discuss the questions.

   1 Where do you think this place is?

   2 Do you ever go hiking? Why/Why not?

   3 How important is it to connect with nature? Why?

PREPARE

2 Read the Scenario and answer the questions.

   1 What are you planning?

   2 What kind of information do you think the group will need to know?

SCENARIO

You are going to lead a fairly inexperienced group on a hike along part of the Appalachian Trail. You plan to attend a talk by an experienced local guide. As group leader, you need to take notes for the rest of the group as not everyone is able to attend.

The talk is interesting but not always focused on the things that are relevant to you and your group. You need to decide what's important and what you can ignore. Then you'll email the group with a summary of 'need-to-know' information.

3 Read the Mediation Skill box. Then answer questions 1 and 2 in relation to the Scenario.

MEDIATION SKILL
taking notes

An important part of taking notes is to be selective about the information you record. Before a talk or lecture, think about what's going to be important to focus on. What do you want to get out of it?

Introductory and concluding remarks will often include important ideas or overviews of key points. Listen for signposting and sequencing words or phrases like:
The most important thing to remember …
There are three main points …
First/Secondly/Finally …

Consider two questions before you take notes:

1 What is the purpose?

What are you going to use the notes for? Sometimes they are just for you to refer back to later on, to use in assignments or essays, and so on.

2 Who is the audience?

If you're taking notes which will be used by other people, or to inform a text you'll write for a particular audience, think about what they need to know.

4 🔊 **MB7.01** | Listen to the first part of the talk and complete the notes.

Appalachian Trail

Notes:

What you need to know

- Physical fitness & ¹ _____ of similar trails, e.g. Dientes Circuit Trek (Chile), but also local ² _____ with pack as heavy as you'll take.

  General fitness key – along with all the other ³ _____ of walking:
  - circulation
  - cardiovascular system
  - lowering blood sugar
  - ⁴ _____ loss
  - bone strength

- Not just a physical challenge – it's ⁵ _____ , too.

  Speaker hit the wall when he was on a hike during college. His friend Jan (later got married!) helped him get back.

  How to prepare mentally:
  - know your answer to question: ⁶ _____ ?
  - have a ⁷ _____ person* (back home) who you can call (check daylight saving ⁸ _____ difference).

*must be someone who'll motivate you

5 Read the script of the first part of the talk. Which information is important for the group of people in the Scenario? Circle the important information and cross out the parts you think are unnecessary.

6 Use your answers in Ex 5 to edit the notes in Ex 4.

MEDIATE

7 🔊 **MB7.02** | Listen to the second part of the talk and take notes.

8 Work in pairs. Compare your notes with your partner. Did you include the same information?

9 Write a summary of the two parts of the talk for your hiking group. Use your notes from Ex 6 and Ex 7 to help you.

The Appalachian Trail is a huge undertaking that requires the right preparation and attitude. You really don't want to hit the trail without your mind, body and kit being ready! So here's what you need to know before you set out on a hike of the Appalachian Trail.

Probably the most important thing is you've got to be physically fit. Hopefully, you've already got a lot of backpacking experience – I think I heard a couple of you have recently undertaken the Dientes Circuit Trek in Chile, which I'd love to hear more about if you have some time after. Even if you're very experienced, it's a great idea to head out on a few local, day hikes with your pack and gear as heavy as you plan to carry on the trail. And, of course, keeping fit and eating right in any other way you can is only going to benefit you on the hike, not to mention the general health benefits that I'm sure we're all aware of: improving circulation and strengthening the cardiovascular system, lowering blood sugar, weight loss, bone strength, etc.

However, this is not purely a physical challenge, it's a mental one, too. There will be times when you're cold, hungry, tired. I remember on my first serious hike, I was probably around nineteen – a freshman at college – and I really hit the wall. I just sat down – and it wasn't because my body had given up, I just couldn't work out why I was putting myself through such an ordeal – till my friend Jan came and talked to me (we ended up getting married as it happens!). There are some other things you can do to prepare for this, which don't involve finding a life partner! First, and before you start out, think of your honest answer to the question 'Why am I doing this?'. And, in the few days leading up to your trip, picture yourself arriving at Mount Katahdin. It sounds kinda corny but visualisation is so crucial to achieving any goal you set yourself, and that picture's a real pick-me-up when you're finding it tough.

Secondly, have a 'support person'. I'm not just talking about a 'buddy' who's on the trail with you, which is great to have, but you also need someone back home that you can call for mental support. Who's going to tell you what you need to hear to get you motivated and back up on your feet? And make sure, whoever it is, they know that you'll probably be calling them sometime, and it may not be at the most convenient time – especially with the time difference for y'all – what is it now? Five hours? Six? Thankfully it's not that time of year when we're out of sync for a coupla weeks with daylight saving. Boy did that get me in trouble a few years back …

8C Working as a team

SPEAKING OUTPUT | a staff meeting
GOAL | make a decision as a group
MEDIATION SKILL | keeping the conversation on track tactfully

WARM-UP

1 **Work in pairs. Look at the photos above and discuss the questions.**

  1 What are the people doing in each photo?

  2 Why do businesses organise events like these for their employees?

PREPARE

2 **Read the Scenario and answer the questions.**

  1 What kind of course is your team going to do?

  2 How are you going to decide which course to take?

SCENARIO

You are a department manager for a company. You have been told that your staff can attend a training course to help create a better working environment and a happier, more productive team. You decide to discuss the options with your colleagues.

You share the descriptions of the courses with them and organise a meeting to choose the one you think will benefit you all the most.

Emotional intelligence for better professional relationships

★★★★☆ | 10 reviews

You'll learn what we mean by 'emotional intelligence' and how we can use it to better understand ourselves and others, to build better professional relationships, resolve conflicts constructively and create a positive atmosphere for teamwork and collaboration.

Building a mindful team

★★★★½ | 10 reviews

Mindfulness is not some faddish new concept. It's based on academic research and is proven to lead to better communication skills, relationships and mental health. Learn how to apply the techniques of mindfulness to lead a happier, more productive life in the workplace and beyond.

Connecting nature and work

★★★★★ | 220 reviews

Learn how to establish a stronger connection with the natural world and implement more sustainable ways of working as an everyday part of business, as we face the climate crisis. You'll discover ways your team can reduce your carbon footprint, boost mental well-being and find out about potential business opportunities.

Creating a stress-free workplace

★★★★☆ | 410 reviews

Stress is widely accepted as just a part of work. But it doesn't need to be that way. Stress is one of the leading causes of mental, as well as physical, health problems. You'll learn how to recognise the signs of stress in yourself and others, and what you can do about it. We'll also focus on prevention by creating a work environment which is more conducive to a stress-free existence.

Nutrition and fitness

★★★★★ | 460 reviews

You and your colleagues will work with one of our personal trainers and a nutrition expert. Underpinned by academic research, you'll learn about the effects of common bad habits, bust some myths and work on ways to integrate a healthier lifestyle into your work routine for a fitter, happier, more productive workforce and workplace.

Overcoming the fear of conflict

★★★★☆ | 70 reviews

We spend much of our lives working with other people. Inevitably, that means some conflict. Rather than fear conflict, your team should be embracing it. It can be one of the most productive forces in the workplace if managed well – increasing creativity and energy. We'll teach you how!

3 Read the Mediation Skill box. Read the sentences (1–8) and decide which section they belong to.

MEDIATION SKILL
keeping the conversation on track tactfully

In meetings, it's important to be able to focus on the task at hand to avoid wasting time. However, it can be tricky to do that in a polite, constructive way. So it's useful to use tentative language. Also, remember to be sensitive to what other people think is important.

Moving the conversation on
These are all great points, but I think we really need to focus on (the business benefit).
OK, some good ideas there, so let's move on to the next option.
Given the time we have left, …

Returning to a point
I want to return to something you mentioned earlier.

Interrupting
Sorry to interrupt, but (we need to move on/we're short of time).
Hold that thought. Maybe we can come back to it in a minute.

Concluding
Have we reached a conclusion about (when will be the best time)?
So, if there are no more suggestions, can we agree that … ?
We can take the (video idea) forward.

---

1 Did anyone have anything else to add on that? No? Great. So moving on to the next point, what do you think about the 'Connecting nature and work' course?

2 Actually, sorry, can we just go back to that last point? I had another idea about that.

3 We've definitely made some important points there. Are we ready to discuss the next option?

4 A: I'd just like to mention that there are some other courses out there which might be worth taking a look at.

   B: If you can hold that thought for a moment. I think we need to discuss what's on the table first, then we can pick that up afterwards if that's OK.

5 Unless anyone has any more ideas, can we agree that we'll vote on the best course and make a decision by the end of the day?

6 To recap, we've agreed to move forward with the conflict training.

7 Thanks everyone, some really useful ideas. We've agreed to move ahead with the mindfulness course. Please check your diaries so we can schedule some dates.

8 I'm not sure we should get into that now. We're short of time.

MEDIATE

4 Work in groups of three. Read the Scenario again. Hold a meeting to discuss each training course.

Student A: You are the manager. Ask your team for their opinion on each of the courses. Keep the meeting on track using the language from the Mediation Skill box.

Students B and C: Choose your favourite course and prepare to persuade the others. Try to keep talking about the course you want as much as possible.

5 Vote for the best course and explain your decision to the rest of the class.

AUDIOSCRIPTS

UNIT 1

Audio 1.01
If it hadn't been for his love of the game, he would have thrown in the towel early on.

Audio 1.02
1 a nurturing environment
2 striving for excellence
3 fostering good relationships
4 fulfilling your potential
5 a quality curriculum
6 rigorous standards
7 taking the initiative
8 mutual respect

Audio 1.03
S = Sarah   R = Rob

S: I'm Sarah Butler and today on the programme we're talking about education. Is our education system fit for purpose? Or perhaps, a more important question might be: how do we make our education system fit for purpose for future generations? In recent decades we've seen class sizes fall, we've seen new technology embraced in classrooms and a shift to students researching information, working, and sharing work online. We've seen the role of the teacher move from dominant instructor – the fount of all knowledge – to the facilitator, an enabler of learning, manager of classroom interaction, with a move towards project and teamwork. Happily, the image of a 19th-century classroom, with students in rows, heads down, writing whatever the teacher says in their notebooks and only speaking to answer a direct question, is something from the dim and distant past. But these reforms have been slow and a long time coming, and by no means are they part of the educational systems in every country. Tradition still holds sway in many parts of the globe and will not be relinquished easily. But our world is now changing at a rapid pace. Consider climate change, advancing technology, increasing political uncertainties – think about shifting job markets, increasing populations. Dealing with the changing nature of the world and global issues which affect us all will require minds that have been educated in a significantly different way to whatever current educational systems can offer. I'm talking today to education expert Rob Taylor about how he believes education for future generations will differ from what we have today. Rob – so, what can we expect and why?

R: Well first, let me say Sarah, I think in your introduction you've laid out exactly what we need to be considering. And you're right, it's the speed of change that will force educators to adapt so rapidly. Were we able to jump forward a hundred years, we'd be looking at a dramatically different educational system. Change is happening, and it's basically because of a refocus on how to equip students in the future; it's all based on how we view 'knowledge' – the crux of any education system – is it 'knowing that' or 'knowing how'? Up to this point in time, 'knowledge' has meant 'knowing that'. By 'that' I mean education has all been about knowing facts and information and the teacher's role has been to pass that knowledge on. The students' role has been to store the knowledge and use it whenever they need it – sadly sometimes simply to pass exams. Here in the UK, whoever makes the big educational decisions has set out that students should know maths, history or geography, English, science and a foreign language. So, I know that Paris is the capital of France, I know that seven times seven is forty-nine, I know that the bones in my foot are called tarsals and metatarsals and so on.

S: Yes, and I know that the Spanish word for sun is 'sol'.

R: Exactly. But all that knowledge takes storage space in our brains, and technology is already helping us offload much of this.

S: Like using GPS to direct us rather than remember instructions or read a map?

R: Yes, and the map you refer to – before GPS became available – the map was a way of offloading the need to remember routes. Humans have always been good at offloading and that is what makes new learning easier. And now we're beginning to offload big time. We don't know something – we google it; we don't remember something – we google it. We've been using calculators to replace mathematical skills for many decades! And in the future smart tech will be taking even more weight of knowledge from our minds. However you look at it, approaches to future education will need to change.

S: So, what sort of knowledge are we going to be needing?

R: Instead of 'knowing that' we'll need to 'know how'. And what I'm talking about here is that it's more than knowing how to play an instrument or cook a meal, or how to perform an operation, it's also about doing what human beings are uniquely placed to do – knowing how to interact, collaborate, creatively problem-solve, how to understand each other, empathise, and so on. And of course, as well as knowing how to use technology, we'll also need to know how to deal with whatever issues it throws up. All the mechanical, repetitive things will get offloaded to machines. Of course, students in the future will adapt to whatever the educational system asks of them.

S: OK, so Rob, on-the-spot time! You say jump forward a hundred years – well, make that jump! What are you seeing?

R: Thanks for that! Right, …

Audio 1.04
R = Rob   S = Sarah

R: Right, this is a great leap in the dark! And I know, I know, I set myself up for this … let me think. Hmm, I guess the student in a hundred years' time most definitely won't spend whole days in a classroom – at least not a physical one.

S: You mean – they will learn everything online?

R: Not everything – I think there will still be physical interactions of some shape or form. But class timings won't be fixed as they are today, and perhaps students will be grouped – online or in a classroom – according to ability, not age. So, a ten-year-old may be in a study group with a fifteen-year-old. Students will also, in all probability, interact with other students internationally, not locally or even within the same country. They may even be able to project a three-dimensional hologram into a study group on another continent. Who knows? What I am very sure of, however, is that VR will play an enormous role in future education. Our student will be able to experience first-hand, for example, the way elephants interact in family units, instead of hearing or reading about them. And gamification will also be a big player. Using role-play games could be an excellent interactive way to inspire students, for example to problem-solve and work collaboratively.

S: Yes – sounds a fun way to learn.

R: I would also say that AI will feature significantly. Although it sounds far-fetched, one idea some experts are floating is that each child will be equipped with an AI companion from birth which will deliver any fact-based knowledge the child needs and will record every single experience the child has, acting as a memory bank if you like. So, the companion will record every conversation, every film, every book – that is if we still have films or books! Or maybe we'll all have computer chips in our brains to download new information! The possibilities are endless and making predictions at this stage is a minefield. All we can say is that future learning will happen in a very different way to today!

Audio 1.05
P = Presenter   J = Jake   K = Kelly
M = Marie

P: OK, so today's big question is whether creativity can be learnt or not. And with me I have a secondary school teacher, Kelly Martin; a businesswoman, Marie McCall; and a novelist, Jake Hawkins. To get the ball rolling, let's start with Jake. You're a successful writer, Jake, so everyone knows that you're a creative guy – in your opinion, is creativity something we can all learn or is it a talent that you're born with?

J: Hmm. It's an interesting question and the short answer is I don't really know. I get a lot of people asking me – Where do I get my ideas?, Have I always had stories in my head? – and it's really a bit of a mystery to me.

K: So, would you say you get flashes of inspiration? I love your books by the way!

J: Thanks! I suppose so. They usually happen when I'm doing something else entirely – I mean, not sitting at a computer trying hard to think of something. But out on a walk or playing with the kids – something will spark my imagination – sometimes completely out of the blue!

K: You see, I think that's important. As you know I teach young people, and I try to develop their creativity by encouraging them to do things just like that – going for a walk, letting the mind wander … , it's amazing what insights and creative thoughts you can get.

P: But surely, we can't all be creative geniuses? There has to be an element of raw talent – something you're born with?

J: OK, I hear what you're saying, maybe there has to be a spark of talent that's innate, but that needs to be nurtured and it doesn't come just like that. I mean, unless you're a Mozart or a Mary Shelley, you have to work at being creative, it takes patience and time, a lot of practising, thinking, rejecting ideas, rethinking and …

M: If I can come in here, I think it all depends on the type of creativity you're talking about. What I'm concerned with is innovation in a business setting, helping people to think outside the box and come up with novel ideas. And for me that means having experience and being versatile, open to new things and so on.

K: Agreed, and going back to what I was saying earlier – encouraging my students to become more creative involves just what you're talking about; that need to be open to the new and unfamiliar – and not pigeon-holing yourself by thinking 'I'm not a creative person, it's not in my nature.' I believe creativity can be learnt.

P: So, you're saying that if I wanted, I could sit down and write a novel, like Jake here …

K: Not at all, … sorry, I didn't mean to cut you off, but no – that's not what I'm saying at all, I'm talking about learning to be a better writer, and become a more creative thinker … not becoming a creative genius. I'd say …

M: Absolutely, you've hit the nail on the head. I don't think anyone is saying that we can all be another Jake! Sorry Kelly, you were saying … ?

K: No worries. I'd like to hear Jake's thoughts on this. Jake?

J: Actually, having listened to the comments, I'd say that there are definitely a lot of 'me's out there – there are writers, artists, musicians and great creative thinkers who just haven't been heard yet or discovered. I was in the right place at the right time. And you're also bang on about creativity. My talent – what there is – is geared towards writing, coming up with storylines, fleshing them out, connecting with readers – but put me in a business meeting and I'd freeze. My mind doesn't think that way.

M: Come on, Jake – don't downplay your talent here – you're wired to think outside the box. To go back to my earlier point – there are ways to teach people to be more creative, but all of that can't make up for a lack of innate talent.

K: Let me pick up on that, Marie – what we do, or at least, I do, is give advice. For instance, we have in-class discussions about getting out of the linear approach to problem-solving, focusing on the importance of patience, relaxing, daydreaming, and there's something I read the other day about the importance of the colour green …

P: Did you just say 'green'? What's that got to do with being creative?

K: If I could just finish?

P: Please – go on. I'm fascinated …

K: OK, what I started to say was … apparently looking at the colour green immediately before doing a creative task can increase creativity – as opposed to blue or yellow which has a more mellowing effect …

M: Well, that's a new one on me.

K: Yes, well … obviously, as we mentioned before, it's important to focus on being open to new experiences, learning new things, looking at other viewpoints, all of which helps to develop creativity.

P: Thanks for that, Kelly. Right guys, the clock's ticking on this one, so if I can just bring Jake back in on the topic of inspiration. Earlier you raised an important point about …

Audio 1.06

1 To get the ball rolling, let's start with …
2 If I can come in here, …
3 … and going back to what I was saying earlier …
4 Sorry, I didn't mean to cut you off …
5 Sorry Kelly, you were saying … ?
6 I'd like to hear Jake's thoughts on this.
7 To go back to my earlier point, …
8 Let me pick up on that …
9 … what I started to say was …
10 … as we mentioned before, …

11 … if I can just bring Jake back in …
12 Earlier you raised an important point about …

Audio 1.07

1 But surely, we can't all be creative geniuses.
2 So you're saying that if I wanted, I could sit down and write a novel?
3 Did you just say 'green'? What's that got to do with being creative?

Audio 1.08

1 But don't you think that's a bit of an exaggeration?
2 So you're saying that anyone can learn to paint a masterpiece?
3 Did you just say 'daydream'? What's daydreaming got to do with it?

UNIT 2

Audio 2.01

1 It's not so much an investment in our future as a quick way of making cash.
2 We couldn't get a better opportunity to put ourselves on the map than this one.
3 The money will drain away as quickly as it comes.

Audio 2.02

I = Interviewer   A = Alan

I: International conferences are huge events where people from a range of cultures come together to share ideas and opinions or to debate, and therefore the need for simultaneous interpretation is vital. It's something that's always fascinated me. What is it like to sit in a booth all day at the United Nations or in a conference, translating at the same time as people are talking? What sort of problems do the interpreters face? Joining me in the studio is Alan Suarez, who is an interpreter for international conferences where he translates between Spanish, German and English. Alan, welcome to the programme.

A: Thanks.

I: So, what would you say are the main challenges you face when you're interpreting?

A: That's something I get asked a lot. There are quite a few challenges and I'm not sure that speakers ever really consider their interpreters. For instance, a surprisingly frequent problem – and one that people find unbelievable – comes from the fact that nowadays sound levels are very carefully checked so microphones and headsets are set for voice level. Some speakers, however, will start off by shouting into their microphones or do that old-fashioned 'testing, testing' thing and tap the microphone, resulting in a loud noise which can be quite painful for the interpreter and in some cases actually cause serious injury.

I: Really? I'd never even considered that! Of course, you're sitting there in your booth with your headset on. Very vulnerable. So, what can you do?

A: Well, it's crucial to educate the speaker and of course, the organisation. I kind of shock them. Tell them that their behaviour can incapacitate the interpreter and in the worst-case scenario there's a risk of hearing loss, of the interpreter actually going deaf.

I: Are you serious?

A: Yes.

I: So, what other things can the speaker do wrong?

A: One of the worst is when they insist on speaking a language in which they're not particularly competent, that they're really not good at. I remember one very high-powered professor from … well, I won't say where … but her English was extremely difficult to follow. I just had to make an educated guess as to what she was trying to say. I usually try to get speeches from all speakers in advance so I at least have the written word to fall back on in these kinds of situations.

I: And I suppose sometimes people speak too fast for you to follow?

A: Yes, to a certain extent, but from experience I've found there's no point in asking them to slow down. Everyone has a natural pace of speaking so the best thing to do is not try to translate word for word but to summarise what they're saying.

I: Right. I can understand that.

A: And then of course there are cultural differences. Humour is an interpreter's nightmare. There's a risk of humorous sayings from one language getting completely lost in translation. Humour doesn't travel well, and jokes are often just not funny.

I: So, what do you do if a speaker is telling a lot of jokes?

A: I'll try and see if I can find an equivalent in the audience's language, but if I can't think fast enough, I'll fall back on the old interpreter's rule of saying, 'the speaker has just made a joke about such and such', which seems to work. Now, one really problematic area is when the speaker uses lots of metaphors, cultural references or indecipherable acronyms. For example, if a U.S. speaker starts using metaphors from American baseball, say, something like, 'I'll take a rain check on that.' Now most audiences won't have a clue about this so I have to translate it as something like, 'He would like to accept your invitation at a later time.' You've got to be very quick-thinking and versatile. You also need to have a fairly broad knowledge of culturally specific things, and do your research on acronyms, etc.

I: Is there anything else you can do about that?

A: Again, I try and educate the speaker. I suggest that they should steer clear of cultural references which seem familiar to them but may not be understood in a different context; instead, they should find references to people or places or events that the audience will understand. But of course, often I only meet the speaker on the day of the conference, so I don't always have a chance to help them prepare for the process. And don't get me started on online conferences – some of the speakers are simply not familiar with different platforms or how they work so they can get really chaotic.

I: That sounds like a lot of problems.

A: Yes, but most problems are fixable as long as there's mutual respect between us, between the speaker and the interpreter. Understanding that we both have an important job to do. And there's one more thing I really must mention. It's a problem I take home with me. You see, I get so used to thinking ahead and predicting what people are going to say that I tend to do the same thing outside work. I anticipate the end of a sentence, so my friends are always complaining: 'You never let me finish!' It's something I keep promising myself I must address!

I: Well, this has been a real insight. Thank you very much for joining us today.

A: My pleasure.

Audio 2.03

1 John and Maya were critical of translation apps, but Tina felt differently.

2 Betina said most words can be translated accurately, but according to Juan there are lots of words that can't be.

3 Paul discussed the difficulty of real-time translation, and the group agreed with his views.

4 While most people agreed about the challenge of translating idiomatic language, Mo felt it wasn't such a big issue.

Audio 2.04

L = Leo   E = Ella   C = Clare

L: I have to say that I, and most of my friends, well, we were brought up to respect older people. And not just older people, but everyone really. It's part of our culture.

E: I'm not arguing there. Respect is important, of course it is. But what I'm saying is that, in my opinion, it's not something that's peculiar to a certain culture – it's international, surely, it's part of being a normal human being, of being part of a civilised community, isn't it?

L: That's a relevant point, and I see where you're coming from. But I don't know that I'm totally in agreement here. In some cultures, respect is automatic, whereas in others it has to be earned. In my culture, for example, it's automatic.

E: But surely respect has to be earned? You can't respect someone who doesn't deserve it. I mean, to take an extreme example, you wouldn't respect a criminal, would you?

L: Oh now, come on. You're looking at things the wrong way round. My upbringing tells me that I should respect people until they cause me to **lose** that respect – doesn't that make sense?

E: OK, I take your point, but I still think politeness and respect are innate human traits, not cultural ones.

L: You know, when I say automatic respect, I'm thinking about, for example, respecting older people automatically because they have lived long lives and have acquired, well, wisdom. In my society, older people are valued, and family ties are strong, so, for example, older family members live with and are looked after by their family – not isolated, as I see happening in many other countries.

E: Fair enough. Yeah, you make a good point. And I must say I have to agree to some extent. But, moving on – and changing the focus of the topic slightly – wouldn't you say that for some reason, in general, there's a lack of respect these days between the generations?

C: If I can come in here. I think that now we're getting to the real point. Today's young people have a total lack of respect, in my opinion. They're rude, absorbed in their phones and ignore you when you're talking to them. They're lazy, sitting in their rooms all day, never helping out. People say I should respect them, but they simply don't respect me!

E: Hey, that's going too far! OK, some young people might appear not to respect anyone outside their age group, but you can't generalise like that. What you're saying is unjustifiable and narrow-minded. You only have to open your eyes and you'll see young people who definitely don't sit in that category.

C: OK, so when was the last time a young person held a door open for you or gave up a seat on a train to an older person? Tell me that!

L: Right, it's clear you both have strong views here. But Clare, I think there's a slight flaw in your argument when you say all young people are lazy. Check out the lists of young entrepreneurs, or volunteering sites for teenagers … it's patently obvious that they aren't all lazy and expect the world to give them a living. Look at Greta Thunberg and how she's rallying young people to fight for the environment!

C: She's an exception.

L: But I appreciate that there are some problems. As I see it, the mutual lack of respect between generations is happening where the culture of respect is not strong, where traditions and family bonds are breaking down. Both the older and the younger generations feel misunderstood by the other, and it's because the cultural – how can I say it – glue, maybe, that holds societies together, is failing.

E: Wow, that's a bit deep! But I think I get where you're coming from. On the other hand, however …

Audio 2.05

1 I'm not arguing there.

2 That's a relevant point.

3 But surely respect has to be earned?

4 You're looking at things the wrong way round.

5 OK, I take your point.

6 Fair enough.

7 You make a good point.

8 It's clear you both have strong views here.

9 I think there's a slight flaw in your argument.

10 I think I get where you're coming from.

Audio 2.06

But surely respect has to be earned?

Audio 2.07

1 But surely it's the other way round?

2 But surely you can't really believe that?

3 But surely there's more to it than that?

4 But surely that's oversimplifying things?

Audio R2.01

Culture shock

It can be a tremendous shock to the system, irrespective of how well prepared you are. Going for the first time to a country where the culture is nothing like your own can be overwhelming. According to the autobiography of a famous traveller, his first trip abroad couldn't have been any more traumatic. His knowledge of the language was so limited as to be practically nonexistent, he was vegan and found himself in a meat-loving country, and he had no knowledge of customs or traditions at all. However, although he acknowledges that culture shock is commonplace, he is insistent that it soon fades, and the long-standing benefits that being immersed in another culture brings are far more important than the initial cultural isolation.

Audio WB2.01

I = Interviewer   S = Signer

I: That's interesting. But what made you choose this line of work in the first place?

S: Well, I always had strong feelings about equal opportunity, that everyone should have the same access to information and official processes, and indeed entertainment. My mother is deaf, and I saw how she was often left out of things – for example the parent-teacher meetings when I was at school.

I: Is that how you learnt to sign?

S: Yes, I grew up signing. It was natural to me, so I had no problem with fluency or with switching between speech and signing.

I: I see. And what are the ups and downs of the job?

S: Oh, there are plenty of positives – I've helped people understand their doctor's instructions about taking medication, so they could do so confidently and independently. The other day I interpreted at a job interview for quite a high-up position. The candidate, who was deaf of course, prepared a fantastic presentation, and my interpretation helped them get the job. I've also done signing for local drama productions.

I: That's incredible. It's just never occurred to me how useful it must be to know sign language.

S: Oh yes, like knowing any language.

I: So, what's the downside of the job?

S: Well, you need to be really quick-thinking and it's quite physical with all the gesturing. It can be draining. And sometimes if I'm conveying bad news, I can get quite down, so it's emotionally draining, too.

I: I can understand that. Otherwise, it sounds like a great job.

S: It is. And I can be well paid! Oh, except the travel – it sounds glamorous, when I get these jobs abroad, but I prefer to sleep in my own bed.

I: Well, thank you for talking with us …

Audio 3.01

A: … and that's the key to finding the career path that's best for you. Thank you all for listening. I'm happy to take questions now. Yes, there in the second row.

B: My question is about actually getting a job in the first place. How can you make sure your application warrants a second look?

A: Well, I can give you some basic guidance. First, you need to tick all the boxes on your CV, and that means highlighting what you can offer. There's a strong likelihood that certain key phrases will come up in a job advertisement. For example, these often refer to 'good organisation and communication skills'. Let's start with organisation. Think about all the information and data we deal with in our everyday lives, and how overwhelming that can be … Well, it's no different in a job, and it's absolutely essential that you have the skills to enable you to manage large amounts of information efficiently: keep your calendar up to date, have clear file-naming systems so that everything is traceable, develop a systematic approach to dealing with emails, and so on.

AUDIOSCRIPTS

B: And what about 'communication skills'?

A: Having good 'social skills' and being able to interact with people well is important on many levels. Face-to-face, interpersonal skills are one element, being able to articulate your ideas clearly is also key. You need to be good at getting people to want to listen to you, whether online or not, to get them to feel it's worth their while. And then of course it's obviously your responsibility to present yourself in the best possible way. You should always demonstrate common sense and discretion in controlling the image you convey in the visible aspect of your personal life. We all have a massive digital footprint that comes from our online activities, and that is a concern for a prospective employer. If there's a problem with your online history, inevitably it will come out at some point. Next question? Yes, go ahead.

C: Could you say something about 'flexibility' and what that means to employers?

A: Ah yes. I think simply put, that means the willingness to turn your hand to anything, to muck in. You might be asked to take on a range of tasks that are not necessarily in your job description and to do this with enthusiasm rather than grudgingly. Saying, 'I'm not going to do this because it's not in my remit' will not go down well. And it makes a strong impression if, in your motivational letter, you can demonstrate experience in stepping up to do what needs to be done for the good of the team.

C: So, it's like being a good team player?

A: Exactly. Now, there's time for one more question. Yes?

D: I've heard from friends that they've had to take part in some different types of job interviews. It seems that it's no longer a case of sitting down face-to-face and answering questions about your strengths and weaknesses!

A: You're right! The job interview has certainly developed in interesting ways and may well continue to do so in the coming years. Of course, there are, as you would expect, remote interviews that are carried out online, which allow employers to interview candidates from a wide range of geographical locations. And there have been developments in the types of things interviewees are asked to do. Some people have been asked to play computer games, or in one case, even dance during an interview! And we've probably all heard of those weird interview questions, like 'If you were a tree, what kind of tree would you be?' or 'What would you take with you to a desert island?' On the surface, these questions and activities seem just plain odd. However, they are indicative of a trend – recruiters want to find out more about employees than simply what they know or what they've done. They want to know how quick-thinking they are, how creative, how they respond under pressure, more about their personality. And how well they work in a team. And with developments in facial- and voice- recognition technology, in the future, recruiters may well be using voice analysis to learn more about the candidates. OK, thank you all for …

Audio 3.02

1 There's a strong likelihood that certain key phrases will come up in a job advertisement.

2 It's absolutely essential that you have the skills to enable you to manage large amounts of information efficiently.

3 … being able to interact with people well is important on many levels …

4 You need to be good at getting people to want to listen to you.

5 It's obviously your responsibility to present yourself in the best possible way.

6 Inevitably it will come out at some point.

7 You might be asked to take on a range of tasks.

8 In the future, recruiters may well be using voice analysis to learn more about the candidates.

Audio 3.03

1 There's a strong likelihood that it will happen.

2 It's absolutely essential that we attend.

3 It's obviously your responsibility to get it done.

4 You should always be aware that others might see it differently.

5 In all probability, this will fail.

Audio 3.04

aggravate	ease	isolation
alleviate	engender	morale
distrust	exacerbate	strengthen

Audio 3.05

At the forefront of our campaign is a determination to bridge the gap between the rich and the poor – the 'haves and the have nots,' the heart of which is work and the resulting standard of living. This will involve allocating resources to deal with the many inequalities in employment – from enforcing regulations to enable equal opportunities for every job seeker, to shaping policy to allow for more apprenticeships, and more scholarships to universities. We shall also not shirk away from tackling inequality in pay scales for men and women and for ethnic minorities. We are the party that will stand up for workers' rights in all areas of employment to eliminate discrimination and encourage diversity.

Audio 3.06

1 Our intention is to bridge the gender pay gap by increasing higher-level work opportunities for women.

2 A major policy of ours going forward will be to allocate more resources to enable more rough sleepers to leave the streets.

3 We realise that eliminating discrimination across the board will be a huge challenge, but we shall enforce existing regulations and pass new laws.

4 Diversity is to be encouraged in every area of life and we shall tackle inequalities wherever we find them.

5 Helping the environment is high on our agenda and our party will stand up for those who want to develop greener energy and shape further policy to fight climate change.

Audio 3.07

A: I thought Philippa Marwell made a good speech about how her party would address the gender pay gap if they got into power at the upcoming election. Did you hear it? She's going to get my vote next week, that's for sure.

B: So, in other words, you're going to vote for her because of one election promise.

A: Not at all. What I said was that she made a good speech. And it was about an issue that concerns me. I mean, look at the number of women in top jobs in the country. There are so few of them. It simply isn't fair, and something needs to be done to even everything up.

B: So, what you're basically saying is that men and women don't have the same opportunities to reach the high-salaried positions.

A: Absolutely. That's exactly what I mean. Don't you agree?

B: Of course I agree – I just don't think Marwell's party will help change anything.

A: So, am I right in thinking that you believe there's nothing more politicians can do to address the glass ceiling for women?

B: OK, I'll put it another way. There are certainly things government can do to help – but I honestly don't think Marwell's party is the one to carry these things through. It's a really tricky problem.

A: You're right. But another approach they could take – and Marwell mentions this, too – is to force companies to be more flexible about their employees' hours, so both men and women could fit work around childcare. They should share the responsibilities.

B: Good thinking – but you shouldn't only be focusing on people with top jobs and salaries – that's still a comparatively small number of men and women.

A: That's not what I'm saying. And it's not what Philippa Marwell is saying either. She wants to raise the pay for lower-income jobs, like carers and nurses, and also introduce targets such as making employers at least encourage women to put in for higher positions.

B: It's pointless though. Whatever policies the next government introduces, the following one could well change them all!

A: Please correct me if I'm wrong, but it sounds like you're talking about a complete lack of progress – that the gender pay gap will always exist.

B: Let me rephrase that. Maybe 'pointless' is too negative a word. Perhaps I should have said 'unlikely'. You know how long it takes to get laws through parliament, and how many are turned around by the next incoming ministers.

A: Well, I must say that I hope your view isn't shared by the electorate. **You** might think it's not worth fighting for, but in my opinion, Philippa Marwell and her party have the right ideas. More opportunities, more flexibility, higher salaries – they're all doable. Whether Marwell's party will actually make good on those promises if they win, is another question. But I'll give them the benefit of the doubt next week.

Audio 3.08

A: I thought Philippa Marwell made a good speech about how her party would address the gender pay gap if they got into power at the upcoming election. Did you hear it? She's going to get my vote next week, that's for sure.

B: So, in other words, you're going to vote for her because of one election promise.

A: Not at all. What I said was that she made a good speech. And it was about an issue that concerns me. I mean, look at the number of women in top jobs in the country. There are so few of them. It simply isn't fair, and something needs to be done to even everything up.

B: So, what you're basically saying is that men and women don't have the same opportunities to reach the high-salaried positions.

Audio 3.09

1 So, what you're basically saying is that men and women don't have the same opportunities to reach the high-salaried positions.
2 Correct me if I'm wrong, but it sounds like you're talking about a complete lack of progress.

UNIT 4

Audio 4.01

1 What fuelled your motivation?
2 If you could pursue an ambition, what would it be?

Audio 4.02

1 It's important to satisfy your curiosity.
2 What worthwhile local projects in your area need to raise funding?
3 How important do you think it is for pioneers to serve science in their endeavours?
4 Many people want to realise a dream although not all succeed.
5 Have you found anybody to back your project?

Audio 4.03

P = Presenter   H = Helen

P: There are a lot of people out there, kind, compassionate people, who are ready, willing and able to give a helping hand to those who are in need – and there are a host of websites that provide a link between those who need the help and those who want to give it. Helen Carter, who, as you're aware, does a weekly round-up of useful websites and apps for us, is here today to report on a charitable organisation, 52 Lives, which seems to be really rather special. Helen?

H: Yes. I'd heard about this website a while back and I'd been meaning to check it out. What it does is try to change someone's life every single week of the year. Each week a story is posted on the website or social media pages, about someone who needs help in some shape or form, things which can really make a difference to their day-to-day lives – not necessarily because they're destitute, but because they might be going through a rough patch, needing something relatively basic to help them face the day. This could be something concrete and simple like a pram, an old computer, or, I don't know, an easy type of can opener for someone with arthritis, or it might be something a whole lot bigger, like a stair lift. It could also be a service, like giving people lifts to hospital appointments. The organisation's supporters, which now number over 100,000, either give help themselves, or if they can't, they spread the word to find others who can.

P: It sounds amazing. Has it been running for a long time?

H: Well, by the end of the month, the woman who started it, Jaime Thurston, will have been working on the project for nine years. It all came about by chance. Apparently, she'd been thinking about doing some volunteering for a while but never got round to it. Like a lot of people, I guess. Anyway, she came across a 'Wanted' advert while she was looking for some second-hand furniture and it had been put up by a woman who needed a rug. Her story touched Jaime's heart. The woman was bringing up children on her own, on a low income, and finding it hard to make ends meet. Her flat had no carpet, which meant

the rooms were very cold. Jaime didn't have a rug, but she contacted the woman and said if she could source a rug then Jaime would pick it up for her. Just that one item made a huge difference to the woman's family and Jaime had the idea that things like this could help an enormous number of people who were struggling. The word just needed to be spread. And so, the idea took off. It started with an online post about this woman's story, then a fundraising page to get money to help install a lift for a boy in a wheelchair, and now has grown into a global community, linking people across a whole range of social media platforms.

P: So, you were saying it's not only giving items but services as well?

H: Or money to fund services – like, a few years ago, redecorating the room of a little girl confined to bed or even things like sending cards and kind messages to young people who are being trolled or bullied. It's quite remarkable. And it's all based on a simple philosophy – that being selfless and spreading kindness empowers people and can change lives. It clearly brings benefits to the person or family in need – and not only the tangible benefits – it's the kindness that complete strangers are showing that people are appreciative of – it's that which makes the big difference. Also, it has a knock-on effect – it benefits the givers – being altruistic and knowing that their kindness to someone – who they will never meet – has helped in a major way, is rewarding.

P: Wow – I just love this idea. Does the organisation do anything else?

H: Oh yes! Jaime won an award for the website in 2016 and used the prize money to set up a School of Kindness. They go into primary schools and work with children, helping them to understand how much difference even very small everyday choices can make, and encourage them to come up with ways of spreading kindness in their circles of friends, families and communities. You know, I'm sitting here, and I'm wondering what on earth this amazing woman is going to do next!

P: It's true though, isn't it? You get a warm glow if a complete stranger does something kind for you, out of the blue, and also if you do something kind for a complete stranger. It has to be a win-win philosophy! What a great website report this week. Thanks, Helen.

Audio 4.04

1 People will always be grateful when you give them a helping hand.
2 It can have a serious knock-on effect.
3 We all go through rough patches; things do get better.

Audio 4.05

1 I'm sitting here and I'm wondering what on earth this amazing woman is going to do next!
2 Jaime Thurston will have been working on the project for nine years.
3 I'd heard about this website a while back and I'd been meaning to check it out.
4 She'd been thinking about doing some volunteering for a while.

Audio 4.06

A: … and the next section was particularly interesting. On the whole, people expressed a curiosity about businesses that had less relevance for them. So, they wanted to know more about services

that they were in fact unlikely to use, which was surprising for us. To cite one example, people who don't have pets tended to be particularly interested in getting information about the pet-related services. Our impression was simply that these businesses had some novelty for them, and their interest presumably reflected amusement more than a genuine desire to use the service. One person said, 'It just never occurred to me that such a business would exist.'

B: Another illustration of this is the number of people who asked for more information about the parking services, and who, as it turned out, don't actually have a car. Generally speaking though, when we asked people about actually using the services, there was limited interest in trying out ones that the survey participants hadn't used in the past. The consensus seems to be that people favour what they already use or know about and are satisfied with the service they're getting for the price they're paying. One might speculate that this reflects human nature – people don't like to go out of their comfort zone – but having said that, some people were attracted to alternatives to services they already use, such as HomeExchange instead of Airbnb.

A: Yes, and in that case there's a real difference in the way the services work, since with Airbnb you pay for what you use, and with HomeExchange you only pay a membership fee, and after that the services are free. Now moving onto the next question …

Audio 4.07

1 On the whole, people expressed a curiosity about how effective the businesses were in significantly reducing waste.
2 To cite one example, people who were interested in sustainable fashion wondered how many times fashion items could be recycled.
3 Our impression was simply that people were interested in the difference between the claims and the actual reality of these business models.
4 Their interest presumably reflected a genuine concern to help protect the planet's finite resources.
5 Another illustration of this is the number of people who asked for more information about second-hand furniture outlets and clothes-swap websites.
6 Generally speaking though, there was limited interest in trying out services that had no proven track record in sustainability and seemed to be profit-driven rather than eco-friendly.
7 The consensus seems to be that people favour businesses that persuade us that they are really committed to a truly circular economy.
8 One might speculate that this way of approaching services will continue to attract consumers and marks a radical shift in the way we will spend money in the future and why.

Audio 4.08

1 To cite one example, businesses which sold upcycled furniture reported a significant increase in customer interest.
2 Generally speaking though, the cost and effort that goes into upcycling tends to lead to very small profit margins.

Audio R4.01

One of the most successful projects of recent years aimed at improving the lives of people living on or below the bread line has been The Big Issue Foundation. Homeless people or those desperately trying to make ends meet have become mini entrepreneurs, selling magazines which have been compiled by people just like themselves. The project has brought many out of poverty, restored their self-esteem and enabled them to face each day with a brighter outlook. People who buy these magazines are not donating to charity but are involved in a transaction which has the knock-on effect of both raising the profile of the homeless (through the articles in the magazine) and helping each vendor on a financial and life-affirming journey. Thousands of vendors are known to have benefitted from the scheme and the lives they live now are infinitely preferable to sleeping rough and not knowing where the next meal is coming from.

UNIT 5

Audio 5.01

AJ: In my opinion, the best way to make a favourable impression on someone is by being confident but not over-confident. If someone talks too loudly or tells me too much about themself at a first meeting, trying to project a certain image, it can definitely lead to a bad first impression.

Keyops17: For me it's all about body language. It tells us how interested that person is in having a conversation with us or if they'd rather be somewhere else! In my case that has a bearing on whether I want to continue a conversation or not!

RayTheLima: Oh, it's all about the eyes. If someone doesn't actually look me in the eye, I assume the person's not that honest. Perhaps they're fine and just have little confidence? We're told things like this can lead to problematic preconceptions, but I can't help it!

Audio 5.02

1 It's a person's accent that tells others whether they can be trusted or not.
2 What disturbs me is when people have really weird facial expressions.
3 What I love is when people make eye contact with you when they're talking to you.
4 It's the way people walk that tells me the most about them.

Audio 5.03

A = Alex   T = Teacher   C = Child
M1 = Man 1   M2 = Man 2   Ty = Ty
Tw = Twiggy   M3 = Man 3   W1 = Woman 1

A: Welcome to the *Digital Human*'s episode about whispers.

T: Tiger's tail is stripey, lion's tail is ropey, cheetah's tail is spotty.

C: Erm, lion's tail is stripey, tiger's tail is ropey …

A: We've all played that game as kids: when we pass the message along, it changes. But hey, that's part of the fun.

C: Tiger's tail's … spotty …

A: But away from the playground as grown-ups we continue to spread rumours and to distort information. Between friends we might embellish or detract, shape, and carve what we hear until it feels right, before passing it on.

M1: People love a story and people love sensation. People don't bother to check their facts. What they do is they see a headline on their Facebook newsfeed, they get outraged by it, they skim the story and then they repost it.

A: But rumour has a bad rep. It's not always untrue. It's simply a kernel of something that's not yet been confirmed or denied. Now though, the interconnectivity of social media means that rumours can spread quickly, unchecked. Passing something too good to keep to yourself to the next person or network only takes a click.

M2: There's an entire world of design possibilities that might help people to think about the information that they're spreading but the entire point of these networks is to have people spreading more and more. Sharing more and more. Sharing what other people spread.

A: Picture a tiger, red and black, stripes, claws, canines – four hundred pounds of pure muscle. This tiger could do real damage. Imagine it stalking the streets of London. Because that is what happened in August 2011. Just at the time the London riots kicked off. Or did it?
That summer Twiggy Garcia and Ty Evans shared a flat in Bethnal Green – one of the neighbourhoods where people were rioting.

Ty: Um, I remember it being sort of, yeah, the start of August, it was quite hot. You know, reading the initial reports about what happened with Mark Duggan. And then, um, I guess from there sort of on the news, websites, and in the papers, it just sort of slowly escalating

Tw: There was too many people causing too much trouble and there was this kind of bravery that people had where they just decided that they could do what they wanted.

M3: Hearing reports that London Zoo was broken into, and a large number of animals have escaped.

A: Cooped up in their flat above the police station, Twiggy, Ty and their mates decided to add their own voice to the chaos of information that was ricocheting around social media.

Ty: The London Eye is on fire.

W1: Reports of tigers roaming round Primrose Hill.

Tw: Is this real?

A: The tiger is on the loose.

Ty: I just typed into Google 'tiger escaped from zoo' and found a black and white grainy photograph of what looked like a tiger stalking down a residential street. Twiggy's obviously got quite a few followers, so I think I tweeted it and he retweeted it and he's got about 5,000 followers, so I think from there it just sort of escalated quite quickly. A couple of hours later we had sort of thousands of people retweeting that animals had escaped from the zoo and then it was that there was animals walking down the streets of Hackney and I think at that point Russian news channels were saying that there was animals all over London, and you could actually hear the tigers roaring and I think Sky News at one point also reported something similar.

A: Twiggy and his following on social media lit the fire, getting the word out there initially, but then the design of Twitter

fanned the flames. Hashtags made the information easy to find and to spread. And besides, there was evidence. There was a photo and pictures, they say a thousand words, right? Unconfirmed information, source credibility, the means to spread it and the so-called conclusive evidence meant that the tiger rumour became one of the most enduring tales of the riots.

Audio 5.04

A = Alex   Tw = Twiggy

A: But just as quickly as it flared up, fellow Twitter users began questioning the 'truthiness' of the rumour.

Tw: I think it was a few hours into it that we started to see voices out there saying that it's not true, but then the difficulty is within social media and the way that people are connected, you don't really, if you've got someone who's saying that it's not true, it's how loud is their voice within the social community and who's listening to them and who's repeating what they say – even two weeks after the tiger story I still heard people at parties and out and about talking about it, saying "Did you hear that?"

A: Did you, did you tell them that you were involved with it?

Tw: Oh, yeah – complete blagging rights.

A: Ha-ha. What was their response?

Tw: Some people were … thought that it was hilarious and then other people said that I was wasting people's time and that I shouldn't have done that because there was lots of stuff going on during the riots and I kind of didn't help the situation, um, but to those people I just say …

Audio 5.05

1 Having shared the story, I instantly felt bad.
2 Knowing what I do now, I wish I hadn't reposted it.
3 Being a smart person, I always check the sources before I share news posts online.
4 Having seen stories like that before, I was wary about it.

Audio 5.06

Hi, can everyone hear me? That's great. I'd like to tell you about escape rooms, which have become one of my favourite free-time activities and which I think might be a great activity to help us work together better. They're everywhere now, and big cities have literally dozens of them. So, what are they? Well, escape rooms are basically these small rooms or floors, usually in rundown or abandoned buildings, and each escape room complex has different rooms with different themes. What you have to do in each one is the same. You go into the room with four or five other people, so you go in with friends, so it's a good social experience. You're locked in the room for 60 minutes and your task is to find a way out of the room. And to do this you have to engage in lots of puzzle solving, collaborative puzzle solving, so you do it together.

The rooms are elaborate. It's like this huge 3D puzzle – and each room has a different theme. To give you an example, let's look at this one. So, the theme of this one is Ancient Egypt. The room is the office of a professor of Ancient Egypt and you're surrounded by locked cupboards. All you have is one key hanging down and there are padlocks everywhere, so you have to find the right lock for the key. Eventually you find it, you open the cupboard and there you find another key or a piece of paper with numbers on it or a paper trail of clues that need some lateral thinking. You've got to communicate a lot with the others, like 'Why do you think we got this piece of paper?' or 'What's this number?' or 'Hey, this number's the same as that number over there, do you think there's something in that?'

All the while you can see that the clock's ticking and it gets a bit frantic. But you can't panic, you can't get out and you can't stop working as a team.

If you succeed, it's great, you did it as a team and you feel really good about it. If you fail, well that's a shame, but you did it as a team and you still feel really good about it. In other words, either way, it's the feeling of teamwork that you take away. And you go for lunch together and talk about it. For hours.

So that's how an escape room works. And who does it suit? Well, it suits people who like doing hands-on work, people who like looking around and taking it all in, trying to connect the dots, and most of all it suits people who like working in a team. You have to enjoy the team element and finding your role in that, whether your role is the foot soldier or the general.

The thing is, it's cooperative, it's collaborative, but it's not competitive.

In short, escape rooms are certainly worth trying once. Not only will you have a unique, exciting experience but you will also share an experience that you'll be talking about for years. I guarantee it. OK, so, I'm ready to take any questions, you can unmute yourselves now, or just pop your questions in the chat.

Audio 5.07

3　But you can't panic, you can't get out and you can't stop working as a team.

7　Not only will you have a unique, exciting experience but you will also share an experience that you'll be talking about for years.

UNIT 6

Audio 6.01

The thing is, they all think he's just a petty criminal, but actually, he's the criminal mastermind.

He's there the whole time, answering the police officers' questions, asking for coffee, pretending just to be this very average crook who walks with a limp and is very low on confidence. Then when they let him go, we suddenly see he doesn't walk with a limp at all. He's been playing with the police all along.

Audio 6.02

See page 71.

Audio 6.03

P = Presenter　A = Andy　K = Kate

P: An interesting topic for discussion today I think, people. We shall be getting to grips with the power of poetry and song and asking a few fundamental and potentially tricky questions, with my two guests – Andy, a performance poet and Kate, a lecturer. First up is **not** the age-old 'what is poetry' question …

A: Thank goodness …

P: It's why do you think poetry sometimes has a bad press? There are no two ways about it: there are those who love poetry and those who find it, well, it just does nothing for them.

A: I know, people's eyes often glaze over when I tell them I'm a poet. To be honest, I think it's down to poetry being misrepresented, and schools are often guilty of this. Students are introduced to poetry through traditional, classical poets who adhere strictly to certain rhyme schemes and rhythms. What the poet is trying to say is often difficult to decipher and poems are clogged up with metaphor and archaic language. It can be quite intimidating.

K: Yeah, that's not all bad though, it's just not always the best way to encounter poetry for the first time – and we all know that first impressions count. Students have to realise that poetry doesn't have to rhyme, it doesn't have to have lines of equal length or rhythm. It can be deceptively simplistic or linguistically complex. It can be punchy like rap, or lyrical, it can tell a story, express a feeling, or be a call to action. It can be pages long or short and sweet – look at the magical effects of a seventeen-syllable Japanese haiku! A poem can be read or it can be listened to. The important thing about a poem is that it has relevance to the reader and is meaningful. It communicates, talks to them, conjures up images, stops them in their tracks and makes them see things from different angles – whether that be a relationship, the environment, politics …

A: Exactly. Poetry can help both the reader and the poet. We should encourage people to use poetry to express their own emotions, frustrations and fears. In the 21st century, poetry can be exciting, thrilling – just go to a poetry slam or listen to performance poets. It's a far cry from Shakespeare's sonnets – sorry Shakespeare, they are pretty special, but …

P: OK, OK. Thanks guys. I do have another question here. Some people question whether songs can be considered poetry, and the songwriters considered poets. Your thoughts?

A: Yes, I can see where the controversy comes in. A song comprises music and lyrics, and of course, we need to add in performance. One version of a song may lift someone's mood, whereas another version, more emotionally charged, will be really moving and poignant and have the ability to reduce you to tears.

K: That is so true. Compare two versions of *The Sound of Silence*, the original by Simon and Garfunkel and a more recent recording by Disturbed, a heavy metal band. The lyrics talk about the dangers of not communicating, but while the original uses harmonies, is purely melodic and relatively melancholic, Disturbed's version is confrontational and rousing, and finishes loud and rasping in its outrage. It took my breath away when I first heard it. Quite brilliant.

P: OK, to bring you back to the question … ?

A: But then poems can be read differently by two people, can't they? In my opinion, lyrics **are** poetry. Just look at the songs of Leonard Cohen, now those really take me back, or more recently, rapper Kendrick Lamar. Lyrics can do the same as poetry – take you out of yourself, make you feel alive, give you solace, stir you, change you.

K: And like poetry they are often open to interpretation. People can identify with the writer or relate to them in different ways. Music adds different shades of meaning to all lyrics, but in essence, the words stand alone as poems. So, yes, I'm definitely not a fusty old traditionalist when it comes to this question. Songwriters can definitely be poets.

A: I wholeheartedly agree!

Audio 6.04

1　There are those who love poetry and those who don't.

2　A poem can be deceptively simplistic or linguistically complex.

3　It doesn't matter whether it's upbeat or slow, hard rock or gentle folk.

Audio 6.05

The Orient Express is definitely one of those classic journeys that every traveller dreams of taking. I finally got the chance to do so a few years back. Some friends who had done it were like, 'Yeah, it's amazing, but it's quite expensive. We had to pay twenty euros for an orange juice!' So, I wasn't sure about it before I started, but in fact it turned out to be really fun.

I was travelling alone, so I booked a single cabin, which was amazing – antique lacquered furniture, plush velvet cushions … it felt like I had travelled back in time!

Anyway, once I'd unpacked, I decided to go and explore the train a bit – see if could meet a few people to hang out with on the trip. So, I ended up sitting with three fellow travellers in the dining car – two young Chinese guys and this Polish guy, a really nice guy, more on him in a minute. No one spoke any English. Fairly typical situation for a traveller in an exotic context, you know what I mean? You'd think it would be awkward, the lack of a *lingua franca* I mean, but to the contrary, it was really nice, sort of relaxed, like 'we're all in this together and let's just enjoy it'. In fact, we did make many attempts at communicating, especially me and the Polish guy, by drawing pictures of things, maps showing where we were from, writing dates for major events in life, family tree and all that. Funny, I don't remember much about him now, but I remember understanding quite a lot about his family, his kids, his house, job, stuff like that. I also remember that he was a really warm-hearted guy and loved to share everything, for example on the first evening I think it was, he pulled out this huge, homemade cake, and simply split it into four pieces, and gave each of us a piece, me and the two Chinese guys.

Every day on the train offered a new experience. One minute you're soaking in the bustling streets of Istanbul, the next you're in some sleepy town in the middle of the Romanian mountains. Anyway, when I was talking about the trip when I first booked it, some guy I know got really excited when I mentioned we'd be going to Lake Balaton. He just kept raving about how beautiful it was and I have to say, he wasn't wrong. We got there just in time to see the sun go down and it was … kind of magical – everything bathed in this orangey blue light. So, anyway, I'm sitting there trying to take a decent photo to send my mate and I noticed that this kid kept looking at me. Eventually, I turned to face him and he just grinned and said, 'Nice hat'. I was wearing this faded old Boston Celtics cap – nothing special really. In fact, I'm not even sure where I got it – I don't know anything about basketball – but he seemed rather taken with it. So, I just, kind of, gave it to him. Stupid thing to do, maybe, but it was one of those moments when you just kind of go with the flow. I wonder if he's still got it?

Audio 6.06

1 Some friends who had done it were like, 'Yeah, it's amazing but it's quite expensive.'
2 Fairly typical situation for a traveller in an exotic context, you know what I mean?
3 It was really nice, sort of relaxed, like 'we're all in this together and let's just enjoy it'.
4 Funny, I don't remember much about him now, but I remember understanding quite a lot about his family, his kids, his house, job, stuff like that.
5 … for example on the first evening I think it was, he pulled out this huge, homemade cake …
6 … some guy I know got really excited when I mentioned we'd be going to Lake Balaton.
7 I noticed that this kid kept looking at me.
8 Stupid thing to do, maybe, but it was one of those moments when you just kind of go with the flow.

Audio 6.07

1 I asked my friend about his trip, and he was like, 'Wow – it was amazing!'
2 The lake was like a huge mirror, you know what I mean?
3 We had all the basics – bread, coffee, milk, stuff like that.

UNIT 6 MEDIATION BANK

Audio MB6.01

1 What a lot of people don't think about is that, if tourism stops overnight, some communities simply won't survive. So what's left for those people to do? They won't have any option but to move to already overcrowded cities and lead less sustainable lives.
And if you think about safari or rainforest tours, for example, they actually opened up opportunities and a way to preserve habitats and the wildlife. They mean that people no longer need to be involved in logging, poaching or big game hunting to make a living. If you shut down tourism, it will be a big boost for some very exploitative and harmful industries. Costa Rica is just one great example of the benefits of the ecotourism boom – during the 1970s, it was one of the most rapidly deforested places on Earth. Fast forward to now, and protected national parks make up more than 30 percent of the land. Tourism is a crucial part of the economy and what has made it all possible.
2 The economic benefits of tourism pale into insignificance when you think of the scale of the economic disaster that awaits if we don't avoid climate catastrophe. People often talk about the benefits of ecotourism, but the fact is that that kind of tourism is very expensive and is a minority interest. Most travel is made up of people flying a few thousand miles, creating tons of CO_2, just so they can be somewhere sunny for a few days, and what are they doing while they're there? Over-consuming and using swimming pools and so on – which themselves are very damaging.
Even worse than that are the incredibly wealthy people who use private jets. I read an article recently saying how private jets are ten times worse in terms of CO_2 emissions than standard commercial aviation – and fifty times worse than trains!

I hear that there are now 'flights to nowhere', too! People are literally flying a couple of hours into foreign airspace so they can get some duty-free shopping, before landing back at the same airport they left from!
3 Clearly some kinds of tourism are more problematic than others – just look at the oversized cruise ships causing Venice's foundations to crumble. So sad when it's one of the most iconic places on the planet, a testament to human ingenuity and creativity. Having said that, I don't think we can just decide 'no more travel'. It's simply not realistic – or even desirable. So what we need to do is learn the lessons from positive tourism and encourage that, and take measures to reduce 'bad tourism'. That could be through tougher regulation on the tourism industry, progressive taxation or even outright bans on certain practices – domestic flights in a country the size of the UK, for example. It's absurd, really. It's probably true that we need to travel, and in particular fly, less often. I would be in favour of legislation there, but we shouldn't give up on travel completely. It's part of what we are as a species.
4 They've just built a new runway and it's made our lives a complete nightmare. The noise pollution, I mean. It's just constant now. At least we used to get a break between midnight and 5 a.m. But since they've expanded the airport, they've changed the rules and it's 24/7. We tried to fight against it, but no one listens to us. Why would they? We haven't got millions of dollars to invest. That's all anyone really cares about – and that's why they won't make any positive change.
5 To be honest, I'm not sure what to think. Every week you hear or read about a different story. We all know that some things have to change – and I try to do my bit, like now – going to work by or whatever, but does it really make a difference? I don't know. It's just daunting really. It puts me off reading the news cos it's easier just to bury our heads in the sand. It's time for the government and big business to take responsibility. Maybe they do need to bring in a law like this, and it'll force airlines to find a cleaner way to fly.

UNIT 7

Audio 7.01

1 umming and ahhing
2 spoilt for choice
3 in a quandary
4 sit on the fence
5 dig your heels in
6 take the path of least resistance

Audio 7.02

P = Presenter   T = Tara

P: All this week on the programme we've been talking to guests about the choice between doing things online or offline, discussing how these experiences differ and what we think the future holds. If you've been tuning in regularly, you'll know that so far there have been several issues up for discussion such as interacting on social media versus meeting face-to-face, how we choose between online retail and actually going shopping, the benefits of online or in-person education and we've even touched on virtual holidays

and sport experiences versus the real thing. We've heard interesting points of view from those who embrace the online world completely and those who express a concern that we are losing valuable real-world experiences. It's been a fascinating exchange of views. Today it's the turn of reading, something that we all do, whether it's reading fact or fiction, checking the news or friends' posts, or reading up on articles for work or college. Technology continues to change the way we access books and information, but will the printed book or newspaper ever totally become a thing of the past? Professor Tara Waters, your thoughts on this?

T: Yes, it's an intriguing topic, isn't it? When e-books first appeared, the predictions were dire – the printed book would eventually disappear, we would all carry our mini libraries with us to dip into wherever and whenever we wanted to. And the die-hard book lovers all threw up their hands in horror; books are physical, they're tactile, there's that wonderful 'smell' of print, how can you flick back in an e-book to find a previous reference and so on? We tended to think that readers were split into two camps: the 'I only read print' camp and the 'I only read digitally' one. Neither the predictions nor the split-camps theory were true. The popularity of e-books plateaued a few years ago and the resilience of the print market is indicative of the value people still place on traditional books – it's clear that there is no great likelihood of screen reading taking over completely. Online and offline reading will coexist in the same way online and offline formats exist in other areas of our lives. In the past, the advent of television was predicted to kill off radio and film, then it was feared that the internet would kill off TV, radio and film, and that cinemas would die out. It hasn't happened.

P: You mentioned the split camps, those who prefer either online or offline reading?

T: Yes. It isn't down to a clear preference for one over the other – it's more that people use the different media for different things or similar things at different times. With phones and tablets we can carry a whole library of reading material with us wherever we go to access when we please. On the other hand, a printed book, hardback or paperback, or an actual printed newspaper or magazine is something like a symbol of the unhurried world! At a time when life is so fast and our interactions with others are immediate, many find pleasure in sitting quietly with printed reading matter, away from a screen, taking pleasure in the turning of pages, and satisfaction with seeing physically how far we have progressed and how much reading still waits for us, indicated by an actual bookmark; for many people a book, or newspaper, has a character all of its own. But the way we read remains basically the same whether it's printed or online. We can plough through dense script or skim information, scrutinise some things in depth or skip to the end. Both forms of reading allow us to follow stories, to pore over details that interest us, to flick through to find what we want or to review something we've read.

P: I've heard that people tend to concentrate more, and remember more, when they're reading print. How true do you think that is?

AUDIOSCRIPTS

T: It's interesting and I have to say that the jury's still out on that. But it's thought that scrolling actually interrupts the flow of reading because the part of our brain that processes the written word is the same as that which deals with spatial awareness. This implies that it focuses best when the page is not moving. Studies have shown that comprehension is better when reading printed matter. But maybe it's just the case that reading is, relatively speaking, a new skill for humans and our brains have not had the chance to catch up with advances in technology.

P: And I have to ask – how do you see the future of reading fiction?

T: OK – the big question. I think that we're going to see a lot of fascinating technological developments, which will have long-term implications for all of us. Just as the form and structure of novels is continually changing – I cite Jeffery Deaver's amazing backwards novel here! – so will online reading. If you cast a quick eye over articles about future developments, you'll find that over the next decades it's expected that we'll undoubtedly peruse books and documents in virtual and augmented reality and illustrations will give way to animated scenes moving around us. I'm also sure that there will be more sophisticated combinations of traditional story telling with technology, with the reader moving across platforms from word to video to picture to game. And we are already able to interact with stories to shape and influence them, tailoring them to our individual preferences; this will become ever more an involvement between writer and reader. The possibilities are endless and exciting, and they're all in the hands of those visionaries of the present and the future. However, there's no getting away from the fact that a bookcase is, and will continue to be, a vital piece of furniture in a room for many people, and a bookcase needs printed books, not least to look good when you're making a video call!

Audio 7.03

1 I don't obsess about whether I read online or offline, I just like reading.

2 I was resistant to getting an e-reader for years, then I gave in and bought one. I love it.

3 If we don't set time aside to read for pleasure, we'll eventually lose the skill to do it.

4 I believe that reading regularly can protect people against certain illnesses.

5 If you skip to the end of a book, you're cheating.

6 I don't comment on other people's taste in fiction, and I expect them not to comment on mine.

Audio 7.04

A: So, what's your take on this article about urban animals? I mean the wolf in that woman's back yard sounds terrifying.

B: Well, I would say that that's a one-off. I mean, they're not like foxes – they haven't taken up residence in towns.

A: Yes, but their numbers **are** increasing throughout Europe, roaming in packs. It's devastating for farmers and downright dangerous when some get into cities. That seems very worrying to me, that there's no control around this, that …

B: Well, I feel like wolves just have a bad name to be honest, you know, you look at any film or story depicting a wolf, it's never positive.

A: Er, no, but there's a good reason for that, which is that they're dangerous wild animals and they've got no place, erm, next to populations of humans – that's just, that's just asking for trouble, isn't it?

B: Well, maybe it's just me, but it feels like the danger is always exaggerated, you know, certainly, erm, in the media they'll blow up any story. Even if one person has a really minor injury, suddenly all wolves are bad. You know, I think it's time to get the balance back and give nature a chance to fight back. I don't think it's fair.

A: I'm no expert, but I think the risk needs to be properly assessed, and I think if you look at where, erm, if you look at the statistics of, of human–wolf interaction, erm, obviously wolves often come off worse because they end up being shot by hunters and the like, but where you …

B: Well, I'm really against any form of hunting, in fact any form of culling them at all. Is that what you're saying? I just don't think that's an answer.

A: And would you feel the same if, say, if those populations of wolves were not in remote wildernesses but were on the doorstep of large cities and potentially taking people's children or pets?

B: It's not a cut and dried question. I don't think all of a sudden – they're in the city, you know, when they weren't before, I just don't think it's that simple. These are single reports – OK, maybe more than just a one-off, but not something to get too het up over.

A: I take your point, but that's not what I'm saying. The evidence is they're **close** to the cities and therefore if you look at what's happened with foxes, for example, which were previously traditionally rural animals, they … well, we now talk about urban foxes, don't we? They're a part of our lives but they, they can be dangerous, they do take people's pets. There are stories about them attacking children, too, and that's just a fox! If you've got a wolf in the same sort of situation, I'm guessing that could cause real problems.

B: Erm, I'm, there are some things that I agree with, but I just think we need to think of other options. Like tourists, for example, erm, tourists bring money to places and it's actually a plus to have wolves because people are actually going to the areas to see them. Did you ever think of it that way?

A: Yeah. Actually, in that respect I'm with you. The idea has a lot going for it, but they'd need to be controlled in some way or maybe penned into a particular reserve …

B: No one would disagree with that. Obviously, you've got to have some sort of control, but I just think some people are taking it out of all proportion, with talk of culling and so on …

A: Er well, no, I don't completely agree with that – people are right to be concerned. I think that we need to ensure that if we want to live, erm, alongside animals like that we need to take necessary precautions and potentially, erm, think about culling to keep the numbers, within reason. You must agree with that, surely?

B: On the face of it, it seems like the only way to stop this problem is to kill animals, but actually I think there are lots of other things you can do. I just think that hunting and culling is really, really inhumane. It's not the right answer.

Audio 7.05

1 The idea has a lot going for it, but they'd need to be controlled.

2 Maybe it's just me, but the danger always feels exaggerated.

3 Well, I'm no expert, but I think the risk needs to be properly assessed.

UNIT 7 MEDIATION BANK

Audio MB7.01
Part 1

The Appalachian Trail is a huge undertaking that requires the right preparation and attitude. You really don't want to hit the trail without your mind, body and kit being ready! So, here's what you need to know before you set out on a hike of the Appalachian Trail.

Probably, the most important thing is you've got to be physically fit. Hopefully, you've already got a lot of backpacking experience – I think I heard a couple of you have recently undertaken the Dientes Circuit Trek in Chile, which I'd love to hear more about if you have some time after. Even if you're very experienced, it's a great idea to head out on a few local, day hikes with your pack and gear as heavy as you plan to carry on the trail. And, of course, keeping fit and eating right in any other way you can is only going to benefit you on the hike, not to mention the general health benefits that I'm sure we're all aware of: improving circulation and strengthening the cardiovascular system, lowering blood sugar, weight loss, bone strength, etc.

However, this is not purely a physical challenge, it's a mental one, too. There will be times when you're cold, hungry, tired. I remember on my first serious hike, I was probably around nineteen – a freshman at college – and I really hit the wall. I just sat down – and it wasn't because my body had given up, I just couldn't work out why I was putting myself through such an ordeal – till my friend Jan came and talked to me (we ended up getting married as it happens!). There are some other things you can do to prepare for this, which don't involve finding a life partner! First, and before you start out, think of your honest answer to the question 'Why am I doing this?'. And, in the few days leading up to your trip, picture yourself arriving at Mount Katahdin. It sounds kinda corny but visualisation is so crucial to achieving any goal you set yourself, and that picture's a real pick-me-up when you're finding it tough.

Secondly, have a 'support person'. I'm not just talking about a 'buddy' who's on the trail with you, which is great to have, but you also need someone back home that you can call for mental support. Who's going to tell you what you need to hear to get you motivated and back up on your feet? And make sure, whoever it is, they know that you'll probably be calling them sometime, and it may not be at the most convenient time – especially with the time difference for y'all – what is it now? Five hours? Six? Thankfully it's not that time of year when we're out of sync for a coupla weeks with daylight saving. Boy did that get me in trouble a few years back …

Audio MB7.02
Part 2

OK, so that's the physical, and mental or psychological challenges covered. But do you know the most frequent reasons for failed hiking trips? It's the little – which isn't to say trivial – practical things. Before you do anything, check your gear is in good, working condition and, even if this sounds obvious, make sure it fits properly **and** you know how to use it. This is another reason to go out on a day hike before you head out on the trail. You won't believe the number of people I've had to stop and help with a tent or camping stove. I once stumbled across a guy practically in tears cos he couldn't work his flashlight. The sun was going down. Would've been a long, dark night for him if we hadn't happened upon him.

Related to the point of equipment, while you need to take certain things, try and pack as light as you can. It stands to reason, but lighter is better so carefully consider what you think is 'important'. I live by a golden rule of never carrying more than twenty-five percent of my body weight. Now, if you're not a big person, that seems a little unfair, right – 'Why can't I take as much just because I'm smaller?'. But see what you can work out between your team to spread the load proportionately – now I hear you bigger guys saying 'Hey, that's not fair either'. If it's any comfort, I know exactly how you feel. I actually lost a few pounds recently, believe it or not, largely thanks to the Appalachian Trail in fact! Anyhow, your team leader will share a checklist and weight calculator that'll ensure you're prepared but without carrying unnecessary weight.

Another great way to do that is with 'bump boxes' – and I hope you've started planning this already – it's a package with supplies you can pick up from the towns on your route. And that doesn't just have to be food – it could be new boots and clothes.

You'll also spend some money when you get to those towns but budget carefully and stick to it. Costs for things like food, a shower or even the occasional warm bed can all add up, especially with the increased cost of living in the region over recent years.

I mentioned food there – that's, without doubt, a critical factor for a successful hike. You can't overestimate how important it is to morale – I'm sure you'll know that already. You need as varied a diet as possible – carbs, protein and yep, some high-sugar. Instant noodles or pasta really won't cut it after the first few nights. One guy I know did just that, pretty much ate noodles and pepperoni for a week and he said it was the best time of his life! But I think that's more the exception than the rule. Generally, the more variety, the better you'll feel physically. And also, in those low moments we spoke about earlier, having something you're looking forward to eating later can give you that push you need. And one last thing: duct tape. No, this is not a joke … people talk about how it can fix just about anything, you know. And it's true! In the past I've used it to mend broken hiking poles, water bottles, whatever it is – it can be a real lifesaver.

UNIT 8

Audio 8.01

a Yes, I was good at music. I seemed to be able to play any instrument after just a couple of lessons. However, it didn't last into my teens, unfortunately.

b Well, unfortunately, I failed my maths exam, which was a huge blow, and I had to retake it a few months later. But I studied hard and passed.

c My friend, Alicia, has this uncanny way with animals. If a dog is barking, she's able to talk to it and can calm it down immediately.

d Oh yes. I once had to give a presentation to a roomful of experts. I was so nervous, but I managed to get through it, and I think it was good for me.

e My team was working on a difficult new project and Tim kept us going with encouragement and advice, never giving up when it was all going wrong. It was a success and completely down to him.

f Not bad. I work out a fair amount, but I don't have enough stamina to do long runs or swims or things like that.

g I don't, but my sister does. She's really patient and can put complex ideas into simple words so that others can understand.

h There was this particular assignment I had to do for college. It was proving really tricky and I couldn't work out how to approach it at first, but I didn't give up and got there in the end.

Audio 8.02

1 He gave a ten-minute speech which was absolutely hilarious.

2 She always keeps her long-term plans in mind – she's very focused.

3 She's someone who will always take part enthusiastically in everything she gets involved in.

4 He has an amazing knack for understanding other people's points of view.

Audio 8.03

1 a ten-minute speech

2 long-term plans

3 who will always take part

4 an amazing knack

Audio 8.04

My shout-out goes to my highly respected colleague, Mikael. He has this rare gift of making other people in our group feel comfortable and is always trying to empathise even when people aren't being all that easy to get along with. He's also the one in the group who's the first to try and get to grips with new things that we're given to do, he just has this amazing drive to keep getting better that I'm pretty jealous of, to be honest!

Audio 8.05

I'll tell you something that I find intriguing and that's how different people react to different sensory input. I would guess it's because our brains are all wired a little differently, though others may disagree. I'm sure you'll have heard that images, sounds and smells have a nostalgic effect and bring back memories, but it's also well documented that many people find certain things unsettling, or even in some cases actually distressing. There are, of course, plenty of sceptics who will insist that this is all nonsense, but the evidence is clearly there. It's quite commonplace that some people will wince on hearing fingernails on a blackboard or at the shrill sound of a dentist's drill, others might find that the sounds of paper ripping or something scraping a bottle is almost painful. But with me it's textures. There are some that will just set my teeth on edge. As a child I had a small suitcase with a handle. The material on the handle wore off with use and my fingers would clutch the metal. For some reason this would trigger a nasty shivery sensation when I touched it. I can still remember the feeling today. I know people who always squirm at the sound or feel of tinfoil and just

won't use it, or who flinch when they touch velvet. And yet there are others who find sensations such as hearing sounds like paper rustling extremely soothing. You may have seen online videos related to something called ASMR? It was quite a trend a few years back. It's the idea that some people have an odd response to certain sounds and sensations. Not only is the particular sensation comforting, but it can actually cause a physical reaction in the form of an involuntary pleasant tingling sensation that starts in the head and runs down the spine – quite hypnotic, really. What is really strange about this is the range and type of sensations that can have this reaction. It can be something as weird as brushing hair, people whispering or even folding towels! There's a plethora of online videos of people doing these things or making these sounds for people to watch.

Audio 8.06

Ja = James   G = Guy   Ju = Julia

Ja: My name's, eh, it's not nice actually. It tastes like chewing gum that's lost most of its flavour.

G: What does your surname taste of?

Ja: It's difficult to describe – it's a bit like sucking on wool trousers. My family have all got, er, their own specific flavours and textures so my mother, for example, who is called Doreen, she has the … I call it a taste, but it's more of an experience. It's like the brain freeze you get when you drink very, very cold water or ice cream. And my father, whose name's Peter, he tastes like processed peas. My sister's blackcurrant yoghurt and my grandmother was very creamy thick condensed milk.

G: In this programme, we explore synaesthesia – a mixing of two or more senses that aren't usually connected. One triggers the other due to differences, not defects, in the brain's wiring. Some synaesthetes for example can hear a colour or taste a sound. I'm Guy Leschziner, a neurologist working in the National Health Service in London.

Ja: When I heard that I'd be speaking to you Guy, the word 'Guy' produces a word sound …

G: This might be worrying. What does 'Guy' taste like?

Ja: It produces a word sound that gives me a taste and texture something similar to fudge, which is rather nice.

G: That's very kind of you.

Ja: Yeah, because some of these are bad. Somebody asked me what their name tasted like, was at a function … Her name's Maureen, err, it's awful!

G: This is James Wonnerton. He has a rare type of synaesthesia where he experiences tastes and textures for every sound he hears. It's most predominant with word sounds and it's involuntary.

Ja: Whenever I hear a word, whenever I read a word, because when you read, you tend to hear the word, in your mind's eye, if you like. Inner speech I call it.

G: What about if you think of a word, is that generating a taste as well?

Ja: It is, yeah, it is. For example, if I see a television screen in the distance, I'll get the taste and texture of jelly.

Ju: My name's Julia Simner, I am a professor of neuropsychology at University of Sussex. Synaesthesia is a rare psychological trait that causes differences in thinking and in sensory perception. It's often described as a merging of the senses because it can cause one sense to become blurred or merged with another. It can either enrich your life or slightly trouble you or it can be something you take absolutely no notice of whatsoever.

G: Roughly four percent of the population has synaesthesia, but in many people, it may be as subtle as to go unrecognised. For James, however, it has always been much more obvious.

Ja: I first remember experiencing tastes and textures specifically when I was going to school aged about four and a half. My mother used to take me to school on the tube and I was learning to read and write at the time, so I used to read out the names of the stations as we passed through, and off the maps, and I used to get tastes and textures. My favourite tube station was Tottenham Court Road because there's so many lovely words in there. Tottenham produced the taste and texture of a sausage, Court was like a lovely crispy fried egg and Road was toast, so there you've got breakfast …

G: A full English fry-up.

Ja: Yeah. Feels like I'm really eating, it's a mouth feel. Oh, I'm getting them now, constantly. One drip and then another drip and another drip – as each of these sounds come in, I get a drip of taste and if it's a particularly strong synaesthetic taste and flavour then it'll take ages to fade.

Audio 8.07
G = Guy   Ju = Julia   Ja = James

G: You'd be forgiven for thinking that James' descriptions are rather far-fetched. Indeed, as a child his doctor dismisses them as simply a boy's wild imagination when he explains how distracting he finds the constant flood of tastes in his mouth. Yet thanks to the advances of science, we now have evidence that synaesthesia is a very real condition.

Unsurprisingly, there are also variations in brain circuitry between synaesthetes and non-synaesthetes.

Ju: Since 1995 we've been able to see those differences using brain scanning. One important study in 2005 showed that synaesthetes' sensory cortices – that's the parts of their brain that do the seeing, and tasting, and hearing and so on – are more active than the average person's. So, colour regions of their brain will light up when they read letters or taste regions might light up when they hear words.

Ja: The actual synaesthetic tastes, this produces a lot of physical side effects. I get stomach acid pumped into my stomach for food that isn't there. It is like eating things all day long.

G: Think about it. James' synaesthesia is extraordinary. There's no food entering his mouth or smells through his nose

creating taste, texture and flavour. Instead, it's his auditory system triggering these sensations and causing him a physical reaction that feels very real. How our brain is structured has a huge influence on how we perceive the world around us. Even those with the same type of synaesthesia almost always disagree on their perceptions. The name Guy will taste of fudge for one and cabbage soup for another. And remember the dress that went viral in 2015 when no one could agree what two colours it was made up of?

Audio 8.08
1 I would guess it's because our brains are all wired a little differently, though others may disagree.
2 I'm sure you'll have heard that images, sounds and smells have a nostalgic effect …
3 There are, of course, plenty of sceptics who will insist that this is all nonsense, but the evidence is clearly there.
4 It's quite commonplace that some people will wince on hearing fingernails on a blackboard …
5 For some reason this would trigger a nasty shivery sensation when I touched it.
6 I know people who always squirm at the sound or feel of tinfoil, and just won't use it.

Audio 8.09
A: They rustle tinfoil at me to make me wince.
B: They'll rustle tinfoil at me to make me wince.

Audio 8.10
1 They'll drum their fingers on the table when they're bored.
2 He'll allow you to ask anything you want.
3 You'll have seen what the teacher wrote on the whiteboard.

Audio 8.11
P = Presenter   L = Lucas   N = Natasha

P: Lucas, let's go with you first. What's your advice for staying healthy?
L: Well, I've recently started doing hot yoga. Don't know if you've ever tried that?
P: 'Hot yoga?' No, I don't know it.
L: So basically, umm, it's yoga but it's much more intense than … it's set in a heated room, a carpeted room, that's thirty-nine degrees and it's just twenty-six positions, but every time you go to the class, it's the same twenty-six positions.
N: Wow – that's a bit excessive, isn't it? And repetitive?
L: But you burn a thousand calories a class, you sweat so much, and they say you can't drink water within the first twenty-five minutes …
N: Hmm, doesn't sound like a good idea.
L: The point is that you come out of that room feeling amazing.
P: And you, Natasha?

N: Well, so I've joined a choir and I feel confident to say that it's really good for your health actually. I'm not that into exercise but it's the same as Lucas has just mentioned, when I come out of the room I just feel completely lifted.
L: That sounds nice. Another real positive about hot yoga is that it's just something that you don't have to think about, there's an instructor there, you meet people, but you don't talk throughout the class so it's something you can just do yourself and it's not …
N: Hmm. So, it's not something where you need to make a big social effort, you can just do it.
L: That's it. And looking at all the benefits, of course you expend energy while doing it.
N: Right. Well, with the choir thing, I think a big plus for me is that it is a part of my day that isn't work or a commute or anything like that. I can just go and be in this room and meet people; it's a really joyful part of my day.
L: Funny you should mention that actually cos, that's what I get out of hot yoga – I enjoy it because I know I'll be at work all day and it's a really stressful environment, you know, living in the city and things like that. So, actually taking that hour and a half to go, do a form of meditation, do some breathing and relaxation just really, you know, **centres** me – without a doubt it's good for me mentally as well as physically. You've only got to look at the number of people who do it to know that it's a good thing.
N: I totally get it. For mental health, the choir is great, too, because if you can regulate your breathing, you can control panic and anxiety – it's just beneficial in so many ways. And I'm speaking from experience here!
L: I guess, though, that there aren't that many people who can sing well enough to join a choir.
N: Ah – it's not that we're all great singers, it's just that we love singing together.
L: Come on, Natasha. Let's be realistic here. You're not going to get someone who's completely tone deaf choosing to join a choir!
P: Hey guys – this isn't a competition! I'm sure both activities are healthy and will appeal to different people. Can we focus on the benefits of …

Audio 8.12
1 It's not that yoga is bad for you, it's just that lots of people find it dull.
2 It's not about meeting people, it's just about being away from the office for a while.
3 The point isn't to make people work harder, the point is to help them feel more relaxed.
4 It's not about forcing people to change diets, it's about making them more aware of what they're eating.

UNIT 1

Opener: BBC Vlogs

1 If there's one thing that I think people should learn to do, it is to learn a language at some point in their lives even if they don't really use it. Learning a language allows you to view things through the eyes of different cultures. It also can be quite practical, help you to travel, and I think it's a very interesting thing to do even if just as another hobby or a pastime.

2 I think one thing everyone should learn to do is cook because you need to cook for yourself, but also it's just a good skill to have socially.

3 I think we all need to learn to think more critically. There is so much information out there at the moment that it can be difficult to determine what's true and what's not. So, we all need to really think about and decide whether there's enough evidence for the claims or the statistics that we're being presented.

4 I think everyone should learn how to swim because it's a really important skill, it keeps you fit. It's a really good form of exercise. And it could save your life if you fall out of a boat.

5 One thing I think that everybody should learn how to do is play chess. It's such a universal strategic game that people from every corner of the globe love to play.

6 In the good and bad moments, you need to learn to say 'thank you' and be grateful.

7 I think everybody should learn basic first aid, so that they can deal with a medical emergency.

8 Everyone should learn to be more empathetic. When you're empathetic, you're able to see how other people see things and that leads to respect, and respect leads to peace.

9 I think everyone should learn how to sew because if you can sew, you can make things, but you can also repair things.

BBC Street Interviews
Exs 2 and 3B

Omri: I enjoy learning about stories and about people mostly. I like hearing the way that other people look at the world and the different like ways that you can look at one situation through different perspectives. So, if it has anything to do with history or with stories of people, then I'm interested in it.

Ollie: I enjoy learning more about things that I know like already. So, if I've watched a TV show or a film like reading a book and finding out more about that. That sort of thing, yeah.

David: I enjoy learning about abstruse bits of history from all over the world. I enjoy learning about cities and visiting them as well.

Serkan: I enjoy learning about architecture, design, design of spaces, different kinds of things that involve the design subject basically.

Farah: I like learning about politics and history and about other people's lives; especially if they're very different from mine. It's always nice to get a new experience.

Samuel: So, I love learning new languages and I love reading about different cultures and the way different people do different things to how we would do them here in the UK.

Rahma: I enjoy learning about history and things in the past and I also enjoy learning about other cultures.

Omri: A good teacher is someone who can connect with you and inspire you on a personal level, who you don't feel like they're lecturing or just there because it's their job, but they're there to help you individually.

Ollie: So, I think having a lot of patience, knowing what your children like, their interests and their hobbies, so you can sort of adjust your teaching to that and make lessons that involve those sort of things. Yeah, so those are the sort of main things, I think.

David: The ability to enthuse the class, the ability to take it forward clearly and the ability to recognise that different pupils have different methods of learning and to take that into account.

Serkan: If they communicate well with the students, if they answer their questions, if they lead them to the answers rather than feeding them with the answers, that will make a good professor.

Farah: Not being dogmatic in their approach like 'I'm a good teacher and you're gonna accept the fact that I'm a good teacher.' Rather 'I'm gonna help you learn.' And not having too much of a power dynamic where 'Oh, I'm the teacher and I'm in the power.' More like 'We're equals here and we're learning together.'

Samuel: Someone who takes their time and listens to your questions, and someone that talks you through the different issues that you're having and helps you with specific problems, rather than just assuming everyone's the same.

Rahma: A good teacher is one that is passionate and really engages with the student and you know that they care in the way that they treat you, the way they take time with you, and a good teacher understands that every student isn't the same.

UNIT 2

Opener: BBC Vlogs

1 I would like to live in Paris because I think it is very elegant and romantic.

2 If I could live anywhere, I would live in India potentially. It seems like a vibrant and interesting place to live. And also I can spend most of my days kind of outside and visiting street food stalls. So yeah, somewhere in India. Not sure where, but yeah.

3 If I could live anywhere in the world, it would have to be Costa Rica in South America. I love nature and I love plants, so I think it would be perfect for me.

4 If I could live anywhere in the world, I would live in Spain because I love the Spanish culture. I do speak Spanish. Living in Spain as well will allow me to maintain a high level of Spanish. And due to Spain being so close to the UK I'm still very able to come back home and visit my friends and family as well.

5 There are many places around the world that simply fascinate me, but I would love to live in Italy because I had the chance to visit Rome and I fell in love with the food, with the culture and the people.

6 If I could live anywhere in the world, hmm, great question. I would love to spend some time living in Brazil. It's a country that I visited in the past. It's a country that I always found fascinating because of history, because of culture, of music, dancing, and it would be a great opportunity for me to learn Portuguese, which is a language that I really really really like.

7 If I could live anywhere in the world, I'd definitely choose an English-speaking country, one that's really beautiful, safe, open. So, this would have to be New Zealand or maybe Canada.

BBC Food
Exs 3 and 4B

Nadiya: LA was part of Mexico until 1847. And ever since, there's been an enduring legacy of immigration.
A stone's throw from the glitz of downtown, there are neighbourhoods where up to 94 percent of the residents come from Latin America.
OK, this is a whole other world.
Mexicans are the largest ethnic group in the city, but there are also millions from Central America, and they have brought with them their unique cuisine.
One of the most authentic places to try it is said to be a night market that's sprung up in a Latino neighbourhood in West Lake.
I've asked chef Wes Avila to show me around.
Hi, Wes!

Wes: How are you doing?

Nadiya: It's wonderful to meet you!

Wes: It's nice to meet you.

Nadiya: It's great, this place, isn't it?

Wes: It's fantastic. It's one of my favourite places to come and eat. This whole street right here is covered with food vendors. It goes down about a block when it's really, really busy.
What's cool about here is you have the Central American stuff, you've got El Salvador, Honduran, you got Guatemalan food, so you'll find things that are a little more unique.

Nadiya: I want to taste LA, I want to know what it's all about. This is a bit of an assault on my senses.

Wes:	Yeah.
Nadiya:	Just, it's so bright and colourful and vibrant. I can just hear that slapping!
Wes:	It's pretty overwhelming. You'll hear that all the way up. People either doing the pupusas or tortillas.
Nadiya:	This place is full of intriguing smells and there are loads of amazing-looking dishes I've never seen before.
Wes:	So, this is what I wanted to show you.
Nadiya:	OK.
Wes:	We've got some chile relleno. It's a stuffed poblano chilli.
Nadiya:	Ah!
Wes:	With, er, potato, green bean and carrot.
[He orders a portion in Spanish.]	
Stall owner:	Yes.
Nadiya:	This is the Guatemalan take on the stuffed chilli. It's fried in batter and loaded with spicy salsa, stacks of seasoned onion and chopped parsley. Where are you from?
Stall owner:	Ah, Guatemala City.
Nadiya:	Guatemala?
Stall owner:	Yes.
Nadiya:	That looks really good. Is this a home-cooked recipe?
Stall owner:	En familia, yes.
Wes:	De tu familia? Yeah, it's a family recipe.
Nadiya:	This is my first taste of Latin food. Ooh! Oh, that's good!
Wes:	That's really good.
Nadiya:	Can I have the recipe? Is it a secret? Yeah! Why is it important for you to make your dishes here?
Stall owner:	[Subtitle – It's really important not to forget your dishes from home when you move to another country.]
Nadiya:	That's pretty special.
Wes:	Yeah.
Nadiya:	You know, that it's a livelihood, but it's also a connection to home …
Wes:	Oh, absolutely!
Nadiya:	That I suppose they don't have?
Wes:	Yeah. It's really important for her to, like, be connected to her country and not to ever forget those roots.
Nadiya:	Dreams are big here. You can feel that, you know, they're all out here happy, laughing, smiling and cooking up foods that their grandparents cooked, that their mothers have cooked and they are the start of the American Dream. Inspired by the Central American flavours of the night market, I'm itching to get cooking, and Wes has invited me to use his restaurant kitchen in the trendy arts district of LA. Wes is Mexican American. He's part of a new breed of chefs using their heritage to fuse flavours from home with contemporary techniques, redefining Californian cuisine. Hi, Wes.
Wes:	How's it going?
Nadiya:	Look at this space! I'm feeling inspired, but I don't think it's going to be very traditional.
Wes:	That's OK, cos what I do, too, is not really traditional.
Nadiya:	Is that allowed?
Wes:	Absolutely. Everything's allowed – it's California, it's LA, it's the Wild West.
Nadiya:	I've taken inspiration from the stuffed chillies I ate in the market, but instead of filling them, I'm using them as a base for a delicious warm chicken salad, topped with a Latin-inspired salsa. I'm making a simple salsa to go with my grilled chicken salad – green tomatoes, radishes and a Latin American classic – barbecued corn.
Wes:	Corn is, uh … It's basically in … in the blood. It's great. Nice and bright. It looks very Angelino.
Nadiya:	I've not heard that one before. What is Angelino?
Wes:	It's somebody who's born and raised here in Los Angeles, able to take flavours and ingredients from different places and reinterpret it. You kind of get the vibe and you feel it.
Nadiya:	It's a vibe.
Wes:	Yeah.
Nadiya:	Ah. Like me, Wes is first generation. His dad immigrated to the US from Mexico in the '70s.
Wes' dad:	Oh, hey.
Nadiya:	Hi! And Wes has invited him to join us for lunch.
Wes:	It's good.
Wes' dad:	Really tasty.
Wes:	Fantastic.
Wes' dad:	He's not cooking just traditional food. Look at his customers, there are not that many Mexicans here.
Wes:	It's like, I cater to Angelinos, which is a big melting pot.
Wes' dad:	Yeah.
Nadiya:	Do you feel like he's living your American Dream?
Wes' dad:	Oh, yeah.
Nadiya:	Why did you come to America?
Wes' dad:	To have a better life. I mean, we don't have any money, so I told my mum, 'I've got to go.' I was eighteen.
Nadiya:	From first leaving Mexico, it took Wes' dad six years to get a green card, allowing him to live permanently in the US. Does America feel like home now?
Wes' dad:	Oh, yeah. I feel like this is my country.
Nadiya:	Yeah. There was something quite powerful about sitting there with Wes and his dad because it made me appreciate the struggles that my dad went through. I've always thought about it from my perspective, but never really thought about it from the immigrant's point of view, the person that had to move, the person that had to make those changes, the sacrifices that they had to make. I hadn't really thought about how big that was.

UNIT 3

Opener: BBC Vlogs

1 The worst job I've ever had was as a dishwasher in a restaurant in a town near where I lived. It was quite intense work. I was given plates every two seconds, and I had to spray them and wash them super super quickly. The actual mental work wasn't that difficult but it was physically really exhausting, so by the end of the day I was so so tired, and it was for very little money, so that's the worst job ever.

2 One of the best jobs I've ever had was making a TV series about cooking. And we worked with brilliant chefs, and the best thing about it was that after they'd demonstrated a dish, we all got to eat it.

3 I think the worst job I ever had was selling advertising on the telephone. Basically, for two weeks people just said: 'no,' 'no,' 'no,' 'not interested,' or sometimes they didn't answer at all. Or they hung up on me! And after two weeks I got fired because I hadn't sold anything. Yep, yep, that wasn't good.

4 The worst job I ever had was being a lawyer. Sure, the money was really good, but the work was really boring and I didn't like the clients very much.

5 The worst job I ever had was when I was eighteen. Before going to university, I worked in a factory where they produced peanuts for supermarkets. The job was so boring that one day I actually fell asleep on top of the peanuts in front of me.

6 I think the worst job I've ever had was probably when I was a student. I was a pizza delivery boy and I would say most of the deliveries were fine, but there were a few that were very challenging. Very maybe difficult people or different places to find in Johannesburg, but it just got to a point where I just I couldn't do it anymore, and I got a job as a waiter, which was much better.

BBC Street Interviews
Exs 2A and 3B

Sagar: If I was changing career, I'd be looking for a company where I can learn, I can grow, learn new skills and things on a daily basis, get paid well of course and work with some fun people as well.

Hazel: I do like to look for a corporate social responsibility policy when I'm applying for a company. I have worked for a company before that prioritised sustainability and a fair supply chain, and I really valued that when I worked for the business.

Michael: Dynamism, I think complexity, you know, a company that had a good, sound financial footing and most importantly a drive, with a purpose, you know, going forward for something that they were looking to try and achieve. And making sure you had a role to fit in that particular space as well.

Nick: For me, it'd definitely be work–life balance, because I do have a lot of hobbies and I kind of like to balance those with my work. I don't want my life to be just all work. So, I think work–life balance for me is a big one. And culture as well. Like a nice culture, where everyone's friendly to you and you can chat to everyone; it's not like a toxic culture, I guess, in the company.

Adeleke: Well, I definitely would like to find something that's economically stable for me. Excluding that, definitely somewhere where there's a community. I've always been somewhere where … I like being in places that are community based, somewhere where I feel like we have shared values in our team. It's looking for always working together and not individual goals.

Sagar: Yes, I would love to travel the world, visit all the restaurants, eat my best favourite foods, watch all the football games I could possibly watch of my favourite teams and just do all the things I've always wanted to do.

Hazel: I don't think I would. I enjoy the social aspect of working and I like using my brain, so I think I'd struggle every day to find a way to like stimulate my brain every day.

Michael: No, I enjoy working. I don't think I would want to not work. It doesn't have to be work in terms of your current field; there's so many other roles and opportunities that you can be involved in doing, but I wouldn't want to just have my feet up.

Nick: I would, yeah. I think with all the hobbies I have, so like playing piano, doing ju-jitsu, I could do those all day and never get bored.

Kirsty: He does do them all day! I would do one week on, one week off, 'cause I do love relaxing, but I think what makes it special is the fact that you do work and you kind of grow and stretch yourself and then have a week off. That would be a perfect balance for me.

Adeleke: Yes, I would take it, but it would be more to not work in standard jobs, and I'm someone who's constantly doing things, so I could sort of focus on I guess things you could say are more hobbies, but volunteering or creating more music or just going out in the world and trying new things. And that would be amazing, just have the freedom to do that as I see fit.

UNIT 4

Opener: BBC Vlogs

1 I think among the most important human qualities are kindness and compassion. I think they're infectious qualities. When people are kind to us, I think it makes it easier for us to be kind to other people, and so it multiplies itself.

2 I think one of the most important human characteristics is humility, the ability to be humble. And I think humility also means knowing what we don't know, acknowledging within ourselves where we need to improve, being more open to different ideas and opinions from others. And basically, the opposite of being prideful or arrogant.

3 I think the most important human quality is curiosity. Why do I say that? Well, without it we wouldn't have such significant developments in a wide range of fields, whether arts, music, science, culture or even sport.

4 I believe an important human characteristic is politeness. I think it's important to have good manners. 'Thank you' when someone holds a door open for you or 'please' when you're ordering a coffee.

5 I think the two most important human characteristics are imagination and creativity. Children have both of those in abundance. Adults less so, but when they do show them, they bring humour, art, colour to our lives. And I think it's impossible to talk about human progress without talking about imagination and creativity, and I think it's what makes us a unique species.

6 I think a good sense of humour is a very important human characteristic to have. Being able to laugh at the smaller most ordinary things in life.

BBC Documentary
Exs 2A and 2C

Extinction: The Facts

Sir David Attenborough: Our planet is home to a seemingly infinite variety of species. From ocean giants to the tiniest insects. We call this abundance of life 'biodiversity'. But today, it's vanishing at rates never seen before in human history.

News presenter: The UN panel of experts has found that one million animal and plant species face extinction.

Prof. Kathy Willis: It is worse than expected. This is happening much faster than we've ever seen before.

Sir David Attenborough: The evidence is that unless immediate action is taken, this crisis has grave impacts for us all.

Prof. Kathy Willis: We're not just losing nice things to look at. We're losing critical parts of Earth's system.

Sir Robert Watson: And it's threatening our food, our water, our climate.

Felicia Keesing: We have a moment when we can change our world and make it better. This is that moment.

Sir David Attenborough: Over the course of my life, I've encountered some of the world's most remarkable species of animals. Only now do I realise just how lucky I've been. Many of these wonders seem set to disappear forever. We're facing a crisis, and one that has consequences for us all.

In 2019, the United Nations asked over 500 scientists to investigate the current state of the natural world.

Prof. Kathy Willis: This is the first time there's been a global assessment where all the evidence has been pooled together – thousands and thousands of papers.

Sir Robert Watson: We're losing biodiversity at a rate that is truly unprecedented in human history.

Dr Stuart Butchart: Since 1970, vertebrate animals – things like birds, mammals, amphibians and reptiles – have declined by 60 percent in total.

Large mammals have, on average, disappeared from three quarters of the range where they were historically found.

Prof. Elizabeth Hadley: What's different is that it's happening simultaneously in the Amazon, in Africa, in the Arctic. It's happening not at one place and not with one group of organisms, but with all biodiversity everywhere on the planet.

Sir Robert Watson: It means that one million species out of eight million species on Earth are now threatened with extinction. 500,000 plants and animals and 500,000 insects.

Sir David Attenborough: Since 1500, 570 plant species and 700 animal species have gone extinct. Studies suggest that extinction is now happening 100 times faster than the natural evolutionary rate, and it's accelerating.

James Mwenda: Many people think of extinction being this imaginary tale told by conservationists, but I have lived it. I know what it is. I am caretaker of the northern white rhinos. We only have two left on the planet. They are mother and daughter.

This is Najin, the mother, who is 30 years old. She is very quiet. And her daughter is Fatu. This is Fatu. Hey, come on. Hey, Fatu. Fatu, no, come on. She's nineteen years old. She's pretty much like a human teenager. She's a little bit unpredictable and can be feisty sometimes, especially when she wants something.

Sir David Attenborough: Northern white rhinos were once found in their thousands in central Africa but were pushed to the brink of extinction by habitat loss and hunting. By 1990, just seven known individuals survived.

James Mwenda: I've seen these beautiful rhinos count from seven down to two. They're here because we've betrayed them. And I think they feel it, this threatening tide of extinction that is pushing on them. They feel their world is collapsing. Unless science saves them, when Najin passes away, she'll leave the daughter Fatu alone forever. The last northern white rhino. And their plight awaits one million more species.

VIDEOSCRIPTS

UNIT 5

Opener: BBC Vlogs

1 The most famous person I've ever met was Benedict Cumberbatch. I was eighteen years old and was lucky enough to be working on the set of *Sherlock* as a runner, and it was basically my job to make him tea and coffee and to make sure that he had everything that he wanted and that he needed. And, because we were filming in London and it rains quite a lot, it was also my responsibility to hold the umbrella next to him and to make sure that he didn't get wet while we were waiting for each scene to set up and for 'action' to be called.

2 I think the most famous person that I've ever met is Nelson Mandela. I was born in South Africa, and I lived there until I was twenty-three years old, so I had the privilege of meeting Nelson Mandela when I was a schoolboy. I received an award from him and I shook his hand, and it was a really incredible experience. You know, he did build the country I was lucky enough to grow up in, and if it wasn't for Nelson Mandela, I have a feeling that I would have had a very different life, and definitely a much worse life.

3 Jack Nicholson. I met him when I was in Colorado, and I was at school in Colorado there. At least I thought it was Jack Nicholson, so I posted a picture and everyone was like 'Wow, that's Jack Nicholson.' Other people thought it wasn't Jack Nicholson and, looking back on it, I think it wasn't actually Jack Nicholson.

4 The most famous person I've met is Barack Obama and I served him a coffee.

5 The most famous person I've met is the Queen of England when I went to Buckingham Palace and had tea in 2011.

6 The most famous person I've ever met was a guy called Jarvis Cocker from a band called Pulp and it went very badly because I was completely starstruck. And I tried to talk to him, but all I could say was 'aeuh …' for several minutes. It was terribly terribly embarrassing.

BBC Street Interviews
Exs 2A and 2C

Jane: The main influence in my life at the moment are my teenage children. They're teaching me how to be more current and to understand the world as it's changing.

Magda: I think I'm always influenced by other people because I like to be surrounded by people and I like to talk to people, get inspired by them, so especially at work, at the gym, I don't know, even at home because of social media, so I think everywhere.

Philo: Yeah, well, the work part is also the same, however, I'm not really on social media, so most of the things I do or the ideas I have come from people who are near and dear to me.

Zoe: I think in every aspect of my life I'm influenced by others. I think in the world at the minute with social media and the internet I feel like it's hard to not be influenced by what other people do and say.

Rory: I think definitely in sort of the clothing that I wear, so I'm very susceptible to what other people are saying and how that affects the way I want to present myself to others. So, sometimes maybe I feel like I'm not presenting myself the way that I want to because I'm worried about what other people are gonna say.

Mohammed: Firstly, I'm influenced like professionally by my parents and my grandparents, like careerwise, like I want to like go down the same path and like learn from them, learn from their mistakes and you know, just like use their mistakes to try and help me be a better person like professionally.

Jane: Probably my grandmother. She was very patient, a wonderful cook and always had an open house. So, yes, my grandmother.

Magda: Actually, I'm thinking of my biology teacher. She was a teacher that gave me the opportunity to start in the medical field and to build up a career in that field, even though I went to a high school that is [for] musician[s]. So, definitely her.

Philo: Yeah, with me it's my basketball trainer. He taught me a lot of principles I can use in my everyday life – discipline and all these things that, yeah, all this knowledge I have for university and all these other things.

Zoe: I think an obvious answer would be politicians 'cause they choose obviously policy, sort of dominates what the culture's like and I feel like that influences me a lot because I study politics as well. That is very influential in my life.

Rory: I think my dad definitely has had the biggest influence on my life. I think from the start, he was sort of the person I aspired to, and so I try to sort of replicate his work ethic, the way that he handles himself in situations that maybe aren't the best. I think he's definitely sort of provided me with a lot of the groundwork that I wanted to grow up and become the person that I want to be.

Mohammed: My friends honestly, like everyone, you know has their own different personalities and everything. So, I like to pick up from their strengths and my friends' weaknesses and try and build it in my character and try and become a better person.

UNIT 6

Opener: BBC Vlogs

1 I really like old things and antiques. I find that things from long ago are designed better, took longer to craft and build. I also like how there is a story behind things that have been around for generations.

2 I think new things aren't necessarily better than old things, especially when it comes to buildings. I live in a building which was constructed in the 20s, and of course some things don't function properly, but there is such a sense of history here, and I feel that architects used to put a lot more care and effort into how they design public spaces. For instance, the staircase, the courtyard, the corridors are simply amazing here.

3 In terms of how we store music these days, it's a lot easier to listen to anything you want wherever you are. It's easy. It's on your phone or whatever. Compared to the old ways which was to have it on a CD or cassette if you're that old. However, there was something nice about having the physical copy as part of a collection of your music.

4 I think from a functional perspective, new things are almost always better than old things, but I think we love the aesthetic of some old things like vinyl records and classic cars and vintage clothes, things like that. So, I think we like both things. I certainly wouldn't swap my smartphone for a 1970s telephone for example.

5 No, I don't think new things are necessarily always better than old things. I think they're just new, and so you're not as bored of them yet.

BBC Documentary
Exs 2A and 2C

Mark: I still love riding my bike today, especially because it's packed full of material science innovation which all came about relatively recently, which is odd because the bicycle seems to me like something that should've been around forever.

It was this man, Baron Karl von Drais, who set the ball rolling in 1820, and he invented something called the *Laufsmaschine* and this is it. Now, it has two wheels, a frame, handles, and it was designed to help you get around, but you had to run. Hence the word *Laufsmaschine*, because *lauf* is the German for *run*.

Designed to support a fully grown Baron, the *Laufsmaschine* was little more than a wooden bench on wheels. Its sturdy frame took the bulk of your weight, but you could still only travel at running speed. It was nearly half a century before that was bettered by this, the 'Boneshaker'. In 1870, this was the cutting edge of bicycle design. It's made of wrought iron and wood, but critically has pedals. The bonus is more speed, but now stopping's the issue, so I'm pleased they added at least some rudimentary brakes. But it was still far removed from the modern bicycle.

Although the Boneshaker is so much better than what came before it, essentially, it's still pretty hopeless. I mean, it's really heavy! And I'm not putting that on, it weighs a tonne! It's slow, it's cumbersome, it's difficult to manoeuvre. It's just … it looks beautiful, but it's not really the thing you want. What you want, is **this**. It's essentially a modern bike, but its basic design dates back to the 1880s. And the reason it is light, stiff and strong is because of the steel tubing and the pneumatic tyres, and what made those possible is not so much an innovation in engineering or design, it's the emergence of new materials.

In the mid-1800s, Henry Bessemer discovered how to turn iron into high-strength steel on a massive scale. That transformed industry and launched a new era of tools and machinery. Unlike iron, steel could easily be made into tubes, though at first, they had welded seams and weren't very strong.

Then, in 1886, a way to make tubes without the seam was invented, and so the bicycle had its frame.

It also had its chain. In 1880, industrial steel was used to make a revolutionary roller-chain, which also made gears possible. But the best was yet to come, the bicycle tyre.

John Dunlop invented his pneumatic tyre in 1888 to give his son's tricycle a comfier ride than its traditional solid wheels did. It was an ingenious idea that's been used on pretty much every bike made since, and almost anything else with wheels.

To show just what a revolution in design the 1880s bicycle was compared to its predecessor, the Boneshaker, I've brought them both here to Herne Hill Velodrome for a rather unusual race.

These racing cyclists are going to help me out by comparing the Boneshaker to its successor.

Club-racer Nigel is going to ride the Boneshaker in a head-to-head pursuit against me. I'll be on the post-1880s bicycle.

So, we've got a super-fit athlete on a Boneshaker, and me on a bike designed just a few years later but featuring pneumatic tyres and tubular steel, not to mention the roller-chain.

Tony: Ready. Go, Nige! Come on! Come on, Nige! He's getting up big speed now, getting stability.

Nigel: Yeah, it might be a touch more than a minute, guys.

Mark: Here he comes.

Nigel: It's the most difficult machine I've ever cycled on, without a shadow of a doubt. I wouldn't be swapping it for my road bike any time soon.

Mark: Sadly, I can't claim any credit for my victory. I owe it all to the revolution in materials that transformed the bicycle from a cumbersome novelty to a genuine speed machine.

UNIT 7

Opener: BBC Vlogs

1 I have to make pretty much all my big life decisions in the next ten years, for example where I live, who I live with, what job I do, if I want to have children. Yeah, all the big ones.

2 I honestly don't expect to be forced to make any important decisions in the next decade. I'm at a point in my life where I worry more about decisions concerning my children than my own. My sons are fourteen and seven so I expect to assist them with their important decisions regarding, for instance, education over the next decade.

3 The biggest decision I have to make over the next ten years is when to retire. I don't want to leave it too late because I've got so many great adventures I'd like to do with my husband, such as trekking across New Zealand.

4 So, over the next ten years I imagine that I'm going to be making a lot of decisions about how I can live sustainably and the impact I have on the environment. So I think I'll be really having to consider the types of businesses that I support and where I buy things from my clothes to my kitchen appliances, pretty much everything where I'm going to buy it and from. And another way that's going to impact my life in terms of living sustainably is how I choose to travel and the places that I visit. I think I'm gonna be making a lot more decisions about those sorts of things than I have done previously.

5 The biggest decision I will have to make in the next decade is whether I want to continue living in Poland or if I want to move abroad. It's actually been my dream forever to live in Iceland, however, I'm not sure whether I would enjoy that cold climate.

6 Do I want to retire? I should perhaps be thinking about retiring around the age of sixty-five, sixty-six, sixty-seven. Do I want to retire, and, secondly, can I afford to retire, because obviously retirement is a much more complex issue than perhaps it was for my parents. I think those are gonna be the biggest decisions that I'll have to make in the next ten years, and at the moment I'm avoiding thinking about them.

BBC Street Interviews
Exs 2A and 2C

Michael: No, I like choice. I think you must always have lots of choice. It's up to you to investigate what are the right choices and that's an interesting process to go through. So, choice is absolutely key.

Dylan: I'd say yes because I myself am quite indecisive, so I would find myself chopping and changing what I want most of the time. But if there is fewer options, then I can narrow it down easier.

Tori: As much as there's like too much choice and as much as I'm like indecisive, I think I love having too much choice. I think it's good to have as many options as possible.

Duncan: Well, you can, I mean some people say, you know, 'I have too much choice in doing things,' but I don't think that's necessarily the case, cos you make your own limitations, and you restrict yourself to whatever choices you think are appropriate. So, in a sense, no, you can't have enough choice. And if other people start to limit your choice, that's worse.

Catherine: I think that's a question for people that are indecisive. So, I like a lot of choice. I like to know that I have choice. I feel restricted if I have no choice. So, I think the answer is no.

Sky: Yes, I think you can have too much choice because I tend to become overwhelmed when there are too many options, and it's hard to really decide, and there are too many variables. So, yes, you can.

Sagar: Yes, cos if you've got too much choice, you'll end up not doing anything, because you got too many things to choose from.

Jane: Definitely too much choice, all the time. I find it very confusing. The older I get, the more confusing it becomes.

Exs 2B and 2C

Michael: I think I make wrong choices all the time. I mean sometimes you're walking down the street and you see people who don't have as much as you, and you sometimes wish you could do more, but you walk past them. That's a wrong choice. So, I make wrong choices all the time.

Dylan: I made the right choice to go to Newcastle University because I love the city and feel like really at home there.

Tori: I made the right choice to study engineering because I get to work with my hands and being able to learn different things about mechanics.

Duncan: My recent job. It's been about eighteen months and I made the right choice in taking up that job. It's really been a massive change, and it's absolutely worked out superbly for me.

Catherine: I was young, I was immature, and I had an opportunity to do a career I really wanted to do. And I started it, and then I decided that partying was so much more fun. And I went off on the partying route and I missed that opportunity for a career choice.

Sagar: The right choice was probably joining the company that I work for right now – I work with some really really fun people. I learn new things every day and new skills. The wrong choice? I don't think there's a wrong choice because as long as you're learning from your decisions that's always a good decision to make, right?

Jane: I've made several wrong choices in my life, but I try and find the positive in that choice. So, I don't really think I've made many wrong choices. It's just finding a solution from the wrong choice.

UNIT 8

Opener: BBC Vlogs

1 A quality I really like about myself is that I think I'm quite positive. I always manage to see the best in any situation or person.

2 I like the fact that I'm able to multitask, which, well, I mean with practical things. It just means I'm able to be quite efficient, especially at the weekend, getting different chores done. It means I get them done a lot more quickly and then I have a lot more time to relax and enjoy myself. Cos I know some people who can't multitask and, yeah, I feel sorry for them.

3   I think the quality that I like most about myself is that I'm really good at keeping in touch with friends. I've got friends from all different times of my life and I think, I like to think that I'm a kind and thoughtful friend and I devote a lot of time to meeting up with people, even, you know, we might have moved many miles apart from one another over the years, and I still make a lot of effort to travel and meet up with friends or if we can't do that then speaking on the phone and just spending a lot of time prioritising my friendships.

4   I like that I have a calm personality. It helps me to get through hard situations, and sometimes I can help others to feel calm, too. And that's really good. But, to be honest, I'm not always calm – sometimes I freak out just like everyone else.

5   Well, I like to think that I'm quite honest. When my children ask me questions, I try to answer them as honestly as possible, and I think I do the same with other people, so yeah.

6   I think I'm quite open-minded. I think I'm quite liberal, which I think is a good quality. I'm also not really intimidated by people, so I don't feel like people are better than me.

BBC Entertainment
Exs 2A and 2B

Stephen Fry:	Good evening, good evening, good evening, good evening, good evening, good evening and welcome to *QI*, where this week I shall be messing with your minds. Tell me this, which do you find most convincing, the IKEA Effect, the Rhyme-as-reason Effect or the Frequency Illusion?
Sarah Millican:	Is the IKEA Effect just arrows on the floor? Is that what that is? Just not being able to get out of anywhere ever.
Stephen Fry:	That, if you can …
Sarah Millican:	Is that prison? Is that prison? Prison with tea lights.
Stephen Fry:	It may be better understood by saying things like if you make crab apple jelly, say, or … or … or jam, in my case apricot jam, I made last year, and it's just the best apricot jam there ever was. I know this, it's a fact. It's the best apricot jam anyone's ever tasted. But I'm told that it's part of the IKEA Effect. In other words, if you've made it yourself from your own ingredients, you just think it's better than anything else that you can buy in a shop or anything else.
Sarah Millican:	Is that why people are really smug about their babies?
Stephen Fry:	Yes! Basically, they are an IKEA Effect. Well, let's move on to the second in our list then, which is the Rhyme-as-reason Effect. What do you think that can be about?
Josh Widdicombe:	Is that like, um, 'no pain, no gain'?
Stephen Fry:	Yes. Yeah.
Sarah Millican:	Never the twain with … no.
Stephen Fry:	They do seem to work, inasmuch as, if you suggest a kind of rhyming piece of advice to someone, and to another group of people you put the same sentiment that doesn't rhyme, they'll believe the rhyming one. So, for example, they gave 'wealth makes health', to a group of people, and almost all of them agreed with it. They then said, 'financial success improves medical outcomes.'
Sarah Millican:	Catchy. It's catchy.
Stephen Fry:	And they didn't agree at all, despite it meaning the same thing. So, it shows there is a strange quality that a rhyming phrase has.
Sarah Millican:	And it's also easier to remember as well, so you're more likely to pass it on to somebody else, aren't you?
Stephen Fry:	Well, that's right.
Sarah Millican:	If it rhymes.
Stephen Fry:	And it seems just to have some sort of authority or imprimatur that an ordinary phrase doesn't. It's also 'the Keats heuristic': because it's beautiful, it must be true. Beauty is truth and truth beauty, is the idea. You've got to be in it …
Josh Widdicombe:	… to win it.
Stephen Fry:	To win it, yes.
Sarah Millican:	Points mean prizes!
Stephen Fry:	Points … no, hang on!
Sarah Millican:	Oh, I'm not very good at this, am I?
Stephen Fry:	An apple a day, of course, yeah …
Josh Widdicombe:	… keeps the doctor away.
Stephen Fry:	Red light in the sky, shepherd's pie. Oh, no. That's not one, is it? Red sky at night, shepherd's delight. That's the one, yes. The Frequency Illusion, does that mean anything to you?
Sarah Millican:	No.
Stephen Fry:	No reason why it should. When I used the word heuristic, it may be that you didn't know the word. But it's quite likely that in a couple of days you might see it in a magazine or hear someone else using it on the radio or television and you'll go, 'That's weird, I only just heard that word for the first time two days ago, and now it keeps cropping up everywhere.' Have you ever had that experience?
Josh Widdicombe:	Yeah. I was talking to someone about this. It was Richard Osman, cos he was complaining about people saying there's always tennis questions on *Pointless*.
Stephen Fry:	Oh, yes.
Josh Widdicombe:	And the moment you think that there's tennis questions on *Pointless*, if you see one, you think, 'Well, that completely reinforces everything.'
Stephen Fry:	Yes, that's right. All these things are called a sort of a cognitive bias, they push you into a way of thinking, some different ways of … So, you can tell the most appalling lie if it rhymes, or it's featured on *QI*.